METHODS IN NUMERICAL ANALYSIS

METHODS
IN
NUMERICAL
ANALYSIS

SECOND EDITION

BY *Kaj L. Nielsen,* PH.D.

DIRECTOR OF SYSTEMS ANALYSIS
BATTELLE MEMORIAL INSTITUTE

THE MACMILLAN COMPANY, NEW YORK
COLLIER-MACMILLAN LIMITED, LONDON

First Printing

Library of Congress catalog card number: 63–20425

THE MACMILLAN COMPANY, NEW YORK
COLLIER-MACMILLAN CANADA, LTD., TORONTO, ONTARIO

PRINTED IN THE UNITED STATES OF AMERICA

To Cheryl Kay

PREFACE TO THE SECOND EDITION

THE SUBJECT of numerical analysis has indeed prospered since the publication of the first edition of this book in 1956. Numerous books have been written. Some are on special topics in numerical analysis (for example, solutions of differential equations, system of linear equations, etc.); some are devoted to the mathematical theory in line with the current tendency to abstraction; others are concerned with programming for lage-scale calculators; still others deal with advanced topics, ultramodern numerical analysis, or applications to specific sciences. All of these topics are important and must have a firm foundation. But the need for a basic, one-semester course at the undergraduate level with ample problems is even greater than before. The philosophy used in the creation of the first edition of this book is preserved in the revision in order to furnish the student with the fundamentals that permit him to progress to special and advanced topics and to the utilization of large computers.

The second edition preserves the theme of the original book in the development of the classical numerical analysis with a minimum of mathematical background. Much of the material has been rewritten for greater clarity, and examples have been added. The major changes are: A] The analysis of empirical data which was formerly in Chapters 8 and 9 has been incorporated into one chapter and reorganized with additional elementary examples; B] a completely new chapter on linear programming has been added to provide an introduction to this important topic and its application to industrial problems; C] 86 new problems have been added.

The author gratefully acknowledges the many valuable suggestions contributed by Professor Robert E. Greenwood of the University of Texas and Mr. Robert V. Esperti of the General Motors Corporation. They have contributed extensively to this revision.

KLN

PREFACE TO THE FIRST EDITION

THE INTEREST in numerical analysis has increased tremendously in recent years, primarily because of the success of the large-scale calculating machines. Problems that used to take hours are now solved in seconds. The ability to obtain numerical answers in a short time has led engineers into lengthy analytical studies, which in turn have placed additional emphasis on numerical methods. Thus, at the annual meeting of the American Society for Engineering Education held in 1954, it was stated that "Every engineer who has mastered the Calculus should also have a course in Numerical Analysis." Practically every university is now teaching a course in numerical analysis, and there is a need for an elementary textbook. It is to meet this need that this book was written.

Since it is a textbook for the practical man, it does not seem appropriate to fill it with mathematical sophistication, but rather to present the methods in a simple manner. The mathematician may peruse this book profitably, however, to obtain a knowledge of today's methods and references to deeper investigations.

Numerical analysis may be divided into two main categories: 1] the analysis of tabulated data, and 2] the numerical method of finding the solutions to equations. Both are treated in this book. Emphasis is placed on the methods which are easily adapted to automatic desk calculators since most engineers and scientists will have these available and because these methods may also be used on the large-scale calculators.

The author is a firm believer in systematic procedures, and many illustrative examples, calculating forms, and schematics are displayed. Many of the numerical methods derived in the book are easily performed with the aid of tables. Consequently, the necessary tables form a part of this book. Exercises with some answers are also given to enable the student to master this subject matter.

An attempt has been made to present not only the classical procedures but also to exhibit the most recent methods which have been developed because of the new calculating machines. It is believed that a knowledge of the material in this book will permit the user to solve the numerical analysis problem that may occur in his investigations.

Many people have contributed to this book, both directly and indirectly. Contribution of subject matter has been acknowledged throughout the text and in the bibliography. The author gratefully acknowledges his indebtedness to his many friends who aided in the preparation of the manuscript and its subsequent publication. He is indebted to Professor Sir Ronald A. Fisher, Cambridge, to Dr. Frank Yates, Rothamsted, and to Messrs. Oliver and Boyd Limited, Edinburgh, for permission to reprint Table No. XVII from their book *Statistical Tables for Biological, Agricultural, and Medical Research*.

Kaj L. Nielsen

CONTENTS

6. *ELEMENTARY EQUATIONS AND SYSTEMS* 172

7. *DIFFERENTIAL AND DIFFERENCE EQUATIONS* 228

8. *EMPIRICAL DATA. PRINCIPLE OF LEAST SQUARES* 265

9. LINEAR PROGRAMMING

MATHEMATICAL SYMBOLS

$=$	is equal to	$\dot{x}$	derivative of x with respect to t
$\neq$	is not equal to	$\sqrt{n}$	square root of n
$\doteq$	is approximately equal to	$n \to \infty$	n approaches infinity
$<$	is less than	$\angle ABC$	angle with vertex at B
$>$	is greater than	$\triangle ABC$	triangle ABC
$\leq$	is less than or equal to	$\ldots$	and so on
$\geq$	is greater than or equal to	Δx	increment of x
$\ll$	is much less than	P_1	P sub 1
$\gg$	is much greater than	$\sum$	sum of
Δ	difference	$\prod$	product of
ln	natural logarithm	log	common logarithm

GREEK ALPHABET

LETTERS		NAMES	LETTERS		NAMES	LETTERS		NAMES
A	α	alpha	I	ι	iota	P	ρ	rho
B	β	beta	K	κ	kappa	Σ	σ	sigma
Γ	γ	gamma	Λ	λ	lambda	T	τ	tau
Δ	δ	delta	M	μ	mu	Υ	υ	upsilon
E	ε	epsilon	N	ν	nu	Φ	φ	phi
Z	ζ	zeta	Ξ	ξ	xi	X	χ	chi
H	η	eta	O	o	omicron	Ψ	ψ	psi
Θ	θ	theta	Π	π	pi	Ω	ω	omega

METHODS IN NUMERICAL ANALYSIS

*I often say ... that when you can measure
what you are speaking about, and express it
in numbers, you know something about it;
but when you cannot measure it, when you
cannot express it in numbers, your knowledge
is of a meagre and unsatisfactory kind; it
may be the beginning of knowledge, but you
have scarcely, in your thoughts, advanced
to the stage of science, whatever the matter
may be.*

LORD KELVIN

I

Fundamentals

I. INTRODUCTION

In general, the application of mathematics eventually requires results in numerical form. The numerical answers desired may result from evaluations of formulas, solutions of equations, or inferences drawn from tabulated data. Numerical analysis is that branch of mathematics which is concerned with obtaining these numerical answers. Frequently, other branches of mathematics will develop theories that yield solutions to problems in "closed form," that is, formulas that represent exact solutions. The work of the numerical analyst is then reduced to a simple evaluation of these formulas for variations in the parameters and variables. On the other hand, often a "closed form" solution cannot be obtained and an approximate method is the alternative. The solution takes the form of a formula that approximates the exact solution, and the difference between the two is reduced to a minimum. It is the work of the numerical analyst to develop approximate formulas in such form that they may be evaluated, to evaluate them, and to state the degree of approximation.

A course in methods of numerical analysis is one that teaches how to perform this work. In so doing the evaluation of mathematical expressions is reduced to the fundamental operations of arithmetic. These operations are then carried out by calculating machines, of which there are many varieties. The methods of this book are those that are best adapted to electrical desk calculators. As is often the case, however, many are equally well adapted to large-scale digital computers.

Since this book is concerned with numbers, it seems appropriate to begin with a discussion of them. Certain mathematical concepts are also basic to this study, and they are reviewed for the reader's benefit.

2.   THE ACCURACY OF NUMBERS

There are two kinds of numbers, those that are absolutely exact and those that denote values to a certain degree of accuracy. Examples of absolutely exact numbers are the integers, 1, 2, 3, ... , rational fractions, $\frac{1}{2}, \frac{1}{4}, \ldots$, and the quantities $\sqrt{3}$, π, e, etc., written in this manner. An approximate number is one that expresses a value that is accurate only to the number of digits recorded. Thus, although $\sqrt{3}$ is exact as written, it cannot be expressed exactly by a finite number of digits; we could write for it the number 1.732 which now is an approximate number approximating the value of the square root of 3. We could also have written 1.73205 which is a better approximation. The digits used to express a number are called *significant figures* if they have a meaning in the number. Thus all of the digits in 1.73205 are significant figures; however, in the number 0.00572 only 5, 7, and 2 are significant figures, the 0 having been used to place the decimal point. If a zero, 0, is used at the end of a number, additional information is required to determine whether it is significant. Thus $525,000 may be exact or it may be an expression of money to the nearest thousand. If exactness is desired, such numbers are usually written in the powers-of-ten notation, which is 5.25×10^5 or 5.25000×10^5, the significant figures being written in the left factor. When this notation is used in tables of numbers, a further abbreviation is obtained by simply writing the power of ten in parentheses after the number; that is, 1.35742 (3) stands for 1.35742×10^3. If many significant digits are retained, it has become customary to separate them in some manner for easy reading; for example, 379843279564 may be written 37   98432   79564.

Frequently arithmetical operations will yield numbers with no termination, and it is necessary to cut them to a usable number of figures. This cutting-off process is called *rounding off*. To carry out such a process, certain arbitrary rules must be established. The following are in practice by most numerical analysts and are recommended. To round off a number to n significant figures, throw away all digits to the right of the nth place, and if this discarded number is

(a) greater than half a unit in the nth place, increase the digit in that place by 1;

(b) less than half a unit in the nth place, leave the digit in that place unaltered;

(c) exactly half a unit in the nth place,

(i) increase an odd digit in the nth place by 1,

(ii) leave an even digit in the nth place unaltered.

The number is then said to be *correct to n significant figures.*

Example 1.1. The following numbers are rounded off to five significant figures.

$$31.35764 \text{ to } 31.358$$
$$10.19313 \text{ to } 10.193$$
$$14.32250 \text{ to } 14.322$$
$$14.32150 \text{ to } 14.322$$

The rule for the case of "exactly half" is quite arbitrary but has been found to be the wisest in most cases. When a set of numbers has to be added, it may be practical to deviate from the rule by increasing in half the cases and leaving unchanged the other half.

In performing a sequence of arithmetical operations on numbers, certain facts must be kept in mind. Of primary importance, in general, is that the results will be no more accurate than the original data used. Thus, if the original data are given to three significant figures, the result is accurate to only three significant figures in most cases. However, this does *not* imply that all computations should be rounded off to the significant figures of the data at each step of the computation. Quite to the contrary, it is advisable to retain more figures during the computation. A good rule to adopt is the following one.

Rule. *During the computation retain at least one more figure than that given in the data and round off after the last operation has been performed.*[1]

Another practice, which has become quite widespread in the use of electric desk calculators, is to set the machine for a fixed number of decimal places, employing at least one more figure than that given in the data, and then to use all the figures to that many decimal places. Frequently, when this practice is followed, no attention is paid to rounding off until the final answer is obtained.

[1]Some people prefer to retain two or three more digits, and if the computations are lengthy this author agrees with this practice.

Example 1.2. Compute the value of N:

$$N = \frac{27.13 \times 3.157}{11.32} + (5.921)(.3214)$$

$$= 9.469.$$

The machine is set to five decimal places. All computation is carried out by employing figures to five decimals, and the final answer is rounded off to four significant figures.

This practice is especially acceptable if tables of values are employed during the computation. The machine is then set to the same decimal accuracy as the tables used.

The two methods described above will, in general, prevent the accumulation of errors during a lengthy computation. However, no rule is infallible. One should always hesitate to throw away numbers during a computation; on the other hand, it is foolhardy to waste a lot of time employing unnecessary numbers.

One of the most troublesome operations in numerical calculations is that of subtraction when the numbers are nearly equal. Thus, if we calculate the difference $.2341 - .2337$, we obtain 0.0004, an answer which has only one significant figure. If this result is used again in a computation, some strange things can happen. In such cases it is desirable to rearrange the computation or change the formula so that the difference may be obtained in a new manner. The classical example is the value of $1 - \cos x$ for small values of x; in this case we use the equivalent expression $2 \sin^2 \frac{1}{2} x$ or expand $\cos x$ in a series.

3.   SOME BASIC CONCEPTS

A review of certain basic mathematical concepts is presented here.

A.   *Formulas and Functions*

Numerical analysis frequently reduces to the evaluation of formulas and functions for variations in the parameters and over a domain of values for the independent variable. We are concerned with two types of functions: one, those that are specified by formulas, and, two, those that are specified by tables of values. In either case we shall usually assume that the functions are continuous, possess as many derivatives as required, and, if singularities exist, defined by appropriate additional information.

The evaluation of a function expressed by a formula is easily accomplished by simply substituting the given values of the variables. It must be remembered, however, that formulas can be rearranged. Thus, for example,

$$y = x^2 + 2x + 3, \tag{3.1}$$

$$y - 3 = x(x + 2), \tag{3.2}$$

$$x = -1 \pm \sqrt{y - 2} \tag{3.3}$$

are all equivalent formulas and express the same relationship. In numerical analysis a formula is more often used to define a process. Formula 3.1, which expresses y explicitly in terms of x, defines the procedure for finding y for given values of x. Formula 3.2, which is an implicit relation, shows a possible form for computation. Formula 3.3, which expresses x explicitly in terms of y, shows the process for finding values of x if y is specified.

The evaluation of a function specified at discrete values of the variable may at first seem to be an easy matter since its values are known at the given points, at least to the accuracy of the table. However, to obtain the value of the function at a point not listed may prove difficult and depends greatly on the behavior of the function. The analysis of tabulated data forms an integral part of numerical analysis and is usually divided into two parts: the finding of a value not listed and the investigation of the behavior of the function. Both topics are considered in subsequent chapters. However, before leaving the subject matter it is well to mention that plotting or graphing of functions specified by empirical data is a great aid in determining the properties of such functions.

B.   Polynomials

The polynomial is an overworked mathematical expression throughout this book. The function

$$f(x) = a_0 x^n + a_1 x^{n-1} + a_2 x^{n-2} + \cdots + a_{n-1} x + a_n, \tag{3.4}$$

where a_i, $(i = 0, \ldots, n)$, are constants, is a *polynomial* of degree n in the unknown x. In a course in algebra the value of a polynomial for a given value of x is found by synthetic division. For example, the value of $f(x)$ at $x = 2$ in the polynomial.

$$f(x) = 3x^4 - 5x^3 + 2x^2 - 3x + 6 \tag{3.5}$$

was found to be 16 by the schematic

$$
\begin{array}{ccccc|c}
3 & -5 & 2 & -3 & 6 & 2 \\
  & 6 & 2 & 8 & 10 & \\
\hline
3 & 1 & 4 & 5 & \boxed{16 = f(2)} &
\end{array}.
$$

Another method of doing synthetic division readily adapted to calculators has been termed the *nesting* process. The polynomial (3.4) may be rewritten in the following nested form:

$$
\begin{aligned}
f(x) &= a_n + x\{a_{n-1} + x[a_{n-2} + \cdots + x(a_1 + a_0x)]\} \\
&= \{[(a_0x + a_1)x + a_2]x + a_3\}x + \cdots + a_n.
\end{aligned}
\tag{3.6}
$$

The value of the polynomial for a given value of x is now found by starting with $a_0x + a_1$, multiplying it by x, adding a_2 to the result, etc. This method is applicable to any finite series. In the example given by the polynomial (3.5) we have

$$
f(x) = \{[(3x - 5)x + 2]x - 3\}x + 6
$$

and at $x = 2$

$$
f(2) = \{[(3 \times 2 - 5)2 + 2]2 - 3\}2 + 6 = 16.
$$

All polynomials of degree n can be factored into n factors,

$$
f(x) = (x - x_0)(x - x_1) \cdots (x - x_{n-1}),
\tag{3.7}
$$

where $x_i(i = 0, \ldots, n - 1)$ are the roots of the equation $f(x) = 0$.

The particular polynomial

$$
P^n(x) = x(x - 1)(x - 2) \cdots [x - (n - 1)]
\tag{3.8}
$$

is called a *factorial polynomial*. If the product on the right is multiplied out, the polynomial may be written in the form

$$
P^n(x) = S_{0,n}x^n + S_{1,n}x^{n-1} + S_{2,n}x^{n-2} + \cdots + S_{n-1,n}x,
\tag{3.9}
$$

where $S_{i,n}$ are the *Stirling numbers of the first kind*. The second subscript, n, denotes the degree of the polynomial[2]; thus a fifth degree factorial polynomial

$$
\begin{aligned}
P^5(x) &= x(x - 1)(x - 2)(x - 3)(x - 4) \\
&= S_{0,5}x^5 + S_{1,5}x^4 + S_{2,5}x^3 + S_{3,5}x^2 + S_{4,5}x.
\end{aligned}
$$

[2]An alternate notation is $S_{i,n} \equiv S_i^{(n)}$.

The Stirling numbers have the most useful property,

$$S_{i,n+1} = S_{i,n} - nS_{i-1,n},\qquad(3.10)$$

which enables us to compute a table of these numbers. (See Table II at the back of this book.)

Any polynomial may be expressed as the sum of factorial polynomials. For example,[3]

$$P(x) = 2x^4 - 3x^3 + 14x^2 + 22x + 10$$
$$= 2P^4(x) + 9P^3(x) + 19P^2(x) + 35P^1(x) + 10P^0(x).$$

This sum, obtained by subtracting $2P^4(x)$ from the original polynomial, leaves a polynomial of degree 3 with leading term $9x^3$. Now subtract $9P^3(x)$ from this difference, etc. Schematically, we have

	x^4	x^3	x^2	x	x^0
$P(x)$ =	2	− 3	14	22	10
$2P^4(x)$ =	2	− 12	22	− 12	
Diff. =		9	− 8	34	10
$9P^3(x)$ =		9	− 27	18	
Diff. =			19	16	10
$19p^2(x)$ =			19	− 19	
Diff. =				35	10
$35P^1(x)$ =				35	
Diff. =					10
$10P^0(x)$ =					10

A special factorial polynomial, namely, the one that has a term $x - i$ missing, is frequently employed in numerical analysis and is given a special notation. Thus we define

$$P_i^n(x) = (x - i)^{-1}P^n(x)$$
$$= x(x - 1)\cdots(x - i + 1)(x - i - 1)\cdots(x - n + 1).\qquad(3.11)$$

Factorial polynomials are basic to the calculus of finite differences, which is continuously finding application to numerical analysis. We list a few useful properties and invite the reader to verify them and to draw the analogy of numbers 5 and 6 to the derivative and integral formulas for a power function.[4]

---

[3]We define $P^0(x) = 1$.
[4]See Louis Brand, *Advanced Calculus*. New York: Wiley, 1955, pp. 545–548.

Properties

1. $P^n(i) = 0, \qquad (i = 0, 1, \ldots, n - 1).$

2. $P_i^n(j) = 0, \qquad j \neq i.$

3. $P_i^n(i) = (-1)^{n-i-1} i!(n - i - 1)!.$

4. $P^n(j) = \dfrac{j!}{(j - n)!}, \qquad (j = n, n + 1, \ldots).$

5. $P^n(x + 1) - P^n(x) = nP^{n-1}(x).$

6. $\displaystyle\sum_{i=0}^{r} P^n(x + i) = \dfrac{1}{n + 1} [P^{n+1}(x + r + 1) - P^{n+1}(x)].$

C. *Binomial Coefficients*

An elementary series is that obtained by applying the binomial theorem to the expression $(1 + x)$:

$$(1 + x)^n = 1 + nx + \frac{n(n - 1)}{2!} x^2 + \frac{n(n - 1)(n - 2)}{3!} x^3 + \cdots. \qquad (3.12)$$

The coefficients of this series, called *binomial*, occur frequently in numerical analysis. The most commonly employed notation is the following:

$$\binom{n}{k} = \frac{n(n - 1)(n - 2) \cdots (n - k + 1)}{k!}, \qquad (3.13)$$

where k is any integer.[5] It is easily seen that the numerator on the right-hand side is a factorial polynomial in n of degree k, so that we can write

$$\binom{n}{k} = \frac{P^k(n)}{k!}. \qquad (3.14)$$

The binomial coefficients possess many interesting properties, of which only a few are listed.

Properties. If n is an integer,

1. $\dbinom{n}{k} = \begin{array}{l} 1, \quad \text{if } k = n, \\ 0, \quad \text{if } k > n. \end{array}$

2. $\dbinom{n}{k} = \dbinom{n}{n - k}.$

[5] For completeness the coefficient is defined as 1 when $k = 0$.

3. $\binom{n}{k} = \dfrac{n!}{k!(n-k)!}$.

4. $\binom{n+1}{k} = \binom{n}{k} + \binom{n}{k-1}$.

As is well known (Pascal's triangle), a table of values for the binomial coefficients can easily be tabulated, and by Property 2, only values to the midpoint need be recorded. (See Table I in the back of the book.)

D. Series

Certain portions of numerical analysis are based on fundamentals obtained from series expansions. It is therefore appropriate to review briefly the concept of series expansion, in particular the representation of functions by power series. The second power series usually encountered by a student of mathematics is the *Maclaurin series*.

$$f(x) = f(0) + f'(0)x + f''(0)\frac{x^2}{2!} + f'''(0)\frac{x^3}{3!}$$
$$+ \cdots + f^{(n)}(0)\frac{x^n}{n!} + \cdots, \qquad (3.15)$$

where

$f^{(n)}(0)$ is the value of the nth derivative of $f(x)$ at $x = 0$.

Another well-known expression is the *Taylor series*:

$$(x) = f(a) + f'(a)(x-a) + f''(a)\frac{(x-a)^2}{2!}$$
$$+ \cdots + f^{(n)}(a)\frac{(x-a)^n}{n!} + \cdots. \qquad (3.16)$$

Both may be written as a finite series plus a remainder by the use of the *extended theorem of mean value*. Thus we have

$$f(x) = f(a) + f'(a)(x-a) + \cdots + f^{(n-1)}(a)\frac{(x-a)^{n-1}}{(n-1)!} + R, \qquad (3.17)$$

where

$$R = f^{(n)}(x_1)\frac{(x-a)^n}{n!}; \qquad (a < x_1 < x). \qquad (3.18)$$

Another form of the same power series is the one which is expanded in powers of h, the increment of x; that is, $x = a + h = x_0 + h$:

$$f(x_0 + h) = f(x_0) + f'(x_0)h + f''(x_0)\frac{h^2}{2} + \cdots + f^{(n)}(x_0)\frac{h^n}{n!} + \cdots. \quad (3.19)$$

If we are concerned with a function of two variables, we have the Taylor series about the point (a, b),

$$\begin{aligned} f(x, y) = {} & f(a, b) + f_x(a, b)(x - a) + f_y(a, b)(y - b) \\ & + \tfrac{1}{2}[f_{xx}(a, b)(x - a)^2 + 2f_{xy}(a, b)(x - a)(y - b) \quad (3.20) \\ & + f_{yy}(a, b)(y - b)^2] + \cdots + R_n, \end{aligned}$$

where

$$f_x = \frac{\partial f}{\partial x}, \qquad f_{xx} = \frac{\partial^2 f}{\partial x^2}, \qquad f_{xy} = \frac{\partial^2 f}{\partial x\, \partial y}, \text{ etc.}$$

By adopting the symbolic notation

$$\left(h\frac{\partial}{\partial a} + k\frac{\partial}{\partial b} \right)^n f(a, b) = \sum_{j=0}^{n} \binom{n}{j} h^j k^{n-j} \frac{\partial^n f(a, b)}{\partial a^j\, \partial b^{n-j}}$$

we can write the series in the form

$$f(a + h, b + k) = f(a, b) + \sum_{i=1}^{n-1} \frac{1}{i!} \left[\left(h\frac{\partial}{\partial x} + k\frac{\partial}{\partial y} \right)^i f(x, y) \right]_{\substack{x=a \\ y=b}} + R_n,$$

where

$$R_n = \frac{1}{n!} \left[\left(h\frac{\partial}{\partial x} + k\frac{\partial}{\partial y} \right)^n f(x, y) \right]_{\substack{x=a+\theta h \\ y=b+\theta k}}, \qquad 0 < \theta < 1.$$

A function of several variables may be expanded in a series by Taylor's formula:

$$\begin{aligned} f(x_1 + \Delta x_1, x_2 + \Delta x_2, \ldots, x_n + \Delta x_n) = {} & f(x_1, x_2, \ldots, x_n) \\ + \sum_{i=1}^{n} \Delta x_i \frac{\partial f}{\partial x_i} + \frac{1}{2}\Bigg[\sum_{i=1}^{n} \Delta x_i^2 \frac{\partial^2 f}{\partial x_i^2} & + 2 \sum_{i=1}^{n} \Delta x_i\, \Delta x_{i+1} \frac{\partial^2 f}{\partial x_i\, \partial x_{i+1}} \Bigg] + \cdots. \quad (3.21) \end{aligned}$$

For a thorough discussion of series the reader is referred to any standard textbook on advanced calculus.[6]

E.   Successive Approximations and Iteration

In this book we make a distinction between two very similar processes which are frequently used in numerical analysis; one is called *the method of successive approximations*, the other, *the method of iteration*. Each is applied to the solution for a particular value of a variable which is involved in a formula or functional relation. Let us, for example, find a root of the equation

$$f(x) = 0. \qquad (3.22)$$

The method of successive approximations is concerned with the finding of a sequence of numbers, $x_0, x_1, x_2, \ldots$, which converges to a limit b such that the equation $f(x) = 0$ is satisfied by $x = b$. The process is based on the development of a recursion formula for x_{i+1} in terms of x_i so that x_{i+1} may be calculated after x_i is known. This formula is derived from general considerations independent of the given relation $f(x) = 0$.

The method of iteration also calculates a sequence of values $x_0, x_1, x_2, \ldots$, which converges to the desired value. The process, however, is based on a recursion formula obtained by an explicit solution for the variable x, in terms of the parameters and x, directly from the given relation $f(x) = 0$.

Example 1.3. Let us find a root of the equation

$$f(x) = x^2 + \sin^2 x - 3 = 0.$$

From elementary calculus it may be recalled that a good recursion formula for x_{i+1} is given by Newton's formula for approximating the roots of an equation:

$$x_{i+1} = x_i - \frac{f(x_i)}{f'(x_i)}. \qquad (3.23)$$

This formula for computation was derived independently of the given equation. If from this formula we were to develop a sequence of numbers $x_0, x_1, x_2, \ldots$, which converges to the desired solution, we would be employing the method of successive approximations.

If, on the other hand, we were to solve the equation explicitly for x, in terms of x and the given parameters,

$$x = \pm \sqrt{3 - \sin^2 x}$$

[6]John M. H. Olmsted, *Advanced Calculus*. New York: Appleton-Century-Crofts, 1961.

and then to write the recursion formula

$$x_{i+1} = \pm\sqrt{3 - \sin^2 x_i}$$

for the determination of a sequence of numbers $x_0, x_1, x_2, \ldots$, we would be employing the *method of iteration*.

F.   Undetermined Coefficients

A technique frequently employed by mathematicians is one that may be called the *method of undetermined coefficients*. In the application of this method the mathematician writes down the desired form of a mathematical expression with arbitrary coefficients, which at this stage are undetermined. A sufficient number of conditions are now imposed on the expression so that these undetermined coefficients may be found, and the mathematical expression becomes a specific formula.

A good example of this method was encountered in calculus in the introduction of the Maclaurin series, in which it is stated that a function of x may be written in the form

$$f(x) = a_0 + a_1 x + a_2 x^2 + \cdots + a_n x^n + \cdots.$$

Then the question was raised regarding the form the coefficients a_i, $(i = 0, 1, \ldots)$ were to take in order that the function might be represented by a power series. The coefficients were determined by letting $x = 0$ in the function and its successive derivatives to obtain the expression for the Maclaurin series (3.15).

G.   Derivatives of $\binom{x}{k}$

If we insert a variable x into the binomial coefficient expression, we may differentiate it with respect to x. There are two ways in which this derivative may be written. The first is obtained by differentiating Formula 3.14 with $n = x$ to obtain

$$\frac{d}{dx}\binom{x}{k} = \frac{1}{k!}\frac{d}{dx}P^k(x)$$

$$= \frac{1}{k!}[kS_{0,k}x^{k-1} + (k-1)S_{1,k}x^{k-2} \tag{3.24}$$

$$+ (k-2)S_{2,k}x^{k-3} + \cdots + S_{k-1,k}],$$

where $S_{i,k}$ are the Stirling numbers of the first kind. The second is obtained by differentiating the binomial coefficient expression as the product of k variables:

$$\frac{d}{dx}\binom{x}{k} = \frac{d}{dx}[x(x-1)(x-2)\cdots(x-k+1)]\frac{1}{k!}$$

$$= \frac{1}{k!}[(x-1)(x-2)\cdots(x-k+1)$$

$$+ x(x-2)(x-3)\cdots(x-k+1)$$

$$+ x(x-1)(x-3)\cdots(x-k+1) + \cdots$$

$$+ x(x-1)(x-2)\cdots(x-k+2)].$$

(3.25)

It is to be noted that the bracketed expression is a sum of factorial polynomials with one factor, $x - i$, $(i = 0, 1, \ldots, k - 1)$, missing from each. If the missing factors are inserted and then divided out, we can write[7]

$$\frac{d}{dx}\binom{x}{k} = \binom{x}{k}\left(\frac{1}{x} + \frac{1}{x-1} + \frac{1}{x-2} + \cdots + \frac{1}{x-k+1}\right)$$

$$= \sum_{i=0}^{k-1} \frac{P^k(x)}{k!(x-i)}.$$

(3.26)

A useful recursion formula for varying k may be developed from the formula in (3.25). Let us introduce the symbol

$$D_k(x) = \frac{d}{dx}\binom{x}{k}$$

(3.27)

and consider $k = i$, $(i = 1, 2, 3, \ldots)$; then

$D_1(x) = 1;$

$D_2(x) = \frac{1}{2}[(x-1) + x] = \frac{1}{2}[(x-1)D_1(x) + xb_1(x)];$

$D_3(x) = \frac{1}{3!}[(x-1)(x-2) + x(x-2) + x(x-1)]$

$= \frac{1}{3}\left\{\frac{1}{2}[(x-1) + x](x-2) + \frac{1}{2}x(x-1)\right\}$

$= \frac{1}{3}[(x-2)D_2(x) + (x-1)b_2(x)];$

[7]See Kaj L. Nielsen, *Differential Equations*. New York: Barnes and Noble, 1962, p. 10.

$$D_4(x) = \frac{1}{4!}[(x - 1)(x - 2)(x - 3) + x(x - 2)(x - 3)$$

$$+ x(x - 1)(x - 3) + x(x - 1)(x - 2)]$$

$$= \frac{1}{4}[(x - 3)D_3(x) + (x - 2)b_3(x)].$$

The general formula is

$$D_{i+1}(x) = \frac{1}{i + 1}[(x - i)D_i(x) + (x - i + 1)b_i(x)], \tag{3.28}$$

$$(i = 1, 2, 3, \ldots),$$

where

$$b_i(x) = \frac{1}{i}(x - i + 2)b_{i-1}(x), \qquad (i = 2, 3, 4, \ldots),$$

$$= \frac{1}{i}\binom{x}{i - 1}, \tag{3.29}$$

and

$$D_1(x) = b_1(x) = 1.$$

Formula 3.28 permits rapid evaluation of the first derivatives for changing k since it is the sum of products of two factors followed by a division.

It is especially interesting to obtain the values of the derivative at $x = i$, $(i = 0, \ldots, k)$. From Formula 3.25 it is easily seen that all the expressions in the bracket are zero except the one in which $x - i$ does not occur. Thus we have for $i < k$

$$D_k(i) = \frac{1}{k!}[x(x - 1)\cdots(x - i + 1)(x - i - 1)\cdots(x - k + 1)]_{x=i}$$

$$= \frac{1}{k!}[i(i - 1)\cdots(2)(1)(-1)(-2)\cdots(i - k + 1)] \tag{3.30}$$

$$= (-1)^{k-i-1}\left[\frac{i!(k - i - 1)!}{k!}\right].$$

In particular

$$D_k(0) = \frac{1}{k!}[(x - 1)(x - 2)\cdots(x - k + 1)]_{x=0}$$

$$= (-1)^{k-1}\left[\frac{(k - 1)!}{k!}\right] = (-1)^{k-1}\left[\frac{1}{k}\right],$$

and from Formula 3.26

$$D_k(k) = \frac{1}{k} + \frac{1}{k-1} + \frac{1}{k-2} + \cdots + \frac{1}{1} = \sum_{j=1}^{k} \left(\frac{1}{j}\right). \qquad (3.31)$$

By direct substitution into Formula 3.30, we can arrive at the recursion formula

$$D_k(i) = -\frac{1}{k-i}[D_k(i-1)], \qquad (i < k). \qquad (3.32)$$

The second derivative is obtained by differentiating the first derivative. From Formula 3.24 we obtain

$$D_k^2(x) = \frac{1}{k!}[k(k-1)S_{0,k}x^{k-2} \qquad\qquad\qquad (3.33)$$
$$+ (k-1)(k-2)S_{1,k}x^{k-3} + \cdots + S_{k-2,k}].$$

From Formula 3.28 we obtain

$$D_{i+1}^2(x) = \frac{1}{i+1}[D_i(x) + (x-i)D_i^2(x) + b_i(x) \qquad\qquad (3.34)$$
$$+ (x-i+1)b_i'(x)].$$

Now from Formula 3.29

$$b_i'(x) = \frac{1}{i}\frac{d}{dx}\left(\frac{x}{i-1}\right) = \frac{1}{i}D_{i-1}(x)$$

and by Formula 3.28

$$\frac{1}{i}(x-i+1)D_{i-1}(x) + b_i(x)$$

$$= \frac{1}{i}[(x-i+1)D_{i-1}(x) + (x-i+2)b_{i-1}(x)] = D_i(x).$$

Thus Formula 3.34 becomes

$$D_{i+1}^2(x) = \frac{1}{i+1}[2D_i(x) + (x-i)D_i^2(x)], \qquad (i = 1, 2, 3, \ldots), \qquad (3.35)$$

with

$$D_1^2(x) = 0 \quad \text{and} \quad D_2^2(x) = 1.$$

The general formula for higher derivatives is

$$D_{i+1}^{(n)}(x) = \frac{1}{i+1}[nD_i^{(n-1)}(x) + (x - i)D_i^{(n)}(x)]. \tag{3.36}$$

H. Orthogonal Polynomials[8]

An important property of polynomials which finds wide application in numerical analysis is known as orthogonality. In general, two functions, $g_m(x)$ and $g_n(x)$, are said to be orthogonal if

$$\int_a^b g_m(x)g_n(x)\,dx = 0 \tag{3.37}$$

and a set of functions, $g_n(x)$, $(n = 1, 2, 3, \ldots)$, is orthogonal in the interval (a, b) if the condition in (3.37) is true when $m \neq n$ for all functions of the set.

If, in particular, we consider the set of polynomials

$$P_m(x) = a_0 + a_1 x + a_2 x^2 + \cdots + a_m x^m, \qquad (m = 0, 1, 2, \ldots), \tag{3.38}$$

they are said to be orthogonal in the interval $[-1, 1]$ if

$$\int_{-1}^{1} P_m(x) P_n(x)\,dx = 0, \quad \text{when } (m \neq n). \tag{3.39}$$

A special set of such polynomials in which the leading and last coefficients are

$$a_0 = 1,$$
$$a_n = \frac{(2n - 1)(2n - 3)\cdots(3)(1)}{n!} \tag{3.40}$$

is known as the *Legendre polynomials*. They may be generated by *Rodrigues'* *formula*

$$P_m(x) = \frac{1}{2^m m!} \frac{d^m}{dx^m}(x^2 - 1)^m. \tag{3.41}$$

This set of polynomials has the further property that when $m = n$

$$\int_{-1}^{1} [P_m(x)]^2\,dx = \frac{2}{2m + 1}, \qquad (m = 0, 1, 2, \ldots). \tag{3.42}$$

The zeros of the Legendre polynomials are all real and distinct.

[8] For a thorough discussion of orthogonal polynomials see R. V. Churchill, *Fourier Series and Boundary Value Problems*. New York: McGraw-Hill, 1941.

I. Dimensional Analysis

In applying mathematical formulas to the solution of problems which occur in the physical sciences, it is essential that uniform dimensions be used. Formulas should always be checked for their dimensional accuracy by using ratios and considering the expressions for the dimensions as algebraic quantities. The equations should be dimensionally balanced, and a check will frequently indicate errors in the construction of the mathematical model.

Example 1.4. If x is given in feet, m in slugs, v in feet per second, and t in seconds, prove that the formula $kx = m(dv/dt)$ is accurate when the spring constant k is given in pounds per foot.

SOLUTION.   Since, by definition, slug $=$ lb-sec$/^2$ft and the rate of change of velocity is ft/sec^2, we have

$$\frac{\text{lb}}{\text{ft}} \times \text{ft} = \frac{\text{lb-sec}^2}{\text{ft}} \times \frac{\text{ft}}{\text{sec}^2}$$

or

$$\text{lb} = \text{lb}.$$

Example 1.5. Prove that the formula on Example 1.4 is not correct if the spring constant k is given in pounds per inch and the other dimensions remain the same.

SOLUTION.

$$\frac{\text{lb}}{\text{in.}} \times \text{ft} = \frac{\text{lb-sec}^2}{\text{ft}} \times \frac{\text{ft}}{\text{sec}^2} \quad \text{or} \quad \frac{1 \text{ ft}}{1 \text{ in.}} = 1,$$

which is not true.

The same procedure may be used to change dimensions, since the ratio of equivalent units of measure is one and the value of any expression is unaltered by the multiplication of such ratios.

Example 1.6. How many feet per second does an automobile travel if its speed is 50 mph?

SOLUTION.

$$x\,\frac{\text{ft}}{\text{sec}} = \frac{50 \text{ mi}}{\text{hr}} = \frac{50 \text{ mi}}{1 \text{ hr}} \times \frac{1 \text{ hr}}{3600 \text{ sec}} \times \frac{5280 \text{ ft}}{1 \text{ mi}}$$

$$= \frac{220 \text{ ft}}{3 \text{ sec}} = 73\tfrac{1}{3} \text{ ft/sec.}$$

We present here some "standard" units of measure in the English and metric systems. Some useful constants and conversion factors are listed in Table XX in the back of the book.

I. MECHANICAL UNITS

QUANTITY	SYMBOL	ENGLISH UNITS	MKS UNITS
Displacement	s or x	foot	meter
Time	t	seconds	seconds
Linear velocity	v	ft/sec	meter/sec
Linear acceleration	a	ft/sec^2	meter/sec^2
Angular velocity	ω	rad/sec	rad/sec
Angular acceleration	α	rad/sec^2	rad/sec^2
Mass	m	slug	kilogram
Force	F	pound	newton
Work	W	foot-pound	joule
Moment of inertia	I	slug-ft^2	kg-meter^2

II. ELECTRICAL UNITS

QUANTITY	SYMBOL	ENGLISH UNITS	MKS UNITS
Current	i	ampere	ampere
Resistance	R	ohm	ohm
Capacitance	C	farad	farad
Inductance	L	henry	henry
Charge	q	coulomb	coulomb
Electromotive force	e or E	volt	volt

4. INHERENT ERRORS

In numerical analysis there are three causes of error: (1) the given data are approximate; (2) the formulas and procedures employed are approximate; and (3) errors are made by the computer. Very little can be done about the first of these. Clearly, attempts can be made to obtain better data, to correct obvious errors in the data, and a few things of that nature. The third is, of course, a mistake and is corrected by redoing the problem; diligence on the part of the operator will minimize this error. In general, the second category can be evaluated, and it is desirable that it be made as small as possible. Errors which are the result of approximate procedures are called *inherent*, and most formulas and procedures should have some expression for them. Errors can be expressed in three ways.

Absolute Error. The numerical difference between the true value and the approximate value:

$$E_a = x - x_1 = \Delta x,$$

where x is the true value and x_1 is the calculated or measured approximate value.

Relative Error. The absolute error divided by the true value:

$$E_r = \frac{E_a}{x} = \frac{\Delta x}{x}.$$

Percentage Error. The relative error multiplied by 100, that is, $100E_r$, is the percentage error.

The error committed by a formula or a functional representative can be determined by a *general error formula*. Let

$$N = f(x_1, x_2, \ldots, x_n) \tag{4.1}$$

denote any function of the independent variables x_i, $(i = 1, \ldots, n)$, each of which is subject to error, say Δx_i, $(i = 1, \ldots, n)$, respectively. There is then an error ΔN in the function so that we have

$$N + \Delta N = f(x_1 + \Delta x_1, x_2 + \Delta x_2, \ldots, x_n + \Delta x_n). \tag{4.2}$$

The right-hand side of (4.2) may be expanded in a Taylor series for several variables [see (3.21)] to give us

$$f(x_1 + \Delta x_1, x_2 + \Delta x_2, \ldots, x_n + \Delta x_n) = f(x_1, x_2, \ldots, x_n)$$
$$+ \left(\Delta x_1 \frac{\partial f}{\partial x_1} + \Delta x_2 \frac{\partial f}{\partial x_2} + \cdots + \Delta x_n \frac{\partial f}{\partial x_n} \right)$$
$$+ \frac{1}{2} \left(\Delta x_1^2 \frac{\partial^2 f}{\partial x_1^2} + \cdots + \Delta x_n^2 \frac{\partial^2 f}{\partial x_n^2} + 2\Delta x_1 \Delta x_2 \frac{\partial^2 f}{\partial x_1 \partial x_2} + \cdots \right.$$
$$\left. + 2\Delta x_{n-1} \Delta x_n \frac{\partial^2 f}{\partial x_{n-1} \partial x_n} \right)$$
$$+ \cdots.$$

Usually the errors in the variables should be relatively small, that is, $\Delta x_i/x_i \ll 1$. It is therefore permissible to ignore the squares, cross products, and higher powers of $\Delta x_i, (i = 1, \ldots, n)$, and to write to a *first-order approximation*

$$N + \Delta N \doteq f(x_1, \ldots, x_n) + \sum_{i=1}^{n} \Delta x_i \frac{\partial f}{\partial x_i}. \tag{4.3}$$

If we now subtract (4.1) from (4.3), we obtain

$$\Delta N \doteq \frac{\partial f}{\partial x_1} \Delta x_1 + \frac{\partial f}{\partial x_2} \Delta x_2 + \cdots + \frac{\partial f}{\partial x_n} \Delta x_n. \tag{4.4}$$

Formula 4.4 is a first-order approximation for the error of a function. It may be noted that it is the same expression as that for the total differential of the function N. A formula for the relative error follows directly.

$$E_r = \frac{\Delta N}{N} \doteq \frac{\partial N}{\partial x_1} \frac{\Delta x_1}{N} + \frac{\partial N}{\partial x_2} \frac{\Delta x_2}{N} + \cdots + \frac{\partial N}{\partial x_n} \frac{\Delta x_n}{N}. \tag{4.5}$$

The error formula may be applied to all functions and serves as an evaluation of all processes that can be expressed in formula form.

Example 1.7. Consider the formula

$$N = \frac{3x^2 y}{z^3}.$$

To evaluate the error in N caused by errors in x, y, z, we first determine the partial derivatives

$$\frac{\partial N}{\partial x} = \frac{6xy}{z^3},$$

$$\frac{\partial N}{\partial y} = \frac{3x^2}{z^3},$$

$$\frac{\partial N}{\partial z} = -\frac{9x^2 y}{z^4}.$$

Then

$$\Delta N \doteq 6xyz^{-3} \Delta x + 3x^2 z^{-3} \Delta y - 9x^2 yz^{-4} \Delta z.$$

Into this formula are now substituted the values of the errors Δx, Δy, Δz, and the partial derivatives are evaluated at the desired point, (x_1, y_1, z_1). In general, the errors, Δx, Δy, Δz, may be positive or negative, and if the sign is not specified it is possible to compute only the maximum error in N, in which case we sum the absolute values of the terms on the right-hand side. Thus

$$\Delta N_{max} \doteq |6xyz^{-3} \Delta x| + |3x^2y^{-3} \Delta y| + |9x^2yz^{-4} \Delta z|.$$

It is important to note that this is the maximum error and thus furnishes an upper bound on the error. To continue the example, suppose $\Delta x = \Delta y = \Delta z = .005$; then the maximum error at the point $(1, 1, 1)$ is

$$\Delta N_{max} \doteq 6(.005) + 3(.005) + 9(.005)$$
$$= 18(.005) = .090.$$

The value of the function at $(1, 1, 1)$ is $N = 3$ and the relative maximum error is

$$E_{r_{max}} = \frac{\Delta N}{N}\bigg|_{max} \doteq \frac{1}{3}(.090) = .030.$$

It should again be emphasized that this is the maximum error and that the actual error can be found only if the algebraic signs of the individual errors are known.

As another example let us apply the error formula to the simple operation of addition.

$$N = x + y;$$
$$\Delta N = \Delta x + \Delta y.$$

The inclusion of higher order terms is demanded only in rare situations. Thus, in the Example 1.7 the second-order term is

$$\frac{1}{2}\left(\frac{\partial^2 N}{\partial x^2} \Delta x^2 + \frac{\partial^2 N}{\partial y^2} \Delta y^2 + \frac{\partial^2 N}{\partial z^2} \Delta z^2\right)$$
$$+ \frac{\partial^2 N}{\partial x \, \partial y} \Delta x \, \Delta y + \frac{\partial^2 N}{\partial y \, \partial z} \Delta y \, \Delta z + \frac{\partial^2 N}{\partial x \, \partial z} \Delta x \, \Delta z.$$

The partial derivatives evaluated at $(1, 1, 1)$ become

$$\frac{\partial^2 N}{\partial x^2} = 6yz^{-3} = 6; \qquad \frac{\partial^2 N}{\partial x \, \partial y} = 6xz^{-3} = 6;$$

$$\frac{\partial^2 N}{\partial y^2} = 0; \qquad \frac{\partial^2 N}{\partial y \, \partial z} = -9x^2z^{-4} = -9;$$

$$\frac{\partial^2 N}{\partial z^2} = 36x^2yz^{-5} = 36; \qquad \frac{\partial^2 N}{\partial x \, \partial z} = -18xyz^{-4} = -18.$$

The squares and cross products of the errors for

$$\Delta x = \Delta y = \Delta z = .005$$

become

$$\Delta x^2 = \Delta y^2 = \Delta z^2 = \Delta x \, \Delta y = \Delta x \, \Delta z = \Delta y \, \Delta z = .000025.$$

The maximum error at $(1, 1, 1)$ including second-order terms is

$$\Delta N_{max} \doteq .090 + [3 + 0 + 18 + 6 + 9 + 18].000025$$
$$= .09135.$$

The errors committed by series expansions can be evaluated by the remainder after n terms. In a normal course in calculus formulas for the remainders in series expansion are given in terms of the nth derivative at an intermediate point. We also list the remainder in integral form which is obtained by repeated integration by parts of

$$\frac{1}{(n-1)!} \int_0^x f^{(n)}(x-t) t^{n-1} \, dt$$

where $f(x-t)$ is a continuous function of t in the interval from 0 to x. Remainder terms for some well-known series are listed.

I. MACLAURIN SERIES (3.15)

$$R_n(x) = \frac{x^n}{n!} f^{(n)}(x_1), \qquad 0 < x_1 < x. \tag{4.6}$$

$$R_n(x) = \frac{1}{(n-1)!} \int_0^x f^{(n)}(x-t) t^{n-1} \, dt. \tag{4.7}$$

II. TAYLOR SERIES (3.16)

Lagrange Form

$$R_n(x) = \frac{(x-a)^n}{n!} f^{(n)}(x_1), \qquad (a < x_1 < x). \tag{4.8}$$

Cauchy Form

$$R_n(x) = \frac{(x-a)(x-x_1)^{n-1}}{(n-1)!} f^{(n)}(x_1), \qquad (a < x_1 < x). \tag{4.9}$$

Integral Form

$$R_n(x) = \frac{1}{(n-1)!} \int_0^{x-a} f^{(n)}(x-t) t^{n-1} \, dt. \tag{4.10}$$

III. TAYLOR SERIES (3.19)

Lagrange Form

$$R_n(x) = \frac{h^n}{n!} f^{(n)}(x_1), \qquad (x_0 < x_1 < x). \qquad (4.11)$$

Integral Form

$$R_n(x) = \frac{1}{(n-1)!} \int_0^h f^{(n)}(x+h-t)t^{n-1} \, dt. \qquad (4.12)$$

For a thorough discussion of Taylor's formula with a remainder the reader is referred to a book on advanced calculus.[9]

Example 1.8. Evaluate the remainder after six terms in the series expansion for e^x at $x = 2$.

SOLUTION. The Maclaurin series for e^x is

$$e^x = 1 + x + \frac{x^2}{2!} + \frac{x^3}{3!} + \frac{x^4}{4!} + \frac{x^5}{5!} + \frac{x^6}{6!} + \cdots + R_n.$$

The sixth term is

$$f^{(5)}(0)\frac{x^5}{5!} = \frac{x^5}{5!};$$

thus $n = 6$ and

$$R_6 = \frac{x^6}{6!} f^{(6)}(x_1), \qquad 0 < x_1 < 2$$

$$= \frac{2^6}{6!} e^{x_1} = \frac{4}{45} e^{x_1}.$$

Since $x_1 < 2$,

$$R_6 < \frac{4}{45} e^2 = \frac{4}{45}(7.38906) = .65681.$$

If we use five-decimal-place accuracy with $x = 2$,

$$1 + x + \frac{x^2}{2!} + \frac{x^3}{3!} + \frac{x^4}{4!} + \frac{x^5}{5!} = 7.26667,$$

so that

$$R_6 = e^2 - 7.26667 = 7.38906 - 7.26667 = .12239.$$

[9]John M. H. Olmsted, *Advanced Calculus.* New York: Appleton-Century-Crofts, 1961. David V. Widder, *Advanced Calculus.* Englewood Cliffs, N. J.: Prentice-Hall, 1961.

To get this value of R_6, we would need to know the particular value of x_1, which could be obtained from the solution of the equation

$$\frac{4}{45} e^{x_1} = .12239 \quad \text{or} \quad x_1 = .32,$$

and the condition $0 < x_1 < 2$ would be satisfied. In practice, of course, we do not know the true value of R_6 or x_1. Instead, we take enough terms of the series so that R_n is less than the desired degree of accuracy. In this example

$$R_{14} < \frac{8}{42567525} (7.38906) = .000001388,$$

so that we would need to take 13 terms of the series to get five-decimal-place accuracy.

5.   CALCULATING MACHINES

Since numerical analysis is concerned with calculations, it depends heavily on calculating machines for the accomplishment of its work. The great amount of labor involved in employing some of the techniques derived in this book would be prohibitive if it were not for modern automatic calculators. In fact, many of the techniques known to mathematicians for years remained dormant awaiting the invention of these machines. The tremendous growth in the computing machinery field in recent years has reactivated interest in numerical analysis and has permitted refinements in techniques dictated by experience and practice. Many of the refinements are presented in this book, but it must be kept in mind that refinements are made every day.

A complete survey of calculating machines has not been attempted here. In fact, the operation of calculators is not taught, since each type of machine has an excellent handbook on operational methods.

This book is written on the assumption that the student will have available an automatic desk calculator and will know how to operate it. One comment may be made in order. If a student writes with his *right* hand, this author strongly recommends that he learn to operate the calculator with his *left* hand and vice versa.

There are many brands of desk calculators now on the market. Each machine has certain specialized features, but, in general, all perform the arithmetical operations in comparable fashion. In the ordinary calculator the operator copies the answers from the dials to a computing paper, although a desk calculator has been joined to a typewriter so that the answers can be automatically recorded. The speed of operation depends on the operator, and in the next section we discuss the benefits to be derived from programming and systematic arrays.

There are many large-scale digital calculators in operation, which have grown from the specialized computers designed for military purposes to commercial ones being sold. It would be impossible to enumerate the features of each. Fundamentally, the machines receive input data and coded instructions from punched cards or tapes, and the operations are performed electronically. The results may be put on punched cards or tapes or printed by a printer. Each problem is programmed for the machine, and special experience with the particular machine is necessary.

6.   PROGRAMMING

The term *programming* has become popular with the innovation of the large-scale machines; however, its widest connotation simply implies the preparation of a problem for a machine and should also apply to desk calculators. The solution of any mathematical problem should be accomplished in a systematic manner. Each problem must be carefully arranged for the machine; recording of intermediate results should be reduced to a minimum, periodic checks should be inserted to spot mistakes, and the results should be neatly presented.

On most desk calculators, whenever possible, the problem should be reduced to a *sum of products of two numbers followed by a division if required*; that is, the formulas should be rearranged into a form of this type insofar as possible:

$$N = \frac{(a)(b) + (c)(d) - (e)(f)}{r}.$$

Furthermore, common factors or constants should be isolated in order that they may be locked into the calculator at the appropriate time. Thus

$$N = kx,$$

where k is a constant, would be accomplished by locking k into the keyboard or multiplier and varying x.

In performing lengthy calculations, it is recommended that columnar paper be used on which the appropriate formulas can be listed at the top and each column specifically labeled. If it is necessary to scale the problem, such scaling should be clearly indicated at each column.

Many examples are presented in this book. It is hoped that the reader will develop a systematic arrangement of his work, for it has been said that one of the great by-products of mathematics is a development of a logical and systematic approach to the solution of problems, and this applies to numerical analysis as well as to other branches.

Example 1.9. Find y for $x = 1.261$, .327, and 2.541 in the formula

$$y = \frac{3.2x^2 - 1.53x + x\sqrt{2x+5}}{x+2.12}.$$

SOLUTION. The formula is rewritten in the form $y = N/D$, where

$$N = x(\sqrt{2x+5} - 1.53 + 3.2x).$$
$$D = x + 2.12,$$

and only D need be recorded as an intermediate value. The values of x are rearranged in ascending order. The calculating sheet would be arranged as follows:

$$y = N/D \qquad\qquad \text{No. 1}$$
$$N = x(\sqrt{2x+5} - 1.53 + 3.2x) \qquad 12/3/63$$
$$D = x + 2.12 \qquad\qquad \text{KLN}$$

x	D	y		
.327	2.447	.2531		
1.261	3.381	1.9573		
2.541	4.661	5.3297		

All calculations should be labeled, paged, dated, and initialed by the calculator.

7.   MATHEMATICAL TABLES

One of the greatest aids to computational procedures is the mathematical table. The reader is already familiar with trigonometric, logarithmic, exponential, and other common tables. Whenever possible, mathematicians have listed values of functions and placed them in tables for others to use. The use of large-scale calculators has permitted the calculations of many tables, and it is indeed difficult to know of all existing ones.[10]

[10]For a good discussion of mathematical tables and an excellent listing of current tables see John Todd, *Survey of Numerical Analysis*. New York: McGraw-Hill, 1962, pp. 93–106.

A *table* is a listing of values of functions or dependent variables for given values of the independent variable usually called the *argument*. All values of the argument cannot be listed, and so tables are given at discrete points, usually at equally spaced intervals of the argument. Once the table is listed, it may be used to find the value of the function or the value of the argument. If it is desired to find the value of either for a given value that is not identical with the given table value, it becomes necessary to approximate between the given values. This process is called interpolation and forms a large part of this book.

Among the many tables now published, there is one type that lists coefficients for numerical processes which is of great importance to the numerical analyst. This is a table of numbers used as multipliers in a numerical method; they are, of course, associated with the process. Those that are most useful are listed in the back of this book.

One word of advice is appropriate at this time and pertains to the finding of an argument from a tabulated function; for example, the finding of an angle from trigonometric functions. Some tables will lead to greater errors than others, and when there is a choice of tables to use the errors should be investigated. Thus it is better to obtain an angle from the tangent function than from the sine function.

8.   EXERCISE I

1. Round off the following numbers correctly to five significant figures:

$$38.46235, \quad 2.37425, \quad .00237135, \quad .700029.$$

2. Find the sum of

$$12.3172, \quad 11.283, \quad 4.3496, \quad 2.4875.$$

3. Evaluate the formula

$$v = \left(\frac{2ghd}{fx}\right)^{1/2}$$

if $g = 32.2$, $h = 92$, $d = \frac{3}{8}$, $f = .025$, and $x = 1250$.

(a) When the given values are considered to be exact.
(b) When the given values are approximate.

4. Find the value of $f(x)$ in

$$f(x) = 7x^4 - 5x^3 + x^2 - 8x + 2$$

for $x = 2, 3, 2\frac{1}{2}, 1.3298$.

5. Express the polynomial

$$P(x) = x^5 + 2x^4 - 7x^3 + 8x^2 - x + 4$$

as the sum of factorial polynomials.

6. Prove the following properties:

(a) $P_n(i) = (-1)^{n-i-1} i!(n-i-1)!$

(b) $P^n(x+1) - P^n(x) = nP^{n-1}(x)$

(c) $\dfrac{d}{dx} P^n(x) = P^n(x) \displaystyle\sum_{i=0}^{n-1} \dfrac{1}{x-i}.$

7. Prove

$$\binom{n+1}{k} = \binom{n}{k} + \binom{n}{k-1}$$

if n is an integer.

8. Expand the following functions in a Maclaurin series:

$$\sin x, \ e^x, \ \cos x, \ \tan x.$$

9. If f is in error by $\Delta f = .005$, what is the error in v in **Problem 3**?

10. Evaluate the remainder after five terms in the series expansion for $\sin x$ at $x = .5$ rad.

11. Plot the family of curves

$$y - c = 4ax^2$$

for $c = 0, 1, 2, 3, 4$.

12. A mathematical model for the drag on a projectile is

$$D = K_D \rho \, d^2 v^2$$

where the drag D is given in (mass)(ft)/sec^2; the air density ρ in (mass)/ft^3; the diameter d of the projectile in ft; and the projectile velocity v relative to the air in ft/sec. Prove that the drag coefficient K_D is dimensionless.

13. Evaluate the formula of Problem 12 for the approximate values

$$K_D = .0398, \quad \rho = .1732, \quad d = .493, \quad V = 2780.$$

14. Given the formula $N = 3x^7 - 6x$, find the percentage error in N at $x = 1$ if the error in x is .05.

15. Derive the first five Legendre polynomials by using Rodrigues' formula and prove that P_3 and P_4 are orthogonal.

16. Check Formula 3.42 for the polynomials of Problem 15.

17. Write $D_3(x)$ and $D_4(x)$ as polynomials in x.

18. Obtain $D_k(x)$ at $x = 0, 1, 2, 3, 4, 5$.

19. Prove $D_k(i) = -i(k-1)^{-1}[D_k(i-1)]$.

20. The solution for the current flowing in a certain electrical circuit is found from the differential equation to be

$$i = 4.3 \cos 120\pi t + 7.5 \sin 120\pi t$$
$$- e^{-600t}(4.3 \cos 200t + 27.1 \sin 200t).$$

Find the value of the current at $t = .01$ and $t = 5$.

21. Use power series to show that $e^{ix} = \cos x + i \sin x$.

22. Evaluate the determinants

$$\begin{vmatrix} -75 & 76 & 20 \\ 94 & 72 & 21 \\ -414 & 55 & 10 \end{vmatrix} \quad \text{and} \quad \begin{vmatrix} -75 & 76 & 20 \\ 94 & 72 & 21 \\ -414 & 55 & 10.01 \end{vmatrix}.$$

23. Given $3P^3(x) - 5P^2(x)$,

(a) find $P(x)$;

(b) change the given expression to one involving only $P^i(x+1)$, $(i = 0, 1, 2, 3)$ (*Hint*. use Property 5);

(c) change to an expression of $P^i(x-1)$ terms.

24. Show that

$$4[P^3(x) + P^3(x+1) + P^3(x+2)] = P^4(x+3) - P^4(x).$$

25. Show that

$$\binom{n}{0} + \binom{n}{1} + \binom{n}{2} + \cdots + \binom{n}{n-1} + \binom{n}{n} = 2^n.$$

2

Finite Differences

9. INTRODUCTION

The calculus of finite differences is employed to a large extent in numerical calculations. It forms the basis for many processes and is used in the derivation of many formulas. It is not the intention here to give a complete discussion of the calculus of finite differences but rather to extract only that which is necessary for numerical methods.[1]

In numerical methods we are concerned with functions of a continuous variable. Such a function may be defined by a formula, and thus its value can be calculated for a given value of the independent variable. On the other hand, a function may be specified by a table of values and not explicitly defined by a formula. In this case, when the function is given at discrete tabular values of the independent variable, it is not formally defined at any other value. However, under the assumption that the function exists for all values of the independent variable in a given interval, we shall seek to obtain a good approximation of its value for any given value of the independent variable in the specified interval. We elaborate on this point in Section 21 and meanwhile turn to the important tool contained in finite differences.

10. FIRST DIFFERENCE

Let the function $y = f(x)$ be given at discrete values of x, so that we have a table of values

[1]See C. Jordan, *Calculus of Finite Differences*. New York: Chelsea, 1947.

x	x_0	x_1	x_2	x_3	x_4	$\cdots$	x_n
y	y_0	y_1	y_2	y_3	y_3	$\cdots$	y_n

If we now subtract from each value of y the preceding value of y,

$$(y_1 - y_0), (y_2 - y_1), \ldots, (y_n - y_{n-1}),$$

the result is called the *first difference* of the function y. We denote these differences by Δy_i in which the subscript of Δy is the same as the *second member* of the difference. Thus

$$y_1 - y_0 = \Delta y_0,$$
$$y_2 - y_1 = \Delta y_1,$$
$$\vdots \qquad\qquad (10.1)$$
$$y_n - y_{n-1} = \Delta y_{n-1}.$$

To illustrate, let us consider the following example.

Example 2.1.

x	y	Δy
1.0	1.36491	
1.1	1.59432	$.22941 = \Delta y_0$
1.2	1.82419	$.22987 = \Delta y_1$
1.3	2.14926	$.32507 = \Delta y_2$
1.4	2.37812	$.22886 = \Delta y_3$
1.5	2.63212	$.25400 = \Delta y_4$
1.6	2.94160	$.30948 = \Delta y_5$
1.7	3.34217	$.40057 = \Delta y_6$
1.8	3.68947	$.34730 = \Delta y_7$
1.9	4.01340	$.32393 = \Delta y_8$

It is easily seen that

$$\Delta y_0 = 1.59432 - 1.36491 = .22941,$$

etc. The differences are usually written on a line between the two numbers for which they represent the differences. To compute the differences of an increasing function on a calculating machine, start with the bottom number and work up the table; this permits locking a number in the keyboard and holding it there for two operations.

II.   HIGHER DIFFERENCES

If we now consider the differences of the first differences, we will obtain a set of quantities called second differences which may be denoted by a superscript on Δ. Thus

$$
\begin{aligned}
\Delta^2 y_0 &= \Delta y_1 - \Delta y_0, \\
\Delta^2 y_1 &= \Delta y_2 - \Delta y_1, \\
&\;\;\vdots \\
\Delta^2 y_i &= \Delta y_{i+1} - \Delta y_i.
\end{aligned}
\tag{11.1}
$$

The process could be continued to define third differences as the difference of second differences.

$$
\Delta^3 y_i = \Delta^2 y_{i+1} - \Delta^2 y_i.
\tag{11.2}
$$

In general, we define the nth differences by the formula

$$
\Delta^n y_i = \Delta^{n-1} y_{i+1} - \Delta^{n-1} y_i.
\tag{11.3}
$$

Although each higher difference is defined in terms of the next lower difference, it is possible by continuous substitution to obtain the higher differences in terms of the values of the function. Thus

$$
\begin{aligned}
\Delta^2 y_0 &= \Delta y_1 - \Delta y_0 = y_2 - y_1 - (y_1 - y_0) = y_2 - 2y_1 + y_0, \\
\Delta^2 y_1 &= \Delta y_2 - \Delta y_1 = y_3 - y_2 - (y_2 - y_1) = y_3 - 2y_2 + y_1,
\end{aligned}
\tag{11.4}
$$

and

$$
\begin{aligned}
\Delta^3 y_0 &= \Delta^2 y_1 - \Delta^2 y_0 = y_3 - 2y_2 + y_1 - (y_2 - 2y_1 + y_0) \\
&= y_3 - 3y_2 + 3y_1 - y_0.
\end{aligned}
\tag{11.5}
$$

The general formula is given by

$$
\begin{aligned}
\Delta^n y_0 &= y_n - \binom{n}{1} y_{n-1} + \binom{n}{2} y_{n-2} - \cdots + (-1)^n y_0 \\
&= \sum_{i=0}^{n} (-1)^i \binom{n}{i} y_{n-i},
\end{aligned}
\tag{11.6}
$$

where $\binom{n}{i}$ is the binomial coefficient notation.

The procedure may be reversed to express a value of y in terms of the initial value of y and differences. From Formula 10.1 we have

$$
y_1 = y_0 + \Delta y_0
\tag{11.7}
$$

and from (11.5) we obtain, on substitution of known values,

$$
\begin{aligned}
y_3 &= y_0 - 3y_1 + 3y_2 + \Delta^3 y_0 \\
&= y_0 + 3\Delta y_1 + \Delta^3 y_0 \\
&= y_0 + 3(\Delta^2 y_0 + \Delta y_0) + \Delta^3 y_0 \\
&= y_0 + 3\Delta y_0 + 3\Delta^2 y_0 + \Delta^3 y_0.
\end{aligned}
\tag{11.8}
$$

In general, we may write

$$
\begin{aligned}
y_k &= y_0 + \binom{k}{1}\Delta y_0 + \binom{k}{2}\Delta^2 y_0 + \cdots + \Delta^k y_0 \\
&= \sum_{i=0}^{k}\binom{k}{i}\Delta^i y_0.
\end{aligned}
\tag{11.9}
$$

12.   DIFFERENCE TABLES

Differences are usually arranged in tabular form, and one of the most commonly employed schemes is the diagonal difference table shown in Table 2.1.

TABLE 2.1.   DIAGONAL DIFFERENCE TABLE

x	y	Δy	$\Delta^2 y$	$\Delta^3 y$	$\Delta^4 y$	$\Delta^5 y$	$\Delta^6 y$	$\Delta^7 y$	$\Delta^8 y$
x_0	y_0								
		Δy_0							
x_1	y_1		$\Delta^2 y_0$						
		Δy_1		$\Delta^3 y_0$					
x_2	y_2		$\Delta^2 y_1$		$\Delta^4 y_0$				
		Δy_2		$\Delta^3 y_1$		$\Delta^5 y_0$			
x_3	y_3		$\Delta^2 y_2$		$\Delta^4 y_1$		$\Delta^6 y_0$		
		Δy_3		$\Delta^3 y_2$		$\Delta^5 y_1$		$\Delta^7 y_0$	
x_4	y_4		$\Delta^2 y_3$		$\Delta^4 y_2$		$\Delta^6 y_1$		$\Delta^8 y_0$
		Δy_4		$\Delta^3 y_3$		$\Delta^5 y_2$		$\Delta^7 y_1$	
x_5	y_5		$\Delta^2 y_4$		$\Delta^4 y_3$		$\Delta^6 y_2$		
		Δy_5		$\Delta^3 y_4$		$\Delta^5 y_3$			
x_6	y_6		$\Delta^2 y_5$		$\Delta^4 y_4$				
		Δy_6		$\Delta^3 y_5$					
x_7	y_7		$\Delta^2 y_6$						
		Δy_7							
x_8	y_8								

As an example of the diagonal difference table, let us complete Example 2.1 to six differences.

x	y	Δy	$\Delta^2 y$	$\Delta^3 y$	$\Delta^4 y$	$\Delta^5 y$	$\Delta^6 y$
1.0	1.36491						
		22941					
1.1	1.59432		46				
		22987		9474			
1.2	1.82419		9520		-28615		
		32507		-19141		59891	
1.3	2.14926		-9621		31276		-100268
		22886		12135		-40377	
1.4	2.37812		2514		-9101		50005
		25400		3034		9628	
1.5	2.63212		5548		527		-28152
		30948		3561		-18524	
1.6	2.94160		9109		-17997		53947
		40057		-14436		35423	
1.7	3.34217		-5327		17426		
		34730		2990			
1.8	3.68947		-2337				
		32393					
1.9	4.01340						

In the construction of this table the decimal points have been omitted in writing the differences. This is common practice to save time and space; it is understood that all numbers are carried to the same accuracy as the given data, and thus the decimal point and the insignificant zeros can easily be restored. For example,

$$\Delta^4 y_3 = .00527,$$

although it is listed in the table as merely 527.

A special form of diagonal difference table is one that is called a central difference table and is identical to the diagonal difference table except that the values of function are ordered around a central value y_0. The values of the independent variable are numbered $\ldots, x_{-3}, x_{-2}, x_{-1}, x_0, x_1, x_2, x_3, \ldots$, and the corresponding values of the function, $\ldots, y_{-3}, y_{-2}, y_{-1}, y_0, y_1, y_2, y_3, \ldots$. A central difference table is shown in Table 2.2.

TABLE 2.2.   CENTRAL DIFFERENCE TABLE

x	y	Δy	$\Delta^2 y$	$\Delta^3 y$	$\Delta^4 y$	$\Delta^5 y$	$\Delta^6 y$	$\Delta^7 y$	$\Delta^8 y$
x_{-4}	y_{-4}								
		Δy_{-4}							
x_{-3}	y_{-3}		$\Delta^2 y_{-4}$						
		Δy_{-3}		$\Delta^3 y_{-4}$					
x_{-2}	y_{-2}		$\Delta^2 y_{-3}$		$\Delta^4 y_{-4}$				
		Δy_{-2}		$\Delta^3 y_{-3}$		$\Delta^5 y_{-4}$			
x_{-1}	y_{-1}		$\Delta^2 y_{-2}$		$\Delta^4 y_{-3}$		$\Delta^6 y_{-4}$		
		Δy_{-1}		$\Delta^3 y_{-2}$		$\Delta^5 y_{-3}$		$\Delta^7 y_{-4}$	
x_0	y_0		$\Delta^2 y_{-1}$		$\Delta^4 y_{-2}$		$\Delta^6 y_{-3}$		$\Delta^8 y_{-4}$
		Δy_0		$\Delta^3 y_{-1}$		$\Delta^5 y_{-2}$		$\Delta^7 y_{-3}$	
x_1	y_1		$\Delta^2 y_0$		$\Delta^4 y_{-1}$		$\Delta^6 y_{-2}$		$\Delta^8 y_{-3}$
		Δy_1		$\Delta^3 y_0$		$\Delta^5 y_{-1}$		$\Delta^7 y_{-2}$	
x_2	y_2		$\Delta^2 y_1$		$\Delta^4 y_0$		$\Delta^6 y_{-1}$		
		Δy_2		$\Delta^3 y_1$		$\Delta^5 y_0$			
x_3	y_3		$\Delta^2 y_2$		$\Delta^4 y_1$				
		Δy_3		$\Delta^3 y_2$					
x_4	y_4		$\Delta^2 y_3$						
		Δy_4							
x_5	y_5								

In our definition of a central difference table we have preserved the original notation for differences, as defined in Section 11, in order not to cause unnecessary confusion. The central difference table is one that focuses attention on those around a horizontal line through the central value.

	Δy_{-1}		$\Delta^3 y_{-2}$		$\Delta^5 y_{-3}$
y_0		$\Delta^2 y_{-1}$		$\Delta^4 y_{-2}$		$\Delta^6 y_{-3}$
	Δy_0		$\Delta^3 y_{-1}$		$\Delta^5 y_{-2}$

It is seen that for this line there are entries for only the even-order differences. For certain kinds of numerical analyses it is desirable to have an entry on this line for the odd differences as well, and this is accomplished by taking the arithmetic mean of the two adjacent differences. Thus in our notation we can define

$$m_{2i-1} = \tfrac{1}{2}(\Delta^{2i-1}y_{-i} + \Delta^{2i-1}y_{-i+1}), \qquad (i = 1, 2, 3, \ldots), \qquad (12.1)$$

so that

$$i = 1: \qquad m_1 = \tfrac{1}{2}(\Delta y_{-1} + \Delta y_0),$$

$$i = 2: \qquad m_3 = \tfrac{1}{2}(\Delta^3 y_{-2} + \Delta^3 y_{-1}), \text{ etc.}$$

The horizontal line through the central value would then have the entries:

y_0	m_1	$\Delta^2 y_{-1}$	m_3	$\Delta^4 y_{-2}$	m_5	$\Delta^6 y_{-3}$	$\cdots$

For some purposes it may be desirable to focus attention on a line between the values y_0 and y_1, which we could call the $y_{\frac{1}{2}}$ line.

y_0		$\Delta^2 y_{-1}$		$\Delta^4 y_{-2}$		$\Delta^6 y_{-3}$	
	Δy_0		$\Delta^3 y_{-1}$		$\Delta^5 y_{-2}$		$\Delta^7 y_{-3}$
y_1		$\Delta^2 y_0$		$\Delta^4 y_{-1}$		$\Delta^6 y_{-2}$	

Here are recorded only the odd-order differences. Following the same procedure, we may now define the arithmetic mean of the adjacent even-order differences by the formula

$$m_{2i} = \tfrac{1}{2}(\Delta^{2i}y_{-i} + \Delta^{2i}y_{-i+1}), \qquad (i = 0, 1, 2, \ldots), \qquad (12.2)$$

so that

$$i = 0: \qquad m_0 = \tfrac{1}{2}(y_0 + y_1),$$

$$i = 1: \qquad m_2 = \tfrac{1}{2}(\Delta^2 y_{-1} + \Delta^2 y_0), \text{ etc.}$$

The horizontal line through these values would then have the entries

m_0	Δy_0	m_2	$\Delta^3 y_{-1}$	m_4	$\Delta^5 y_{-2}$	m_6	$\Delta^7 y_{-8}$	$\cdots$

By combining all of the foregoing into one central difference table we can present Table 2.3.

TABLE 2.3.   CENTRAL DIFFERENCE TABLE WITH ARITHMETIC MEANS

x	y	Δy	$\Delta^2 y$	$\Delta^3 y$	$\Delta^4 y$	$\Delta^5 y$	$\Delta^6 y$	$\Delta^7 y$	$\Delta^8 y$	$\Delta^9 y$
x_{-4}	y_{-4}									
		Δy_{-4}								
x_{-3}	y_{-3}		$\Delta^2 y_{-4}$							
		Δy_{-3}		$\Delta^3 y_{-4}$						
x_{-2}	y_{-2}		$\Delta^2 y_{-3}$		$\Delta^4 y_{-4}$					
		Δy_{-2}		$\Delta^3 y_{-3}$		$\Delta^5 y_{-4}$				
x_{-1}	y_{-1}		$\Delta^2 y_{-2}$		$\Delta^4 y_{-3}$		$\Delta^6 y_{-4}$			
		Δy_{-1}		$\Delta^3 y_{-2}$		$\Delta^5 y_{-3}$		$\Delta^7 y_{-4}$		
x_0	y_0	m_1	$\Delta^2 y_{-1}$	m_3	$\Delta^4 y_{-2}$	m_5	$\Delta^6 y_{-3}$	m_7	$\Delta^8 y_{-4}$	
	m_0	Δy_0	m_2	$\Delta^3 y_{-1}$	m_4	$\Delta^5 y_{-2}$	m_6	$\Delta^7 y_{-3}$	m_8	$\Delta^9 y_{-4}$
x_1	y_1		$\Delta^2 y_0$		$\Delta^4 y_{-1}$		$\Delta^6 y_{-2}$		$\Delta^8 y_{-3}$	
		Δy_1		$\Delta^3 y_0$		$\Delta^5 y_{-1}$		$\Delta^7 y_{-2}$		
x_2	y_2		$\Delta^2 y_1$		$\Delta^4 y_0$		$\Delta^6 y_{-1}$			
		Δy_2		$\Delta^3 y_1$		$\Delta^5 y_0$				
x_3	y_3		$\Delta^2 y_2$		$\Delta^4 y_1$					
		Δy_3		$\Delta^3 y_2$						
x_4	y_4		$\Delta^2 y_3$							
		Δy_4								
x_5	y_5									

Example 2.2. To illustrate the central difference table, the differences have been calculated with $x_0 = 1.5$. The values for m_r are simply the arithmetic means of the vertically adjacent differences and are calculated after the differences have been evaluated. In this example all differences above the fifth are zero.

x	y	Δy	$\Delta^2 y$	$\Delta^3 y$	$\Delta^4 y$	$\Delta^5 y$
1.0	−3.00000					
		137372				
1.1	−1.62628		40840			
		178212		10620		
1.2	.15584		51460		2160	
		229672		12780		240
1.3	2.45256		64240		2400	
		293912		15180		240
1.4	5.39168		79420		2640	
		373332		17820		240
1.5	9.12500	421952	97240	192600	2880	240
	11.47786	470572	107590	20700	3000	240
1.6	13.83072		117940		3120	
		588512		23820		240
1.7	19.71584		141760		3360	
		730272		27180		240
1.8	27.01856		168940		3600	
		899212		30780		
1.9	36.01068		199720			
		1098932				
2.0	47.00000					

By direct reference to the definitions and some algebraic manipulation, it is possible to solve for any difference in terms of other differences. Of particular importance are formulas that express the differences of y_0 in terms of the entries on the horizontal lines through y_0 and $y_{\frac{1}{2}}$. We shall derive some of these expressions. Consider first those in terms of quantities on the line through y_0. From the definitions in (11.1) and (12.1) we have

$$\Delta y_0 = \Delta^2 y_{-1} + \Delta y_{-1}$$
$$= \Delta^2 y_{-1} + 2m_1 - \Delta y_0,$$

and solving for Δy_0 we obtain

$$\Delta y_0 = m_1 + \tfrac{1}{2}\Delta^2 y_{-1}. \qquad (12.3)$$

Before proceeding, we note that in general from the definitions we have

$$\Delta^{2i}y_{-i} = \Delta^{2i-1}y_{1-i} - \Delta^{2i-1}y_{-i},$$

$$2m_{2i-1} = \Delta^{2i-1}y_{1-i} + \Delta^{2i-1}y_{-i},$$

from which we get by an addition and division by 2

$$\Delta^{2i-1}y_{1-i} = m_{2i-1} + \tfrac{1}{2}\Delta^{2i}y_{-i}. \qquad (12.4)$$

To obtain an expression for $\Delta^2 y_0$, we write from the definition and (12.4) with $i = 2$

$$\begin{aligned}
\Delta^2 y_0 &= \Delta^2 y_{-1} + \Delta^3 y_{-1} \\
&= \Delta^2 y_{-1} + m_3 + \tfrac{1}{2}\Delta^4 y_{-2}.
\end{aligned} \qquad (12.5)$$

For $\Delta^3 y_0$ we have

$$\begin{aligned}
\Delta^3 y_0 &= \Delta^3 y_{-1} + \Delta^4 y_{-1} \\
&= m_3 + \tfrac{1}{2}\Delta^4 y_{-2} + \Delta^4 y_{-1},
\end{aligned}$$

in which we wish to replace $\Delta^4 y_{-1}$, since it is not on the line through y_0. From the definition and (12.4) with $i = 3$ we have

$$\begin{aligned}
\Delta^4 y_{-1} &= \Delta^4 y_{-2} + \Delta^5 y_{-2} \\
&= \Delta^4 y_{-2} + m_5 + \tfrac{1}{2}\Delta^6 y_{-3}
\end{aligned}$$

so that

$$\Delta^3 y_0 = m_3 + \tfrac{3}{2}\Delta^4 y_{-2} + m_5 + \tfrac{1}{2}\Delta^6 y_{-3}. \qquad (12.6)$$

The procedure is now quite clear, and for $\Delta^4 y_0$ we have

$$\begin{aligned}
\Delta^4 y_0 &= \Delta^4 y_{-1} + \Delta^5 y_{-1} \\
&= \Delta^4 y_{-2} + \Delta^5 y_{-2} + \Delta^5 y_{-2} + \Delta^6 y_{-2} \\
&= \Delta^4 y_{-2} + 2\Delta^5 y_{-2} + \Delta^6 y_{-3} + \Delta^7 y_{-3} \\
&= \Delta^4 y_{-2} + 2(m_5 + \tfrac{1}{2}\Delta^6 y_{-3}) + \Delta^6 y_{-3} + m_7 + \tfrac{1}{2}\Delta^8 y_{-4} \\
&= \Delta^4 y_{-2} + 2m_5 + 2\Delta^6 y_{-3} + m_7 + \tfrac{1}{2}\Delta^8 y_{-4}.
\end{aligned} \qquad (12.7)$$

Similarly,

$$\Delta^5 y_0 = m_5 + \tfrac{5}{2}\Delta^6 y_{-3} + 3m_7 + \tfrac{5}{2}\Delta^8 y_{-4} + m_9 + \tfrac{1}{2}\Delta^{10} y_{-5}. \qquad (12.8)$$

The processes may be continued as far as desired.

To obtain y_0 and the corresponding differences in terms of quantities on the line through $y_{\frac{1}{2}}$, we proceed in the same manner. First we note that

$$y_0 = y_1 - \Delta y_0$$
$$= 2m_0 - y_0 - \Delta y_0$$

and

$$y_0 = m_0 - \tfrac{1}{2}\Delta y_0. \qquad (12.9)$$

Corresponding to Formula 12.4, we combine

$$\Delta^{2i+1} y_{-i} = \Delta^{2i} y_{1-i} - \Delta^{2i} y_{-}$$
$$2m_{2i} = \Delta^{2i} y_{1-i} + \Delta^{2i} y_{-i}$$

to give

$$\Delta^{2i} y_{1-i} = m_{2i} + \tfrac{1}{2}\Delta^{2i+1} y_{-i}. \qquad (12.10)$$

Then with $i = 1$ in (12.10) we have

$$\Delta^2 y_0 = m_2 + \tfrac{1}{2}\Delta^3 y_{-1}. \qquad (12.11)$$

For $\Delta^3 y_0$ we have

$$\Delta^3 y_0 = \Delta^3 y_{-1} + \Delta^4 y_{-1}$$
$$= \Delta^3 y_{-1} + m_4 + \tfrac{1}{2}\Delta^5 y_{-2}. \qquad (12.12)$$

Similarly, we obtain

$$\Delta^4 y_0 = \Delta^4 y_{-1} + \Delta^5 y_{-1}$$
$$= \Delta^4 y_{-1} + \Delta^5 y_{-2} + \Delta^6 y_{-2}$$
$$= m_4 + \tfrac{1}{2}\Delta^5 y_{-2} + \Delta^5 y_{-2} + m_6 + \tfrac{1}{2}\Delta^7 y_{-3} \qquad (12.13)$$
$$= m_4 + \tfrac{3}{2}\Delta^5 y_{-2} + m_6 + \tfrac{1}{2}\Delta^7 y_{-3}.$$

Again the process may be continued as far as desired.

13.   ERRORS IN TABULATED VALUES

One of the simplest applications of differences is that of checking for errors in tabulated values of function. Let us suppose that there is an error, ϵ, in the value of y_0; the growth of this error in the difference table is shown in Table 2.4.

TABLE 2.4. THE GROWTH OF AN ERROR

y	Δy	$\Delta^2 y$	$\Delta^3 y$	$\Delta^4 y$
y_{-3}				
	Δy_{-3}			
y_{-2}		$\Delta^2 y_{-3}$		$\Delta^4 y_{-4} + \epsilon$
	Δy_{-2}		$\Delta^3 y_{-3} + \epsilon$	
y_{-1}		$\Delta^2 y_{-2} + \epsilon$		$\Delta^4 y_{-3} - 4\epsilon$
	$\Delta y_{-1} + \epsilon$		$\Delta^3 y_{-2} - 3\epsilon$	
$y_0 + \epsilon$		$\Delta^2 y_{-1} - 2\epsilon$		$\Delta^4 y_{-2} + 6\epsilon$
	$\Delta y_0 - \epsilon$		$\Delta^3 y_{-1} + 3\epsilon$	
y_1		$\Delta^2 y_0 + \epsilon$		$\Delta^4 y_{-1} - 4\epsilon$
	Δy_1		$\Delta^3 y_0 - \epsilon$	
y_2		$\Delta^2 y_1$		$\Delta^4 y_0 + \epsilon$
	Δy_2			
y_3				

It is noted that the effect of the error grows in the difference table and spreads fanlike through the higher differences. The following characteristics can also be observed:

1. The coefficients of the ϵ's are the binomial coefficients with alternating signs.

2. The algebraic sum of the errors in any difference column is zero.

3. The maximum error in the even differences is in the same horizontal line as the tabular value that is in error.

These characteristics enable us to locate and correct a random error and may be used also to smooth tabular values obtained from experimental measurements.

Example 2.3. In this example the values of x and y are given and the differences are calculated.

x	y	Δy	$\Delta^2 y$	$\Delta^3 y$	$\Delta^4 y$
1.0	1.0000				
		5191			
1.1	1.5191		354		
		5545		-24	
1.2	2.0736		330		24
		5875		0	
1.3	2.6611		330		24
		6205		24	
1.4	3.2816		354		51
		6559		75	
1.5	3.9375		429		-84
		6988		-9	
1.6	4.6363		420		186
		7408		177	
1.7	5.3771		597		-84
		8005		93	
1.8	6.1776		690		51
		8695		144	
1.9	7.0471		834		
		9529			
2.0	8.0000				

It is noted that the fourth differences are oscillating for the larger values of x. The largest numerical fourth difference of 186 is at $x = 1.6$. If the table is regular, this suggests an error in the y value for $x = 1.6$. The dashed fan lines are now drawn, and we note from Table 2.4 that

$$\Delta^4 y_{-4} + \epsilon = 51,$$
$$\Delta^4 y_{-3} - 4\epsilon = -84,$$
$$\Delta^4 y_{-2} + 6\epsilon = 186,$$
$$\Delta^4 y_{-1} - 4\epsilon = -84,$$
$$\Delta^4 y_0 + \epsilon = 51.$$

Assuming now that we want all fourth differences to be alike, we could eliminate $\Delta^4 y$ between any two of the compatible equations and solve for ϵ; thus, subtracting the second equation from the first,

Then
$$5\epsilon = 135; \qquad \epsilon = 27.$$

or
$$y(1.6) + \epsilon = 4.6363$$

and
$$y(1.6) + 27 = 4.6363$$

$$y(1.6) = 4.6336.$$

If this correction is made, all of the fourth differences become 24, thus defining a smoother function for y. It may be noted that the error was one of transposing numbers; that is, writing 63 instead of 36. This is a common error in numerical analysis which has an additional characteristic. A transposition of two adjacent digits which differ by m will produce an error of $9m$. In the example we noted that $\epsilon = 27 = (9)(3)$ so that $m = 3$ and that the difference between 6 and 3, the transposed numbers, is 3.

Note. A word of caution is necessary. If the values of the function, y, are rounded off to a given number of significant digits, they are in error by not more than $\frac{1}{2}$ in the last significant figure. This error, however, grows in the difference table, and it may appear that a correction should be made on the tabular value of y when in reality it should not. A fairly good rule to follow is: *Do not correct a tabular value if the correction is only one unit in the last significant digit.*

It is also advantageous to have some criterion for the fluctuations in the differences that may be tolerated. We state one given by Comrie.[2] Fluctuations in the nth order differences less than the following limits may be accepted:

n	1	2	3	4	5	6	8	10
limits	± 1	± 2	± 3	± 6	± 12	± 22	± 80	± 300

To see the effect of rounding off, it is suggested that the reader obtain the values of $y = \cos x$ for $15° \leq x \leq 25°$ at $\Delta x = 1°$ from a five-place table and calculate the third differences; then round off the values to four places and calculate the differences. See also Problem 11 at the end of this chapter.

14.   DIFFERENCES OF A POLYNOMIAL

The computation of the successive differences of a polynomial derives an important property. Let us consider a polynomial of the nth degree:

$$y = f(x) = a_0 x^n + a_1 x^{n-1} + \cdots + a_{n-1} x + a_n; \qquad (14.1)$$

---

[2]L. J. Comrie, Chambers's 6-Figure Mathematical Tables. New York: Van Nostrand, 1949, Vol. 2, p. xxxi.

let the increment on x be $h = \Delta x$ and the difference between two consecutive values of y be Δy so that we will have

$$y + \Delta y = a_0(x + h)^n + a_1(x + h)^{n-1} + \cdots + a_{n-1}(x + h) + a_n \quad (14.2)$$

Upon taking the difference $(14.2) - (14.1)$, we obtain

$$\Delta y = a_0[(x + h)^n - x^n] + a_1[(x + h)^{n-1} - x^{n-1}] + \cdots$$
$$+ a_{n-1}[(x + h) - x] + [a_n - a_n]$$
$$= a_0\left[x^n + nhx^{n-1} + \binom{n}{2}h^2x^{n-2} + \cdots + h^n - x^n\right]$$
$$+ a_1\left[x^{n-1} + (n-1)hx^{n-2} + \binom{n-1}{2}h^2x^{n-3}\right. \quad (14.3)$$
$$\left. + \cdots + h^{n-1} - x^{n-1}\right]$$
$$+ \cdots$$
$$+ a_{n-1}(x + h - x),$$

where $\binom{n}{k}$ are the binomial coefficients. By completing the subtraction and collecting the coefficients of the powers of x, we obtain

$$\Delta y = a_0 nhx^{n-1} + \left[a_0 h^2\binom{n}{2} + a_1 h\binom{n-1}{1}\right]x^{n-2}$$
$$+ \left[a_0 h^3\binom{n}{3} + a_1 h^2\binom{n-1}{2} + a_2 h\binom{n-2}{1}\right]x^{n-3} \quad (14.4)$$
$$+ \cdots$$
$$+ (a_0 h^n + a_1 h^{n-1} + \cdots + a_{n-1}h).$$

Since we assume that h is a constant, the bracketed expressions are all constants and we may write

$$\Delta y = a_0 nhx^{n-1} + b_1 x^{n-2} + b_2 x^{n-3} + \cdots + b_{n-2}x + b_{n-1}. \quad (14.5)$$

This is the first difference of the polynomial of the nth degree and is a polynomial of degree $n - 1$.

If we now difference this polynomial in the same manner, we will have

$$\Delta y + \Delta(\Delta y) = a_0 nh(x + h)^{n-1} + b_1(x + h)^{n-2}$$
$$+ b_2(x + h)^{n-3} + \cdots + b_{n-1}, \tag{14.6}$$

and subtracting (14.5) from (14.6) yields

$$\Delta^2 y = a_0 nh[(x + h)^{n-1} - x^{n-1}] + b_1[(x + h)^{n-2} - x^{n-2}]$$
$$+ \cdots + [b_{n-1} - b_{n-1}]$$
$$= a_0 nh\left[x^{n-1} + (n - 1)hx^{n-2} + \binom{n-1}{2}h^2 x^{n-3}\right.$$
$$\left. + \cdots - x^{n-1}\right]$$
$$+ b_1\left[x^{n-2} + (n - 2)hx^{n-3} + \binom{n-2}{2}h^2 x^{n-4}\right. \tag{14.7}$$
$$\left. + \cdots - x^{n-2}\right]$$
$$+ \cdots$$
$$= a_0 n(n - 1)h^2 x^{n-2} + c_1 x^{n-3} + c_2 x^{n-1} + \cdots + c_{n-2}.$$

Thus the second difference is a polynomial of degree $n - 2$. The process may be continued until we find for the nth difference

$$\Delta^n y = a_0[n(n - 1)(n - 2) \cdots 1]h^n x^{n-n} = a_0 h^n n! \tag{14.8}$$

This is a polynomial of degree $n - n = 0$, or a constant, and all higher differences will be zero.

For this derivation we specified h as a constant or, in other words, that chose values of the independent variable x at equally spaced intervals. We may now state the proposition:

For equally spaced intervals of the independent variable, the nth differences of a polynomial of the nth degree are constant.

Since there exist functions that are not polynomials whose nth differences for equally spaced intervals are constants, the direct converse of the foregoing statement is not true. However, we can make the following modified statement:

If the nth differences of a function tabulated at equally spaced intervals are constant, the function may be represented by a polynomial of degree n.

This proposition permits us to analyze a tabulated function. Thus, if the nth differences are constants (or nearly so since rounding-off errors may prevent them from being exactly equal), we draw the conclusion that the function may be represented by a polynomial of the nth degree. Let us refer back to Example 2.2. It is noted that the fifth differences are all equal, and we conclude that the tabulated function may be represented by a polynomial of the fifth degree with $a_0(.1)^5(5!) = .00240$ or $a_0 = 2$. In fact, it is

$$y = 2x^5 - 3x^4 + 5x^3 - x^2 + x - 7.$$

The remaining coefficients may be determined by the method of undetermined coefficients discussed in 3F.

15.   TABULATION OF POLYNOMIALS

We have already discussed a couple of methods of calculating the values of polynomials (*see* 3B). The proposition discussed in Section 14 furnishes still another method for building up a table of values for polynomials if we choose equally spaced intervals for the independent variable. Since we know that the nth differences are constant, we may construct the lower order differences for the polynomial from the formula

$$\Delta^{n-1} y_{i+1} = \Delta^n y_i + \Delta^{n-1} y_i \qquad (15.1)$$

which is obtained from Formula 11.3 by solving for $\Delta^{n-1} y_{i+1}$ once we have the value of the nth difference. Thus it is necessary to compute n values and the initial n differences. Then the lower order differences, computed for the next line by Formula 15.1, yield the next value of the polynomial. It is advisable to check the values periodically. Let us consider an example.

Example 2.4. Let us build up the table of values for the polynomial

$$y = x^3 - 3x^2 + 5x + 2$$

for integral values of x in the interval $0 \le x \le 10$.

SOLUTION. We calculate the first four values, the initial differences, and the value for $x = 10$ for a check. We then build up the difference table, line by line, starting with the third difference, which is a constant for this third-degree polynomial.

x	y	Δy	$\Delta^2 y$	$\Delta^3 y$
0	2			
		3		
1	5		0	
		3		6
2	8		6	
		9		6
3	17		12	
		21		6
4	38		18	
		39		6
5	77		24	
		63		6
6	140		30	
		93		6
7	233		36	
		129		6
8	362		42	
		171		6
9	533		48	
		219		
10	752 check			

Although it is necessary to compute only the first four values for a third-degree polynomial, it is recommended that one more value and the differences be computed as a check on the start. This is indicated by the dotted line in the table of values. The calculation adapts itself readily to a calculating machine, as it is simply a sequence of additions. Thus for the values at

$$
\begin{array}{cc}
x = 5: & x = 7: \\
\hline
6 & 6 \\
+12 & +24 \\
\hline
18 & 30 \\
+21 & +63 \\
\hline
39 & 93 \\
+38 & +140 \\
\hline
77. & 233.
\end{array}
$$

When it is necessary to round off the values of the function, an extra value should always be calculated, since the nth differences are not always exactly constant to the number of significant figures carried. Furthermore, the differences and initial values should be carried to one more significant number than that desired in the values for the function. This is illustrated in the next example.

Example 2.5. List a table of values of the function

$$y = 1.3x^3 - 2.6x^2 + 4.9x - 1$$

in the interval $0 \leq x \leq .15$ with $\Delta x = .01$ and correct to five decimals.

SOLUTION.

x	y	Δy	$\Delta^2 y$	$\Delta^3 y$
0	-1.000000			
		48741		
.01	$-.951259$		-512	
		48229		8
.02	$-.903030$		-504	
		47725		7
.03	$-.855305$		-497	
		47228		8
.04	$-.808077$		-489	
		46739		8
.05	$-.761338$		-481	
		46258		8
.06	$-.71508$		-473	
		45785		8
.07	$-.66930$		-465	
		45320		8
.08	$-.62398$		-457	
		44863		8
.09	$-.57912$		-449	
		44414		8
.10	$-.53471$		-441	
		43973		8
.11	$-.49074$		-433	
		43540		8
.12	$-.44720$		-425	
		43115		8
.13	$-.40408$		-417	
		42698		8
.14	$-.361385$		-409	
		42289		
.15	$-.31911$	check		
	$-.31910$			

Six initial values were computed and carried to one more significant figure than desired. From the initial third differences the value 8 was decided on. (The three values could be averaged and rounded off to six decimals, which in the example would yield 8.) The function values were then calculated by building up the differences. The check value at $x = .15$ shows the value from the differences to be off by one unit in the fifth place. This is to be expected, and if the table is to be expanded the calculated value at $x = .15$ should be used and another periodic check established.

16. DIFFERENCES OF A FUNCTION OF TWO VARIABLES

The differences for a function of two variables are considerably more complex than those for a function of a single variable. Let us consider the function $z = f(x, y)$ to be any function of the two independent variables x and y. The value of the function for given values of the independent variables, say x_i and y_j, may be denoted by $z_{ij} = f(x_i, y_j)$. By following the usual notation of the first subscript denoting the row and the second subscript denoting the column, we now form a table of values of the function according to this scheme.

TABLE 2.5. FUNCTION OF TWO VARIABLES

	y_0	y_1	y_2	y_3	$\cdots$	y_m
x_0	z_{00}	z_{01}	z_{02}	z_{03}	$\cdots$	z_{0m}
x_1	z_{10}	z_{11}	z_{12}	z_{13}	$\cdots$	z_{1m}
x_2	z_{20}	z_{21}	z_{22}	z_{23}	$\cdots$	z_{2m}
x_3	z_{30}	z_{31}	z_{32}	z_{33}	$\cdots$	z_{3m}
$\cdot$						
$\cdot$						
$\cdot$						
x_n	z_{n0}	z_{n1}	z_{n2}	z_{n3}	$\cdots$	z_{nm}

In calculating the first differences we can do so either along a row or in a column, and, of course, the distinction must be made. This is similar to partial differentiation. We may hold y constant and difference with respect to x or vice versa. A subscript on the difference symbol Δ denotes the variable with respect to which we are differencing. The definition for the *first difference of a function of two variables* is given by

$$\Delta_x z_{ij} = z_{i+1,j} - z_{ij},$$
$$\Delta_y z_{ij} = z_{i,j+1} - z_{ij}. \tag{16.1}$$

For example,

$$\Delta_x z_{00} = z_{10} - z_{00},$$

$$\Delta_x z_{01} = z_{11} - z_{01},$$

$$\Delta_x z_{10} = z_{20} - z_{10}, \qquad (16.2)$$

$$\Delta_x z_{22} = z_{32} - z_{22},$$

and

$$\Delta_y z_{00} = z_{01} - z_{00},$$

$$\Delta_y z_{01} = z_{02} - z_{01},$$

$$\Delta_y z_{10} = z_{11} - z_{10}, \qquad (16.3)$$

$$\Delta_y z_{22} = z_{23} - z_{22}.$$

If we wish to difference with respect to both x and y, we are automatically dealing with *second differences*. Thus

$$
\begin{aligned}
\Delta_{xy} z_{ij} &= \Delta_x z_{i,j+1} - \Delta_x z_{ij} \\
&= z_{i+1,j+1} - z_{i,j+1} - (z_{i+1,j} - z_{ij}) \\
&= (z_{i+1,j+1} - z_{i+1,j}) - (z_{i,j+1} - z_{ij}) \\
&= \Delta_y z_{i+1,j} - \Delta_y z_{ij}.
\end{aligned} \qquad (16.4)
$$

The definition of *second differences* is completed with the following formulas:

$$
\begin{aligned}
\Delta_{x^2} z_{ij} &= \Delta_x z_{i+1,j} - \Delta_x z_{ij} \\
&= z_{i+2,j} - 2z_{i+1,j} + z_{ij}, \\
\Delta_{y^2} z_{ij} &= \Delta_y z_{i,j+1} - \Delta_y z_{ij}, \\
&= z_{i,j+2} - 2z_{i,j+1} + z_{ij},
\end{aligned} \qquad (16.5)
$$

in which the symbol $\Delta_{x^2} z_{ij}$ denotes the *second difference of z_{ij} with respect to x while y is being held constant* and the equivalent definition with respect to y.

In general, we shall let the symbol $\Delta_{x^m y^n} z_{ij}$ denote the *$m + n$ difference of z_{ij}, taking m differences with respect to x and n differences with respect to y.*

To define third differences specifically, we would need four formulas, one for each of $\Delta_{x^3} z_{ij}, \Delta_{y^3} z_{ij}, \Delta_{x^2 y} z_{ij}$, and $\Delta_{xy^2} z_{ij}$. They are

$$\Delta_{x^3} z_{ij} = \Delta_{x^2} z_{i+1,j} - \Delta_{x^2} z_{ij}$$

$$= z_{i+3,j} - 3z_{i+2,j} + 3z_{i+1,j} - z_{ij},$$

$$\Delta_{y^3} z_{ij} = \Delta_{y^2} z_{i,j+1} - \Delta_{y^2} z_{ij}$$

$$= z_{i,j+3} - 3z_{i,j+2} + 3z_{i,j+1} - z_{ij}, \tag{16.6}$$

$$\Delta_{x^2 y} z_{ij} = \Delta_{x^2} z_{i,j+1} + \Delta_{x^2} z_{ij}$$

$$= \Delta_y z_{i+2,j} - 2\Delta_y z_{i+1,j} + \Delta_y z_{ij},$$

$$\Delta_{xy^2} z_{ij} = \Delta_{y^2} z_{i+1,j} - \Delta_{y^2} z_{ij}$$

$$= \Delta_x z_{i,j+2} - 2\Delta_x z_{i,j+1} + \Delta_x z_{ij},$$

in which the last two formulas may be reduced to the functional values by (16.5) or (16.1).

Certain characteristics in the formulas are beginning to become apparent. It appears that the coefficients of the right-hand side are the binomial co-efficients with alternating signs. It is immaterial with respect to which variable we difference first. Keeping these characteristics in mind, we now formulate the general formula for *higher order differences of a function of two variables*:

$$\Delta_{x^m y^n} z_{ij} = \Delta_{x^m} z_{i,j+n} - \binom{n}{1} \Delta_{x^m} z_{i,j+n-1} + \binom{n}{2} \Delta_{x^m} z_{i,j+n-2}$$

$$+ \cdots + (-1)^n \Delta_{x^m} z_{ij}$$

$$= \Delta_{y^n} z_{i+m,j} - \binom{m}{1} \Delta_{y^n} z_{i+n-1,j} + \binom{m}{2} \Delta_{y^n} z_{i+n-2,j} \tag{16.7}$$

$$+ \cdots + (-1)^m \Delta_{y^n} z_{ij},$$

and the right-hand side may be further expanded by a repetition of this general formula; that is,

$$\Delta_{x^m} z_{ij} = z_{i+m,j} - \binom{m}{1} z_{i+m-1,j} + \binom{m}{2} z_{i+m-2,j} + \cdots + (-1)^m z_{ij}. \tag{16.8}$$

A difference table may be constructed for the first differences, but those for higher differences are too complex to be practical. To construct a difference table for first differences, arrange the functional values as shown in Table 2.5 but leave a blank space between entries both horizontally and vertically. The appropriate differences may be entered in these blank spaces. It is further recommended that the differences be entered in a different color to distinguish them from the functional values. In other words, the following tables are superimposed on each other.

TABLE 2.6. FUNCTION OF TWO VARIABLES

	y_0	y_1	y_2	y_3
x_0	z_{00}	z_{01}	z_{02}	z_{03}
x_1	z_{10}	z_{11}	z_{12}	z_{13}
x_2	x_{20}	z_{21}	z_{22}	z_{23}
x_3	z_{30}	z_{31}	z_{32}	z_{33}
x_4	z_{40}	z_{41}	z_{42}	z_{43}

TABLE 2.7. FIRST DIFFERENCE TABLE FOR TWO VARIABLES

	y_0		y_1		y_2		y_3
x_0		$\Delta_y z_{00}$		$\Delta_y z_{01}$		$\Delta_y z_{02}$	
	$\Delta_x z_{00}$		$\Delta_x z_{01}$		$\Delta_x z_{02}$		$\Delta_x z_{03}$
x_1		$\Delta_y z_{10}$		$\Delta_y z_{11}$		$\Delta_y z_{12}$	
	$\Delta_x z_{10}$		$\Delta_x z_{11}$		$\Delta_x z_{12}$		$\Delta_x z_{13}$
x_2		$\Delta_y z_{20}$		$\Delta_y z_{21}$		$\Delta_y z_{22}$	
	$\Delta_x z_{20}$		$\Delta_x z_{21}$		$\Delta_x z_{22}$		$\Delta_x z_{23}$
x_3		$\Delta_y z_{30}$		$\Delta_y z_{31}$		$\Delta_y z_{32}$	
	$\Delta_x z_{30}$		$\Delta_x z_{31}$		$\Delta_x z_{32}$		$\Delta_x z_{33}$
x_4		$\Delta_y z_{40}$		$\Delta_y z_{41}$		$\Delta_y z_{42}$	

Example 2.6. Form a table of first differences for the function $z = f(x, y)$ given in the table of values:

SOLUTION.

	y	0		1		2		3
x								
0		1	-5	-4	-5	-9	-5	-14
		4		4		4		4
1		5	-5	0	-5	-5	-5	-10
		6		6		6		6
2		11	-5	6	-5	1	-5	-4
		8		8		8		8
3		19	-5	14	-5	9	-5	4
		10		10		10		10
4		29	-5	24	-5	19	-5	14

Note that $\Delta_y z_{ij} = -5$ for all i, j, which means that the function is linear in y. Note also that the first differences with respect to x differ by 2; that is, all second differences are constant, which means that the function is quadratic in x. The function used is

$$z(x, y) = x^2 + 3x - 5y + 1.$$

Although it is possible to define difference formulas for functions of more than two variables, the formulas are too unwieldy to be practical. For functions of more than two variables it is recommended that the variance study be made on families of functions of two variables, using the other variables as parameters. Thus if we had a function

$$R = f(x, y, v),$$

we could choose v as a parameter and for chosen values of v, say $v_1, v_2, \ldots$, study the functions

$$R_1 = f(x, y, v_1)$$
$$R_2 = f(x, y, v_2)$$

$$\text{etc.,}$$

each of which is a function of two variables.

17.   DIVIDED DIFFERENCES

If a difference is divided by the interval length of the independent variable it spans, it is called a *divided difference*. This general definition is better understood in terms of formulas. Let us again consider the function $y = f(x)$ to be tabulated for x_i, $(i = 0, \ldots, n)$. The *first-order divided difference* is then defined by

$$[x_i x_j] = \frac{y_i - y_j}{x_i - x_j} = \frac{y_j - y_i}{x_j - x_i}. \tag{17.1}$$

If i and j are consecutive integers, the numerator is Δy_i, the first difference. Formula 17.1 also shows that the order inside the bracket is immaterial, since, clearly, $[x_i x_j] = [x_j x_i]$; however, it must be remembered that the differences in the numerator and denominator must be in the same direction. Although i and j are usually consecutive integers, the definition is quite general, and first-order divided differences can be calculated for any integral values of i and j.

In the definition of the first-order divided difference the bracket notation $[x_i x_j]$ was used. There is no generally accepted notation for divided differences, and although the bracket notation is quite popular it becomes somewhat cumbersome for those of higher order. We therefore modify the notation somewhat and adopt the notation

$$\Delta^n[x_i x_k] \equiv \text{the } n\text{th-order divided differences between } x_i \text{ and } x_k. \quad (17.2)$$

In this notation i and k embrace a sufficient number of consecutive integers to permit the taking of n differences. They themselves can be consecutive integers for only first-order divided differences. If divided differences for values of the independent variable which cannot be ordered by consecutive integral notation are required, all values of the x_i are written out; that is, for example,

$$\Delta^2[x_1 x_3 x_5] \equiv \text{second-order divided difference between } x_1 \text{ and } x_5$$
$$\text{with } x_3 \text{ as the intermediate value.} \quad (17.3)$$

Let us now define the higher order divided differences. The differences of the first-order divided difference divided by the interval of the independent variable they span is called the *second-order divided difference*.

$$\Delta^2[x_1 x_3] = \frac{\Delta[x_1 x_2] - \Delta[x_2 x_3]}{x_1 - x_3} = \frac{\Delta[x_2 x_3] - \Delta[x_1 x_2]}{x_3 - x_1}. \quad (17.4)$$

The first of the two formulas is preferred, since it gives consecutive sequence to the subscripts.

We may now proceed in a similar manner to formulate the *third-order divided difference*,

$$\Delta^3[x_0 x_3] = \frac{\Delta^2[x_0 x_2] - \Delta^2[x_1 x_3]}{x_0 - x_3}, \quad (17.5)$$

and the *fourth-order divided difference*,

$$\Delta^4[x_0 x_4] = \frac{\Delta^3[x_0 x_3] - \Delta^3[x_1 x_4]}{x_0 - x_4}. \quad (17.6)$$

In general, we have the *nth-order divided difference*,

$$\Delta^n[x_0 x_n] = \frac{\Delta^{n-1}[x_0 x_{n-1}] - \Delta^{n-1}[x_1 x_n]}{x_0 - x_n}. \quad (17.7)$$

A divided difference table can be constructed by using the principle for ordinary difference tables. The general form is given in Table 2.8. Each difference is obtained by differencing the numbers in the adjacent left-hand column and dividing by the interval length it spans. The interval length is indicated in the notation or can be found by "fanning" back from the value being computed. Thus, in computing $\Delta^3[x_1 x_4]$, the divisor is $x_1 - x_4$, which is

TABLE 2.8. DIVIDED DIFFERENCE TABLE

x	y	$\Delta[x_i x_j]$	$\Delta^2[x_i x_k]$	$\Delta^3[x_i x_k]$	$\Delta^4[x_i x_k]$
x_0	y_0				
		$\Delta[x_0 x_1]$			
x_1	y_1		$\Delta^2[x_0 x_2]$		
		$\Delta[x_1 x_2]$		$\Delta^3[x_0 x_3]$	
x_2	y_2		$\Delta^2[x_1 x_3]$		$\Delta^4[x_0 x_4]$
		$\Delta[x_2 x_3]$		$\Delta^3[x_1 x_4]$	
x_3	y_3		$\Delta^2[x_2 x_4]$		$\Delta^4[x_1 x_5]$
		$\Delta[x_3 x_4]$		$\Delta^3[x_2 x_5]$	
x_4	y_4		$\Delta^2[x_3 x_5]$		
		$\Delta[x_4 x_5]$			
x_5	y_5				

indicated by the subscript on the x's in the bracket. The divisor can also be found by following the slant lines that form a fan, as shown in Table 2.8.

If the values of the independent variable are given in equally spaced intervals, the divisor for the divided differences is constant for each order. This is easily seen, for in this case

$$x_0 - x_1 = x_1 - x_2 = x_2 - x_3 = \cdots = h$$

for the first order,

$$x_0 - x_2 = x_1 - x_3 = x_2 - x_4 = \cdots = 2h$$

for the second order, and, in general,

$$x_0 - x_k = x_1 - x_{k+1} = x_2 - x_{k+2} = \cdots = kh$$

for the kth order.

Example 2.7. Find the divided differences up to the fifth order for the table of (x, y) as given.

SOLUTION.

x	y	$\Delta[x_i x_j]$	$\Delta^2[x_i x_k]$	$\Delta^3[x_i x_k]$	$\Delta^4[x_i x_k]$	$\Delta^5[x_i x_k]$
-4	-4320					
		2040				
-2	-240		-392			
		80		52		
1	0		-28		-7	
		-60		-11		1
3	-120		-105		3	
		-480		13		1
5	-1080		-40		14	
		-600		125		1
6	-1680		710		23	
		2240		286		
9	5040		2140			
		10800				
10	15840					

The higher order divided differences which are defined in terms of the next lower order may be written in terms of the ordinates y_i by continuous substitution. If we keep in mind the symmetric property that we may interchange the order of differencing in numerator and denominator simultaneously, we may write

$$\Delta[x_i x_{i+1}] = \frac{y_i - y_{i+1}}{x_i - x_{i+1}} = \frac{y_i}{x_i - x_{i+1}} + \frac{y_{i+1}}{x_{i+1} - x_i} \tag{17.8}$$

and

$$\Delta^2[x_0 x_2] = \frac{\Delta[x_0 x_1] - \Delta[x_1 x_2]}{x_0 - x_2}$$

$$= \frac{1}{x_0 - x_2}\left(\frac{y_0}{x_0 - x_1} + \frac{y_1}{x_1 - x_0} - \frac{y_1}{x_1 - x_2} - \frac{y_2}{x_2 - x_1}\right)$$

$$= \frac{y_0}{(x_0 - x_1)(x_0 - x_2)} \tag{17.9}$$

$$+ \frac{1}{x_0 - x_2}\left[\frac{(x_0 - x_2)y_1}{(x_1 - x_0)(x_1 - x_2)}\right] + \frac{y_2}{(x_2 - x_0)(x_2 - x_1)},$$

$$= \frac{y_0}{(x_0 - x_1)(x_0 - x_2)} + \frac{y_1}{(x_1 - x_0)(x_1 - x_2)} + \frac{y_2}{(x_2 - x_0)(x_2 - x_1)}.$$

Similarly, the third-order divided difference can be reduced to

$$\Delta^3[x_0 x_3] = \frac{y_0}{(x_0 - x_1)(x_0 - x_2)(x_0 - x_3)}$$

$$+ \frac{y_1}{(x_1 - x_0)(x_1 - x_2)(x_1 - x_3)}$$

$$+ \frac{y_2}{(x_2 - x_0)(x_2 - x_1)(x_2 - x_3)} \qquad (17.10)$$

$$+ \frac{y_3}{(x_3 - x_0)(x_3 - x_1)(x_3 - x_2)}.$$

In general, we have

$$\Delta^n[x_0 x_n] = \frac{y_0}{(x_0 - x_1)(x_0 - x_2) \cdots (x_0 - x_n)}$$

$$+ \frac{y_1}{(x_1 - x_0)(x_1 - x_2) \cdots (x_1 - x_n)} + \cdots \qquad (17.11)$$

$$+ \frac{y_n}{(x_n - x_0)(x_n - x_1) \cdots (x_n - x_{n-1})}.$$

It is noted that the denominator of y_i is a product polynomial evaluated at x_i; that is,

$$(x - x_0)(x - x_1) \cdots (x - x_{i-1})(x - x_{i+1}) \cdots (x - x_n),$$

evaluated at x_i.

18.   DIFFERENCE OPERATORS

The calculus of finite differences employs certain useful operators. We define a few of them here. The symbol Δ, which we have used throughout this chapter, may be thought of as an operator in that when it prefixes the functional notation $y = f(x)$ it defines the operation of taking the difference between two values of y; it may then be called *the difference operator*. The symbol Δ is also used to denote an increment on the independent variable which is in agreement with its use as an operator, since $x_2 = x_1 + \Delta x$. In the following we consider $y = f(x)$.

I. THE OPERATOR, E. This operator is defined by

$$Ey = f(x + \Delta x) \qquad (18.1)$$

where $y = f(x)$ and Δx is the usual increment on the independent variable.

This operator is often referred to as the *shift operator*, since it results in another value of the function. If the functional values, $y_i, (i = 0, \ldots, n)$, are given for known values of $x_i, (i = 0, \ldots, n)$, then

$$Ey_i = y_{i+1}. \tag{18.2}$$

The inverse operator E^{-1} is defined by

$$E^{-1}y = f(x - \Delta x), \tag{18.3}$$

so that

$$E^{-1}y_i = y_{i-1}. \tag{18.4}$$

Since we have already defined

$$\begin{aligned} \Delta y_i &= y_{i+1} - y_i \\ &= Ey_i - y_i, \end{aligned} \tag{18.5}$$

we see that

$$Ey_i = \Delta y_i + y_i.$$

In other words, the operators are related by the expression

$$E = \Delta + 1. \tag{18.6}$$

II. THE CENTRAL DIFFERENCE OPERATOR, δ. This operator is defined by

$$\delta y = f(x + \tfrac{1}{2}\Delta x) - f(x - \tfrac{1}{2}\Delta x). \tag{18.7}$$

If we employ the operator E, we can write

$$\delta y = E^{1/2}y - E^{-1/2}y,$$

so that the relationship between the operators is

$$\delta = E^{1/2} - E^{-1/2}. \tag{18.8}$$

III. THE AVERAGING OPERATOR, μ. This operator is defined by

$$\begin{aligned} \mu y &= \tfrac{1}{2}[f(x + \tfrac{1}{2}\Delta x) + f(x - \tfrac{1}{2}\Delta x)] \\ &= \tfrac{1}{2}(E^{1/2}y + E^{-1/2}y), \end{aligned} \tag{18.9}$$

and the relationship between the operators is

$$\mu = \tfrac{1}{2}(E^{1/2} + E^{-1/2}). \tag{18.10}$$

As an application of difference operators, let us consider the alternating series $u_0 - u_1 + u_2 - u_3 + \cdots$ and write it in terms of the operators

$$u_0 - u_1 + u_2 - u_3 + \cdots = (1 - E + E^2 - \cdots)u_0 = (1 + E)^{-1}u_0$$
$$= (2 + \Delta)^{-1}u_0 = \tfrac{1}{2}(1 + \tfrac{1}{2}\Delta)^{-1}u_0$$
$$= \tfrac{1}{2}u_0 - \tfrac{1}{4}\Delta u_0 + \tfrac{1}{8}\Delta^2 u_0 - \tfrac{1}{16}\Delta^3 u_0 + \cdots.$$

We have thus transformed[3] the given alternating series into another in terms of the differences, $\Delta^i u_0$. It can be used to find the sum of the series.

Example 2.8. Find the value of ln $\tfrac{3}{2}$ from the power series for ln $(1 + x)$.

SOLUTION.

$$\ln\frac{3}{2} = \ln\left(1 + \frac{1}{2}\right) = \frac{1}{2} - \frac{1}{8} + \frac{1}{24} - \frac{1}{64} + \frac{1}{160} - \frac{1}{384} + \cdots + \frac{1}{n}\left(\frac{1}{2}\right)^n + \cdots.$$

We could apply the transformation directly to the series, but it is more expedient to apply it to the tail. Thus

$$\ln\frac{3}{2} = \frac{1}{2} - \frac{1}{8} + \frac{1}{24} - \frac{1}{64} + \frac{1}{160} - \frac{1}{384} + \sum_{i=0}^{\infty} u_i.$$

We form the difference table by listing values of $u_i \times 10^3 = U_i$.

U	ΔU	$\Delta^2 U$	$\Delta^3 U$	$\Delta^4 U$	$\Delta^5 U$	$\Delta^6 U$
1.116071						
	−627790					
.488281		356522				
	−271268		−204611			
.217013		151911		118790		
	−119357		−85821		−69836	
.097656		66090		48954		41615
	−53267		−36867		−28221	
.044389		29223		20733		
	−24044		−16134			
.020345		13089				
	−10955					
.009390						

$$\sum u_i = [\tfrac{1}{2}(1.116071) + \tfrac{1}{4}(.627790) + \tfrac{1}{8}(.356522) + \tfrac{1}{16}(204611)$$
$$+ \tfrac{1}{32}(118790) + \tfrac{1}{64}(.069836) + \tfrac{1}{128}(.041615)] \times 10^{-3}$$

[3]This is called the Euler transformation.

and
$$\ln \tfrac{3}{2} = .404687501 + .000777463 = .405464964.$$

The true value to seven places is .4054651.

A complete discussion of difference operators and their properties is beyond the scope of this book, and we conclude this section with the interesting property that

$$\mu\delta = \tfrac{1}{2}(E - E^{-1}), \tag{18.11}$$

which can be obtained by combining Formulas 18.8 and 18.10. From this we have

$$\begin{aligned}
\mu\,\delta y &= \tfrac{1}{2}[f(x + \Delta x) - f(x - \Delta x)] \\
&= \tfrac{1}{2}[f(x + \Delta x) - f(x) + f(x) - f(x - \Delta x)] \tag{18.12} \\
&= \tfrac{1}{2}[\Delta y_i + \Delta y_{i-1}],
\end{aligned}$$

which is the arithmetic mean of two consecutive first differences. In Section 12 we denoted these differences by m_1; thus

$$\mu\,\delta y = m_1. \tag{18.13}$$

Also, we can obtain

$$\mu\,\delta^3 y = m_3 \tag{18.14}$$

and other similar properties.

19.   DIFFERENCES AND DERIVATIVES

The relation between differences and derivatives can be understood by a consideration of their respective definitions. We recall the definition of a derivative

$$\frac{dy}{dx} = \lim_{\Delta x \to 0} \frac{f(x + \Delta x) - f(x)}{\Delta x}, \tag{19.1}$$

where $y = f(x)$. The numerator of

$$\frac{f(x + \Delta x) - f(x)}{\Delta x} = \frac{\Delta y}{\Delta x}$$

is the first difference of y and the fraction is known as a *difference quotient*. If the function is tabulated at discrete values of x, the foregoing is in accord with the definitions of Section 10.

The second derivative is defined as the derivative of the first derivative, and the difference quotient would be the difference of first differences. This is true of all higher order derivatives; thus we can state in general

$$\frac{d^n y}{dx^n} = \lim_{\Delta x \to 0} \frac{\Delta^n y}{(\Delta x)^n}. \tag{19.2}$$

By the theorem of mean value we have

$$f(x + \Delta x) - f(x) = (\Delta x) f'(x + \theta \Delta x), \tag{19.3}$$

where $0 < \theta < 1$. In terms of differences, this states

$$\Delta y = (\Delta x) f'(x + \theta \Delta x), \qquad (0 < \theta < 1), \tag{19.4}$$

which can be generalized to the nth difference

$$\Delta^n y = (\Delta x)^n f^{(n)}(x + n\theta \Delta x), \qquad (0 < \theta < 1). \tag{19.5}$$

20.   EXERCISE II

1. Calculate the difference table for

x	1.0	1.1	1.2	1.3	1.4	1.5	1.6	1.7	1.8
y	1.0000	1.5191	2.0736	2.6611	3.2816	3.9375	4.6336	5.3771	6.1776

2. Find and correct the error by means of differences if it is known that $y(x)$ is a polynomial in x of some degree

	(a)			(b)	
	x	y		x	y
	1.0	0		0	2
	1.1	$-.54549$		1	5
	1.2	$-.96768$		2	8
	1.3	-1.25307		3	17
	1.4	-1.39776		4	38
	1.5	-1.40625		5	75
	1.6	-1.29024		6	140
	1.7	-1.06734		7	233
	1.8	$-.76032$		8	362
	1.9	$-.39501$		9	533
	2.0	0		10	752

3. By the method of differences, tabulate the values of the polynomial:

$\quad$ (a) $y = 2x^3 - 3x^2 + x - 5$ $\quad$ in $\quad 0 \le x \le 1;$ $\qquad \Delta x = .1;$

$\quad$ (b) $y = 5x^3 + 2.07x^2 - .3$ $\quad$ in $\quad 0 \le x \le .1;$ $\qquad \Delta x = .01.$

4. Compute the values of $z = 2x^2 - 3y^2 + xy$ for $x = 0, 1, 2, 3, 4$ and $y = 0, 1, 2, 3$ and construct a table of first differences.

5. Construct a table of divided differences for the values

x	-4	-2	0	3	5	8
y	-4320	-240	0	-120	-1080	0

6. Show that $\mu \delta^3 y = m_3$.

7. Prove that

$$\Delta[x_1 x_2] = \begin{vmatrix} 1 & y_1 \\ 1 & y_2 \end{vmatrix} \div \begin{vmatrix} 1 & x_1 \\ 1 & x_2 \end{vmatrix}.$$

8. Prove that $\Delta^2[x_0 x_2]$ is the quotient of the two determinants

$$\begin{vmatrix} 1 & x_0 & y_0 \\ 1 & x_1 & y_1 \\ 1 & x_2 & y_2 \end{vmatrix} \quad \text{divided by} \quad \begin{vmatrix} 1 & x_0 & x_0^2 \\ 1 & x_1 & x_1^2 \\ 1 & x_2 & x_2^2 \end{vmatrix}.$$

9. Find the divided differences up to the fourth order of $y = \cos x$ for $0° \le x \le 30°$ with $\Delta x = 5°$.

10. Find the difference table for A_0 in Table VIII in the back of the book, for $0 \le p \le .1; \Delta p = .01$.

11. Tabulate the values of the function $y = 0.1x^4$ for $1 \le x \le 10$ correct to the nearest integer and calculate the difference table. Check the fluctuations of the fifth differences (which should be zero) with Comrie's table (see p. 43).

12. Tabulate the true values for y in Problem 11 and obtain the difference table.

13. Use the Euler transformation to evaluate ln 2 from a series.

14. We present here the tabulated values of four functions: $y_i(i = 1, 2, 3, 4)$ for $-2 \le x \le 2$. These functions are used in many of the problems in the following chapters.

$\quad$ (a) Obtain a complete set of differences for each function and retain for future use.

$\quad$ (b) Find the divided differences.

$\quad$ (c) Find the difference table by using values of y at $x_0 + j \Delta x$ with $\Delta x = .2$.

$\quad$ (d) Find the difference for a tabulation with $\Delta x = 0.5$.

x	y_1	y_2	y_3	y_4
−2.0	2.0000	.0000	−32.00000	−9.000
.9	1.3041	−1.7199	−22.21329	−7.859
.8	.7936	−2.9184	−14.43648	−6.832
.7	.4361	−3.6519	−8.36681	−5.913
.6	.2016	−3.9744	−3.73056	−5.096
.5	.0625	−3.9375	−.28125	−4.375
.4	−.0064	−3.5904	2.20096	−3.744
.3	−.0279	−2.9799	3.91077	−3.197
.2	−.0224	−2.1504	5.01888	−2.728
.1	−.0079	−1.1439	5.67319	−2.331
−1.0	.0000	.0000	6.00000	−2.000
.9	−.0119	1.2441	6.10521	−1.729
.8	−.0544	2.5536	6.07552	−1.512
.7	−.1359	3.8961	5.97963	−1.343
.6	−.2624	5.2416	5.86944	−1.216
.5	−.4375	6.5625	5.78125	−1.125
.4	−.6624	7.8336	5.73696	−1.064
.3	−.9359	9.0321	5.74527	−1.027
.2	−1.2544	10.1376	5.80288	−1.008
.1	−1.6119	11.1321	5.89569	−1.001
.0	−2.0000	12.0000	6.00000	−1.000
.1	−2.4079	12.7281	6.08371	−.999
.2	−2.8224	13.3056	6.10752	−.992
.3	−3.2279	13.7241	6.02613	−.972
.4	−3.6064	13.9776	5.78944	−.936
.5	3.9375	14.0625	5.34375	−.875
.6	−4.1984	13.9776	4.63296	−.784
.7	−4.3639	13.7241	3.59977	−.657
.8	−4.4064	13.3056	2.18688	−.488
.9	−4.2959	12.7281	.33819	−.271
1.0	−4.0000	12.0000	−2.00000	.000
.1	−3.4839	11.1321	−4.87779	.331
.2	−2.7104	10.1376	−8.34048	.728
.3	−1.6399	9.0321	−12.42737	1.197
.4	−.2304	7.8336	−17.17056	1.744
.5	1.5625	6.5625	−22.59375	2.375
.6	3.7856	5.2416	−28.71104	3.096
.7	6.4881	3.8961	−35.52573	3.913
.8	9.7216	2.5536	−43.02912	4.832
.9	13.5401	1.2441	−51.19931	5.759
2.0	18.0000	.0000	−60.00000	7.000

3

Interpolation

21.   INTRODUCTION

Interpolation is a fundamental operation in mathematics. The reader was probably first introduced to the process in a course in trigonometry when it became necessary to find values of the trigonometric functions for the values of the angles other than those given in the table or perhaps when logarithms were first studied. In a lighter vein, interpolation has been said to be the art of reading between the lines of tabulated values of a function. We may now make a distinction between interpolation and extrapolation. The latter is the art of reading before the first line or after the last line of a tabulated function. More specifically, we may define interpolation as the *process* of finding the values of a function for any value of the independent variable *within an interval* for which some values are given and extrapolation as the *process* of finding the values *outside this interval.*

The process of interpolation becomes important in advanced mathematics when dealing with functions which either are not known at every value of the independent variable within an interval or their expression is so complicated that the evaluation of the function is prohibitive. It is then that the function is replaced by a simple function which assumes the known values of the given function and from which the other values may be computed to the desired degree of accuracy. This is the broader sense of interpolation.

In precise mathematical language we are concerned with a function, $y = f(x)$, whose values, $y_0, y_1, \ldots, y_n$, are known for the values $x_0, x_1, \ldots, x_n$ of the independent variable. Interpolation now seeks to replace $f(x)$ by a simpler function, $I(x)$, which has the same value as $f(x)$ for $x_0, x_1, \ldots, x_n$

and from which other values can easily be calculated. The function $I(x)$ is said to be an *interpolating formula* or *interpolating function*. In many engineering applications this function is called a *smoothing function*. We, however, use the term smoothing in a slightly different sense; namely, a function that does not take on the tabulated values exactly but instead evens out these given values into a smooth curve; that is, replaces the tabulated values by "smoothed" values.

A desired characteristic of interpolating functions is that they be simple. Consequently, the most frequently employed forms are the polynomial and the finite trigonometric series. In these cases we refer to the process as *polynomial interpolation* or *trigonometric interpolation*. The latter is used if the given values indicate that the function is periodic. The interpolating function can, of course, be arbitrarily chosen and can take any form; thus it could be exponential, logarithmic, etc. One such form frequently used is the rational fraction. However, it should always be as simple as possible.

The use of the polynomial and trigonometric series is based on *Weierstrass' theorems*.

1. Every function, $f(x)$, which is continuous in an interval (a, b) can be represented there, to any degree of accuracy, by a polynomial $P(x)$, that is,

$$|f(x) - P(x)| < \epsilon$$

for all $a < x < b$ and where ε is any preassigned positive quantity.

2. Every continuous function, $f(x)$, of period 2π can be represented by a finite trigonometric series:

$$T(x) = a_0 + a_1 \cos x + a_2 \cos 2x + \cdots + a_n \cos nx + b_1 \sin x$$
$$+ b_2 \sin 2x + \cdots + b_n \sin nx$$

such that

$$|f(x) - T(x)| < \epsilon$$

for $a < x < b$ and $\epsilon > 0$.

22.   LINEAR INTERPOLATION

The simplest of all interpolation is that in which the interpolating polynomial is linear. In a course in trigonometry this is accomplished by multiplying the tabular difference, Δy, by the increase in the independent variable, $x - x_0$, divided by the tabular difference in x, Δx, and adding to the value of y corresponding to x_0; thus

$$y = y_0 + \frac{(x - x_0)\,\Delta y}{\Delta x}. \tag{22.1}$$

One of the most convenient methods of writing the linear interpolating function for machine calculations is given by

$$I(x) = \frac{1}{x_1 - x_0} \begin{vmatrix} y_0 & x_0 - x \\ y_1 & x_1 - x \end{vmatrix}. \tag{22.2}$$

If we expand the determinant, we obtain

$$I(x) = \frac{1}{x_1 - x_0} [y_0(x_1 - x) - y_1(x_0 - x)]$$
$$= \frac{1}{x_1 - x_0} [(y_1 - y_0)x + y_0 x_1 - y_1 x_0], \tag{22.3}$$

which is linear in x and which reduces to Formula 22.1 if we let $\Delta y = y_1 - y_0$ and $\Delta x = x_1 - x_0$.

The right-hand side of Formula 22.2 is easily evaluated, since it is the difference of two products, $y_0(x_1 - x) - y_1(x_0 - x)$, followed by a division by Δx and is thus accomplished on a calculator without recording any intermediate values

Example 3.1. Find y at $x = .3421$ given

i	x_i	y_i	$x_i - x$
0	.3412	.1946	-9
1	.3432	.1273	11

SOLUTION. The given data are augmented by the column $x_i - x$, the values for which are calculated. The difference $x_1 - x_0 = (20)$ is calculated and recorded if it is not a simple subtraction that can be done mentally. Since we can remove common factors from $x_i - x$ and $x_1 - x_0$, which cancel each other in the division, the values for these terms are reduced to integers. Thus we have

$$y(.3421) = \tfrac{1}{20}[(.1946)(11) - (.1273)(-9)] = \boxed{.1643}.$$

This method is especially handy when obtaining one trigonometric function from another and linear interpolation is sufficiently accurate.

Example 3.2. Find $\sin A$ if $\cos A = .74061$ and given the first three columns

i	$\cos A_i$	$\sin A_i$	$\cos A_i - \cos A$
0	.74120	.67129	59
1	.74022	.67237	-39

SOLUTION. Compute the fourth column. Then

$$\sin A = -\tfrac{1}{98}[(.67129)(-39) - (.67237)(59)] = \boxed{.67194}.$$

23.   CLASSICAL POLYNOMIAL FORMULAS

There are many polynomial interpolating functions based on finite differences which have become classical in numerical analysis. We now derive and display these formulas. Although they may be derived in a number of ways, we use the more classical approach. It is recommended that Chapter 2 be thoroughly reviewed before proceeding.

In the following we consider $y = f(x)$ to be a function that takes the values $y_0, y_1, \ldots, y_n$ for equidistant values of the independent variable $x_0, x_1, \ldots, x_n$. Let $I(x)$ be a polynomial of the nth degree and write it in the form

$$\begin{aligned}
I(x) = a_0 &+ a_1(x - x_0) + a_2(x - x_0)(x - x_1) \\
&+ a_3(x - x_0)(x - x_1)(x - x_2) + \cdots \\
&+ a_n(x - x_0)(x - x_1) \cdots (x - x_{n-1}).
\end{aligned} \tag{23.1}$$

It is now desired to determine the coefficients $a_i, (i = 0, \ldots, n)$, such that

$$I(x_0) = y_0, I(x_1) = y_1, \ldots, I(x_i) = y_i, \ldots, I(x_n) = y_n.$$

Since the values $x_i, (i = 0, \ldots, n)$, are chosen at equidistant values, we have

$$x_i - x_0 = ih, \qquad (i = 1, \ldots, n), \tag{23.2}$$

where h is the interval length Δx.

Now let x assume the values $x_i, (i = 0, \ldots, n)$, in Formula 23.1 and set $I(x_i) = y_i$; then we have

$$I(x_0) = y_0 = a_0,$$

$$I(x_1) = y_1 = a_0 + a_1(x_1 - x_0) = a_0 + a_1 h,$$

$$I(x_2) = y_2 = a_0 + a_1(x_2 - x_0) + a_2(x_2 - x_0)(x_2 - x_1)$$

$$= a_0 + a_1(2h) + a_2(2h)(h), \tag{23.3}$$

$$\vdots$$

$$I(x_i) = y_i = a_0 + a_1(ih) + a_2(ih)[(i - 1)h] + \cdots + a_i(i)! h^i,$$

$$\vdots$$

$$I(x_n) = y_n = a_0 + a_1(nh) + a_2(n)(n - 1)h^2 + \cdots + a_n(n)! h^n.$$

These equations may be solved for $a_i,\ (i = 0, \ldots, n)$. By continuous substitution and recalling the definitions of finite differences we have

$$a_0 = y_0,$$

$$a_1 = \frac{y_1 - a_0}{h} = \frac{y_1 - y_0}{h} = \frac{\Delta y_0}{h},$$

$$a_2 = \frac{1}{2h^2}(y_2 - a_0 - 2ha_1) = \frac{1}{2h^2}(y_2 - 2y_1 + y_0)$$

$$= \frac{\Delta_2^2 y_0}{2h^2},$$

$$\tag{23.4}$$

$$a_3 = \frac{1}{3! h^3}(y_3 - 3y_2 + 3y_1 - y_0) = \frac{\Delta^3 y_0}{3! h^3},$$

$$\vdots$$

$$a_i = \frac{\Delta^i y_0}{i! h^i},$$

$$\vdots$$

$$a_n = \frac{\Delta^n y_0}{n! h^n}.$$

If we put these values for the coefficients into Formula 23.1, we have

$$I(x) = y_0 + \frac{\Delta y_0}{h}(x - x_0) + \frac{\Delta^2 y_0}{2h^2}(x - x_0)(x - x_1)$$

$$+ \cdots \tag{23.5}$$

$$+ \frac{\Delta^n y_0}{n! h^n}(x - x_0)(x - x_1) \cdots (x - x_{n-1}).$$

Let us now make a transformation on the variable by letting

$$x = x_0 + hu \quad \text{or} \quad u = \frac{x - x_0}{h} \tag{23.6}$$

and note that

$$\frac{x - x_i}{h} = \frac{x - (x_0 + ih)}{h} = \frac{x - x_0}{h} - i = u - i \qquad (23.7)$$

for $(i = 1, \ldots, n - 1)$. It is also seen that each term of Formula 23.5 contains an h in the denominator for each parenthetical expression $(x - x_i)$, so that by (23.7) we have

$$I_{N_1}(u) = y_0 + u \, \Delta y_0 + \binom{u}{2} \Delta^2 y_0 + \binom{u}{3} \Delta^3 y_0 + \cdots$$
$$+ \binom{u}{i} \Delta^i y_0 + \cdots + \binom{u}{n} \Delta^n y_0, \qquad (23.8)$$

where $\binom{u}{j}$, $(j = 2, \ldots, n)$ are the binomial coefficients. This is *Newton's forward interpolation formula*. It is written in terms of u and higher order finite differences. It is called the forward interpolation formula since it utilizes y_0 and higher order differences of y_0. Consequently, it is used to find values of y at the *beginning of a table*.

We could also write an interpolating function in a form similar to that of (23.1), but focusing our attention on the end point (x_n, y_n) rather than the initial point. Thus

$$I(x) = a_0 + a_1(x - x_n) + a_2(x - x_n)(x - x_{n-1}) + \cdots$$
$$+ a_n(x - x_n)(x - x_{n-1}) \cdots (x - x_1). \qquad (23.9)$$

The formulas for the coefficients a_i, $(i = 0, \ldots, n)$, can be obtained by substituting in the values $x_n, x_{n-1}, \ldots, x_1$ for x and letting $I(x_i) = y_i$, $(i = 1, \ldots, n)$. We find that

$$a_i = \frac{\Delta^i y_{n-i}}{i! \, h^i}, \qquad (i = 0, \ldots, n). \qquad (23.10)$$

After substituting these values into (23.9), we make a transformation on the variable x by letting

$$u = \frac{x - x_n}{h} \quad \text{or} \quad x = x_n + hu,$$

so that

$$\frac{x - x_i}{h} = \frac{x - (x_n - ih)}{h} = u + i. \qquad (23.11)$$

Formula 23.9 then takes the form

$$I_{N_2}(u) = y_n + u \, \Delta y_{n-1} + \binom{u}{2}^* \Delta^2 y_{n-2} + \binom{u}{3}^* \Delta^3 y_{n-3}$$

$$+ \cdots + \binom{u}{n}^* \Delta^n y_0, \qquad (23.12)$$

where

$$\binom{u}{i}^* = \frac{u(u+1)(u+2)\cdots(u+i-1)}{i!}, \qquad (i = 1, \ldots, n). \quad (23.13)$$

This is *Newton's backward interpolation formula*. It utilizes the end value of the function y_n and the higher order differences on the upward diagonal line from y_n. The formula is used to find values of the function near the *end of a table*.

Newton's two formulas adapt themselves to the diagonal difference table exhibited in Table 2.1. The initial value of the function y_0, can, of course, be chosen any place in the table, and thus the formulas could also be adapted to the central difference table shown in Table 2.2. However, in such cases it is better to utilize values of y on both sides of y_0, and we shall now derive some interpolating formulas which employ values on a horizontal line of the central difference table. In Section 12 we developed the relationships between $\Delta^i y_0$, and the differences on the line through y_0. (See Formulas 12.3 through 12.8.) If we substitute these expressions into Newton's formula (23.8), we obtain

$$I(u) = y_0 + u\left(m_1 + \frac{1}{2}\Delta^2 y_{-1}\right)$$

$$+ \binom{u}{2}\left(\Delta^2 y_{-1} + m_3 + \frac{1}{2}\Delta^4 y_{-2}\right)$$

$$+ \binom{u}{3}\left(m_3 + \frac{3}{2}\Delta^4 y_{-2} + m_5 + \frac{1}{2}\Delta^6 y_{-3}\right)$$

$$+ \binom{u}{4}\left(\Delta^4 y_{-2} + 2m_5 + 2\Delta^6 y_{-3} + m_7 + \frac{1}{2}\Delta^8 y_{-4}\right) \qquad (23.14)$$

$$+ \binom{u}{5}\left(m_5 + \frac{5}{2}\Delta^6 y_{-3} + 3m_7 + \frac{5}{2}\Delta^8 y_{-4} + m_9\right.$$

$$\left. + \frac{1}{2}\Delta^{10} y_{-5}\right)$$

$$+ \cdots.$$

When the coefficients of the differences are collected the formula becomes

$$I(u) = y_0 + um_1 + \left[\frac{1}{2}u + \binom{u}{2}\right]\Delta^2 y_{-1}$$

$$+ \left[\binom{u}{2} + \binom{u}{3}\right]m_3$$

$$+ \left[\frac{1}{2}\binom{u}{2} + \frac{3}{2}\binom{u}{3} + \binom{u}{4}\right]\Delta^4 y_{-2} \qquad (23.15)$$

$$+ \left[\binom{u}{3} + 2\binom{u}{4} + \binom{u}{5}\right]m_5$$

$$+ \left[\frac{1}{2}\binom{u}{3} + 2\binom{u}{4} + \frac{5}{2}\binom{u}{5} + \binom{u}{6}\right]\Delta^6 y_{-3}$$

$$+ \cdots.$$

These coefficients can now be simplified.

$$\frac{1}{2}u + \binom{u}{2} = \frac{1}{2}[u + u(u-1)] = \frac{1}{2}u^2,$$

$$\binom{u}{2} + \binom{u}{3} = \frac{1}{6}[3u(u-1) + u(u-1)(u-2)]$$

$$= \frac{1}{6}[u(u-1)(u+1)]$$

$$= \frac{1}{3!}[u(u^2-1)] = \binom{u+1}{3},$$

$$\frac{1}{2}\binom{u}{2} + \frac{3}{2}\binom{u}{3} + \binom{u}{4} = \frac{1}{4!}[6u(u-1) + 6u(u-1)(u-2)$$

$$+ u(u-1)(u-2)(u-3)]$$

$$= \frac{1}{4!}[u^2(u^2-1)],$$

$$\binom{u}{3} + 2\binom{u}{4} + \binom{u}{5} = \frac{1}{5!}[u(u^2-1)(u^2-2^2)] = \binom{u+2}{5}, \text{ etc.}$$

Let us designate the coefficients of m_{2i-1} by S_{2i-1} and those of $\Delta^{2i}y_{-i}$ by S_{2i} for $(i = 0, \ldots, n)$. Then, in general, we have

$$S_0 = 1,$$

$$S_1 = u,$$

$$S_{2i-1} = \frac{1}{(2i-1)!}\{u(u^2 - 1^2)(u^2 - 2^2)\cdots[u^2 - (i-1)^2]\}$$

$$= \binom{u+i-1}{2i-1}, \tag{23.16}$$

$$S_{2i} = \frac{1}{(2i)!}\{u^2(u^2 - 1^2)(u^2 - 2^2)\cdots[u^2 - (i-1)^2]\}$$

$$= \frac{u}{2i}S_{2i-1}.$$

Formula 23.15 then becomes

$$I_s(u) = y_0 + S_1 m_1 + S_2 \Delta^2 y_{-1} + S_3 m_3 + S_4 \Delta^4 y_{-2} + S_5 m_5$$
$$+ \cdots + S_{2n-1}m_{2n-1} + S_{2n}\Delta^{2n}y_{-n}, \tag{23.17}$$

where the coefficients S_k are defined by the formulas in (23.16). This is *Stirling's interpolation formula*. It is used with a central difference table in which all the entries on the line through y_0 have been made.

If the values for $\Delta^i y_0$ in terms of the quantities on the line through $y_{\frac{1}{2}}$ (see Formulas 12.9 through 12.13) were substituted into Newton's formula (23.8), the result would be

$$I(u) = m_0 - \frac{1}{2}\Delta y_0 + u\,\Delta y_0 + \binom{u}{2}\left(m_2 + \frac{1}{2}\Delta^3 y_{-1}\right)$$

$$+ \binom{u}{3}\left(\Delta^3 y_{-1} + m_4 + \frac{1}{2}\Delta^5 y_{-2}\right) \tag{23.18}$$

$$+ \binom{u}{4}\left(m_4 + \frac{3}{2}\Delta^5 y_{-2} + m_6 + \frac{1}{2}\Delta^7 y_{-3}\right)$$

$$+ \cdots.$$

We can again collect the coefficients of the differences, and, letting B_{2i} denote the coefficient of m_{2i} and B_{2i+1} denote the coefficient of $\Delta^{2i+1}y_{-i}$ with i assuming the values from 0 to n, we find

$$B_0 = 1,$$

$$B_1 = u - \frac{1}{2},$$

$$B_2 = \binom{u}{2},$$

$$B_3 = \frac{1}{2}\binom{u}{2} + \binom{u}{3},$$

$$B_4 = \binom{u}{3} + \binom{u}{4},$$

$$B_5 = \frac{1}{2}\binom{u}{3} + \frac{3}{2}\binom{u}{4} + \binom{u}{5}, \text{ etc.,}$$

which upon simplifying become

$$B_0 = 1,$$

$$B_1 = u - \frac{1}{2},$$

$$B_{2i} = \frac{1}{(2i)!}[u(u-1)(u+1)(u-2)(u+2)\cdots$$
$$(u-i)(u+i-1)], \quad (23.19)$$

$$B_{2i+1} = \frac{1}{(2i+1)!}\left[\left(u - \frac{1}{2}\right)(u)(u-1)(u+1)\cdots\right.$$
$$\left.(u-i)(u+i-1)\right],$$

$$= \frac{1}{2i+1}\left(u - \frac{1}{2}\right)B_{2i} = \frac{1}{2i+1}B_1 B_{2i},$$

and we can write

$$I_B(u) = m_0 + B_1\Delta y_0 + B_2 m_2 + B_3 \Delta^3 y_{-1} + B_4 m_4 + \cdots$$
$$+ B_{2n}m_{2n} + B_{2n+1}\Delta^{2n+1}y_{-n}, \quad (23.20)$$

where the coefficients B_k are defined by Formula 23.19. This is *Bessel's interpolation formula*. It is used with a central difference table in which all of the entries on the line through $y_{\frac{1}{2}}$ have been made. The formula can be changed slightly by combining the first two terms. Thus

$$m_0 + B_1\,\Delta y_0 = \tfrac{1}{2}(y_0 + y_1) + (u - \tfrac{1}{2})(y_1 - y_0)$$
$$= \tfrac{1}{2}y_0 + \tfrac{1}{2}y_1 + uy_1 - \tfrac{1}{2}y_1 - uy_0 + \tfrac{1}{2}y_0$$
$$= y_0 + u(y_1 - y_0)$$
$$= y_0 + u\,\Delta_0$$

and

$$I_B(u) = y_0 + u\,\Delta y_0 + \sum_{i=1}^{n} B_{2i}m_{2i} + \sum_{i=1}^{n} B_{2i+1}\,\Delta^{2i+1}y_{-i}. \qquad (23.21)$$

Two other changes are frequently made on this formula. The first is to let $u = \tfrac{1}{2}$, which results in a formula for *interpolating to halves*. We note that in this case $B_1 = 0$ and thus $B_{2i+1} = 0$ for $i = 1, \ldots, n$. The coefficients for the remaining terms can be evaluated to obtain

$$I_B\!\left(\frac{1}{2}\right) = m_0 - \frac{1}{8}m_2 + \frac{3}{128}m_4 - \frac{5}{1024}m_6 + \cdots$$
$$+ (-1)^n \frac{[1 \cdot 3 \cdot 5 \cdots (2n-1)]^2}{2^{2n}(2n)!}\, m_{2n}. \qquad (23.22)$$

The second is to let $u = v + \tfrac{1}{2}$, which adds symmetry to the coefficients B_k;

$$B_{2i} = \frac{1}{(2i)!}\left\{\left[v^2 - \left(\frac{1}{2}\right)^2\right]\left[v^2 - \left(\frac{3}{2}\right)^2\right]\cdots\left[v^2 - \left(\frac{2i-1}{2}\right)^2\right]\right\},$$
$$(23.23)$$
$$B_{2i+1} = \frac{v}{2i+1}\,B_{2i}.$$

Turn to Exercise 3, Problem 7.

Let us combine two consecutive terms of Bessel's formula (23.20), say

$$B_2 m_2 + B_3\,\Delta^3 y_{-1} = \tfrac{1}{2}B_2(\Delta^2 y_{-1} + \Delta^2 y_0) + B_3\,\Delta^3 y_{-1}.$$

We recall that

$$\Delta^3 y_{-1} = \Delta^2 y_0 - \Delta^2 y_{-1}$$

so that on combining

$$B_2 m_2 + B_3\,\Delta^3 y_{-1} = (\tfrac{1}{2}B_2 + B_3)\Delta^2 y_0 + (\tfrac{1}{2}B_2 - B_3)\Delta^2 y_{-1}.$$

By Formula 23.19 we have

$$B_3 = \tfrac{1}{3}(u - \tfrac{1}{2})B_2$$

so that finally

$$B_2 m_2 + B_3 \Delta^3 y_{-1} = \tfrac{1}{3}(u + 1)B_2 \Delta^2 y_0 + \tfrac{1}{3}(2 - u)B_2 \Delta^2 y_{-1}. \tag{23.24}$$

Thus we can eliminate all odd-order differences from Bessel's formula and reduce it to a polynomial in the even-order differences by combining two consecutive terms. The combination of the first two terms yields

$$m_0 + B_1 \Delta y_0 = \tfrac{1}{2}(y_0 + y_1) + (u - \tfrac{1}{2})(y_1 - y_0)$$
$$= [\tfrac{1}{2} - (u - \tfrac{1}{2})]y_0 + \tfrac{1}{2} + u - \tfrac{1}{2}y_1$$
$$= (1 - u)y_0 + u y_1.$$

In general,

$$B_{2i} m_{2i} + B_{2i+1} \Delta^{2i+1} y_{-i} = \tfrac{1}{2}B_{2i}(\Delta^{2i} y_{-i} + \Delta^{2i} y_{-i+1})$$
$$+ B_{2i+1}(\Delta^{2i} y_{-i+1} - \Delta^{2i} y_{-i})$$
$$= (\tfrac{1}{2}B_{2i} - B_{2i+1})\Delta^{2i} y_{-i}$$
$$+ (\tfrac{1}{2}B_{2i} + B_{2i+1})\Delta^{2i} y_{-i+1}$$

since

$$B_{2i+1} = \frac{1}{2i + 1}\left(u - \frac{1}{2}\right)B_{2i}$$

we have

$$\frac{1}{2}B_{2i} - B_{2i+1} = \frac{i + 1 - u}{2i + 1}B_{2i}$$

$$\frac{1}{2}B_{2i} + B_{2i+1} = \frac{u + i}{2i + 1}B_{2i}$$

and

$$B_{2i} m_{2i} + B_{2i+1} \Delta^{2i+1} y_{-i} = \frac{i + 1 - u}{2i + 1}B_{2i}\Delta^{2i} y_{-i}$$
$$+ \frac{u + i}{2i + 1}B_{2i}\Delta^{2i} y_{-i+1}. \tag{23.25}$$

By changing Bessel's formula we have an interpolating formula in terms of the even-order differences at the beginning and end of an interval, that is, the even-order differences on the lines through y_0 and y_1 in the central difference table. This formula may be written in the form

$$I_E(u) = E_{00}y_0 + E_{10}\Delta^2 y_{-1} + E_{20}\Delta^4 y_{-2} + E_{30}\Delta^6 y_{-3} + \cdots$$
$$+ E_{01}y_1 + E_{11}\Delta^2 y_0 + E_{21}\Delta^4 y_{-1} + E_{31}\Delta^6 y_{-2} + \cdots \tag{23.26}$$

and is known as *Everett's central difference formula*. The coefficients can be simplified by the introduction of another letter; let $t = 1 - u$. We then have

$$E_{00} = 1 - u = t,$$

$$E_{10} = \frac{1}{3}(2 - u)B_2 = \frac{1}{6}(2 - u)u(u - 1)$$

$$= \frac{1}{6}(1 + t)(1 - t)(-t)$$

$$= \frac{1}{3!}t(t^2 - 1^2) = \binom{t + 1}{3},$$

$$E_{20} = \frac{3 - u}{5}B_4 \tag{23.27}$$

$$= \frac{3 - u}{5}\left[\frac{1}{4!}(u)(u - 1)(u + 1)(u - 2)\right]$$

$$= \frac{1}{5!}[(2 + t)(1 - t)(-t)(2 - t)(-t - 1)]$$

$$= \frac{1}{5!}[t(t - 1)(t + 1)(t - 2)(t + 2)]$$

$$= \frac{1}{5!}[t(t^2 - 1^2)(t^2 - 2^2)] = \binom{t + 2}{5},$$

and, in general for the coefficients at the beginning of the interval, we have from Formulas 23.24 and 23.19

$$E_{i0} = \frac{i + 1 - u}{2i + 1}B_{2i}$$

$$= \frac{i + 1 - u}{2i + 1}\left(\frac{1}{(2i)!}\right)[u(u - 1)(u + 1)\cdots(u - i)(u + \ - 1)]$$

$$= \frac{1}{(2i + 1)!}[t(t^2 - 1^2)(t^2 - 2^2)\cdots(t^2 - i^2)] \tag{23.28}$$

$$= \binom{t + i}{2i + 1}.$$

For the coefficients at the end of the interval we have

$$E_{01} = u,$$

$$E_{11} = \frac{1}{3}(u+1)B_2 = \frac{1}{6}(u+1)u(u-1)$$

$$= \frac{1}{3!}u(u^2 - 1^2) = \binom{u+1}{3}, \tag{23.29}$$

$$E_{21} = \frac{1}{5}(u+2)B_4 = \frac{1}{5!}(u+2)u(u-1)(u+1)(u-2)$$

$$= \frac{1}{5!}u(u^2 - 1^2)(u^2 - 2^2) = \binom{u+2}{5},$$

and in general from Formulas 23.25 and 23.19

$$E_{i1} = \frac{1}{(2i+1)!}[u(u^2 - 1^2)(u^2 - 2^2)\cdots(u^2 - i^2)]$$

$$= \binom{u+i}{2i+1}. \tag{23.30}$$

It is noted that the form of the function $E_{i1}(u)$ is identical to that of $E_{i0}(t)$.

24.   USE OF CLASSICAL POLYNOMIAL FORMULAS

Each of the classical polynomial formulas may be used in interpolating for values of a function other than those that are tabulated, provided a sufficient number of differences are available to obtain the desired degree of accuracy. There are, however, special cases for which each is especially efficient, and we shall concentrate on their application to these special cases.

Newton's two formulas [(23.8) and (23.12)] adapt themselves to the cases in which we wish to find the values of a function near the beginning or the end of a table. They utilize the diagonal difference table. The interpolating polynomials $I_{N_1}(u)$ and $I_{N_2}(u)$ are evaluated by summing the products of the coefficients and the differences which have been "blocked off," as shown in Table 3.1.

The coefficients N_{i1} and N_{i2} may be evaluated and entered directly above and below the difference into which each is multiplied, as shown in Table 3.1.

TABLE 3.I. USE OF NEWTON'S FORMULAS

x	y	Δy	$\Delta^2 y$	$\Delta^3 y$	$\Delta^4 y$	$\Delta^5 y$
x_0	y_0	N_{11}				
		Δy_0	N_{21}			
x_1	y_1		$\Delta^2 y_0$	N_{31}		
				$\Delta^3 y_0$	N_{41}	
x_2	y_2				$\Delta^4 y_0$	N_{51}
						$\Delta^5 y_0$
$\cdots$	$\cdots$	$\cdots$	$\cdots$	$\cdots$	$\cdots$	$\cdots$
						$\Delta^5 y_{n-5}$
x_{n-2}	y_{n-2}				$\Delta^4 y_{n-4}$	N_{52}
				$\Delta^3 y_{n-3}$	N_{42}	
x_{n-1}	y_{n-1}		$\Delta^2 y_{n-2}$	N_{32}		
		Δy_{n-1}	N_{22}			
x_n	y_n	N_{12}				

Example 3.3. Find the values of $f(.53)$ and $f(1.18)$ from the table of values.

GIVEN		SOLUTION					
x	$y = f(x)$	Δy	$\Delta^2 y$	$\Delta^3 y$	$\Delta^4 y$	$\Delta^5 y$	
.5	.34375	.3					
		53241	−.105				
.6	.87616		6840	.0595			
		60081		2790	−.040162		
.7	1.47697		9630		600	.029720	
		69711		3390		120	
.8	2.17408		13020		720		
		82731		4110		120	
.9	3.00139		17130		840		
		99861		4950		120	
1.0	4.00000		22080		960	−.025536	
		121941		5910	−.0336		
1.1	5.21941		27990	−.048			
		149931	−.08				
1.2	6.71872	−.2					

(a) For $f(.53)$

$$N_{11} = u = \frac{x - x_0}{h} = \frac{.53 - .5}{.1} = .3,$$

$$N_{21} = \binom{u}{2} = \frac{1}{2}(.3)(-.7) = -.105,$$

$$N_{31} = \binom{u}{3} = \frac{1}{3} N_{21}(u - 2) = .0595,$$

$$N_{41} = \binom{u}{4} = \frac{1}{4} N_{31}(u - 3) = -.040162,$$

$$N_{51} = \binom{u}{5} = \frac{1}{5} N_{41}(u - 4) = .029720,$$

$$f(.53) = \sum_{i=0}^{5} N_{i1} \Delta^i y_0 = \boxed{.49775}.$$

Note that the differences are numbers to five decimals, although only the significant digits are recorded.

(b) For $f(1.18)$

$$N_{12} = u = \frac{x - x_n}{h} = \frac{1.18 - 1.20}{.1} = -.2,$$

$$N_{22} = \tfrac{1}{2} u(u + 1) = \tfrac{1}{2}(-.2)(.8) = -.08,$$

$$N_{32} = \tfrac{1}{3} N_{22}(u + 2) = \tfrac{1}{3}(-.08)(1.8) = -.048,$$

$$N_{42} = \tfrac{1}{4} N_{32}(u + 3) = -.0336,$$

$$N_{52} = \tfrac{1}{5} N_{42}(u + 4) = -.025536,$$

$$f(1.18) = \boxed{6.39328}.$$

The coefficients N_{i1} and N_{i2} may be calculated for given values of u once and for all and tabulated. This has been done for N_{i1} with $0 \le u \le 2.0$ at intervals of .01 and $1 \le i \le 6$. It can be shown that

$$N_{i1}(u) = -N_{i2}(-u), \qquad (i = 1, 3, 5),$$

$$N_{i1}(u) = N_{i2}(-u), \qquad (i = 2, 4, 6),$$

so that for $-2 \le u \le 0$ for N_{i2} the values for N_{i1} and N_{i2} can be placed in the same table by changing the headings of the columns. These values have been tabulated in Table III, p. 352.

Example 3.4. Using Table III, find $f(.57)$ and $f(1.11)$ from the data of Example 3.3.

SOLUTION.

(a) For $f(.57)$ $u = \dfrac{.57 - .5}{.1} = .70.$

From Table III for $u = .70$ we have the coefficients

$$.70, \ -.10500, \ .04550, \ -.026162, \ .017267.$$

Thus $f(.57) = \boxed{.71039}$.

(b) For $f(1.11)$ $u = \dfrac{1.11 - 1.20}{.1} = -.9.$

From Table III for $u = -.9$ we have the coefficients

$$-.90, \ -.045, \ -.0165, \ -.008662, \ -.005371.$$

Thus $f(1.11) = \boxed{5.35568}$.

Stirling's and Bessel's formulas [(23.17) and (23.20)] employ the central difference table; Stirling's formula utilizes the entries on the line through y_0 and Bessel's formula, the entries on the line through $y_{\frac{1}{2}}$. For this reason these two formulas should be used whenever it is possible to obtain a sufficient number of higher order central differences for the desired degree of accuracy. They cannot be used at the beginning or at the end of a table of values. The coefficients are computed by Formulas 23.16 and 23.19.

Example 3.5. Find the value of $f(.82)$ from the data of Example 3.3.

SOLUTION. Choose $x_0 = .8$. Then $u = (x - x_0)/h = .2$. For Stirling's formula we compute the entries on the line through x_0 and the coefficients

x	y	m_1	$\Delta^2 y$	m_3	$\Delta^4 y$	m_5
.8	2.17408	.76221	.13020	.03750	.00720	.00120
S_i	1	.2	.02	$-.032$	$-.0016$	.006336

$$S_1 = u = .2,$$

$$S_2 = \frac{1}{2}u^2 = .02,$$

$$S_3 = \frac{1}{3!}(u)(u^2 - 1) = \frac{1}{6}(.2)(-.96) = -.032,$$

$$S_4 = \frac{1}{4!}(u^2)(u^2 - 1^2) = \frac{u}{4}S_3 = -.0016,$$

$$S_5 = \frac{1}{5!}u(u^2 - 1^2)(u^2 - 2^2) = \frac{1}{20}S_3(u^2 - 4) = .006336,$$

$f(.82) = $ sum of the vertical products of the entries

$$= \boxed{2.32792}.$$

For Bessel's formula we compute the entries on the line through $x_{\frac{1}{2}}$ and the coefficients

x	m_0	Δy	m_2	$\Delta^3 y$	m_4	$\Delta^5 y$
.85	2.587735	.827310	.150750	.041100	.007800	.001200
B_i	1	$-.3$	$-.08$	.008	.0144	$-.000864$

$$B_1 = u - \tfrac{1}{2} = .2 - .5 = -.3,$$

$$B_2 = \tfrac{1}{2}u(u - 1) = .5(.2)(-.8) = -.08,$$

$$B_3 = \tfrac{1}{3}B_1B_2 = \tfrac{1}{3}(-.3)(-.08) = .008,$$

$$B_4 = \tfrac{1}{12}(u + 1)(u - 2)B_2 = \tfrac{1}{12}(1.2)(-1.8)(\ .08) = .0144,$$

$$B_5 = \tfrac{1}{5}B_1B_4 = \tfrac{1}{5}(-.3)(.0144) = -.000864,$$

$f(.82) = $ sum of the vertical products of the entries

$$= \boxed{2.32792}.$$

The coefficients S_j and B_k may be computed and tabulated as was done for the coefficients N_{kj}. They are given in Tables IV and VI, p. 356 and p. 360, respectively.

Everett's formula (23.26) employs only even-order differences at the beginning and end of an interval. It is therefore used with tabular values for which these differences have been computed and recorded. Since only the even-order differences are involved, the recording of the values is cut in half, and the trend is to publish tables with the even-order differences recorded.

Example 3.6. Work Example 3.5 with Everett's formula.

SOLUTION. The beginning of the interval is at $x = .8$ and the end at $x = .9$. The values and even differences are

x	y	$\Delta^2 y$	$\Delta^4 y$
.8	2.17408	13020	720
.9	3.00139	17130	840

The coefficients are found from $u = .2$ and $t = .8$:

$$E_{00} = t = .8,$$

$$E_{10} = \binom{t+1}{3} = \frac{1}{6}(.8)(.64 - 1) = -.048,$$

$$E_{20} = \binom{t+2}{5} = \frac{1}{20}E_{10}(t^2 - 4) = .008064,$$

$$E_{01} = u = .2,$$

$$E_{11} = \binom{u+1}{3} = \frac{1}{6}(.2)(.04 - 1) = -.032,$$

$$E_{21} = \binom{u+2}{5} = \frac{1}{20}E_{11}(.04 - 4) = .006336.$$

By combining them into one table we have

E_{i0}	.8	$-.048$	.008064
.8	2.17408	.13020	.00720
.9	3.00139	.17130	.00840
E_{i1}	.2	$-.032$	.006336

The value of the function is found by summing the vertical products of this table:

$$f(.82) = (2.17408)(.8) + (.13020)(-.048) + (.00720)(.008064)$$
$$+ (3.00139)(.2) + (.17130)(-.032) + (.00840)(.006336)$$
$$= \boxed{2.32792}.$$

The coefficients E_{ij} may be computed for given values of u and tabulated.

Values for $0 \le u \le 1$ are listed in Table V, p. 358, at increments of $\Delta u = .01$. Thus the values we have computed can be read directly from this table.

When the coefficients are obtained from the tables, they are not written down on the work sheet because they can be entered directly into the calculating machine. It is to be noted that with the use of tables of coefficients all formulas of this section are sums of products of two numbers and are therefore easily evaluated on a desk calculator. Let us consider a summary example.

Example 3.7. Find the value of $f(1.63)$ in the table of values by using each of the classical polynomial interpolating formulas we have discussed.

SOLUTION. Calculate the table of differences.

x	y	Δy	$\Delta^2 y$	$\Delta^3 y$	$\Delta^4 y$	$\Delta^5 y$	
1.3	24.27685						
		10.29755					
1.4	34.57440		3.22180				
		13.51935		.70110			
1.5	48.09375		3.92290		.09480		
		17.44225		.79590		.00600	
1.6	65.53600	19.80165	4.71880	.84630	.10080	.00600	Stirling
	76.616525	22.16105	5.16715	.89670	.10380	.00600	Bessel
1.7	87.69705		5.61550		.10680		
		27.77655		1.00350		.00600	
1.8	115.47360		6.61900		.11280		
		34.39555		1.11630		.00600	
1.9	149.86915		7.73530		.11880		
		42.13085		1.23510			
2.0	192.00000		8.97040				
		51.10125					
2.1	243.10125						

Let $x_0 = 1.6$; then $u = (x - x_0)/h = .3$ and $t = .7$. The coefficients are now obtained from the tables and

$$f_{N_1}(1.63) = 71.65004,$$
$$f_S(1.63) = 71.65004,$$
$$f_B(1.63) = 71.65004,$$
$$f_E(1.63) = 71.65004.$$

The reader should perform the arithmetic and check the calculations.

25.   INHERENT ERRORS

In the preceding sections we have derived some polynomial formulas which approximate a given function within an interval. The polynomials were made to coincide with the given function at the points (x_i, y_i), $(i = 0, \ldots, n)$, and by Weierstrass' theorem we can make the approximation as close as we wish by increasing the number of points indefinitely. This would, of course, change the polynomials to infinite series, and for this reason they are frequently called *interpolation series*. In application we employ only a finite number of terms and thus, as in the case of all such series, there is a remainder term. This remainder term is a good estimation of the inherent error committed by the interpolating polynomial resulting from the use of only a finite number of terms.

The remainder terms for the classical interpolating polynomials may be derived in the same manner as those for the well-known series taught in a study of the calculus. The general procedure may be summarized. Let $f(x)$ denote the given function and $I(x)$ a polynomial interpolation formula of degree n, in the interval (x_0, x_n). Then form the arbitrary function in the "dummy" variable z,

$$F(z) = f(z) - I(z) - [f(x) - I(x)] \frac{(z - x_0)(z - x_1) \cdots (z - x_n)}{(x - x_0)(x - x_1) \cdots (x - x_n)}.$$

This function satisfies the conditions of Rolle's theorem to the extent that its $(n + 1)$th derivative vanishes at some point $z = \xi$ in the interval (x_0, x_n); thus, since $I^{(n+1)}(z) = 0$,

$$F^{(n+1)}(z) = f^{(n+1)}(z) - [f(x) - I(x)] \frac{(n + 1)!}{(x - x_0)(x - x_1) \cdots (x - x_n)}$$

$$= 0 \text{ at } z = \xi,$$

from which we solve for

$$f(x) - I(x) = \frac{f^{(n+1)}(\xi)}{(n + 1)!} (x - x_0)(x - x_1) \cdots (x - x_n)$$

$$= R_n = \text{error}.$$

This expresses the remainder in terms of the $(n + 1)$th derivative, which may not be available in tabulated functions; consequently, it is necessary to estimate the value of $f^{(n+1)}(\xi)$. This is usually done by an approximation in terms of differences:

$$f^{(n+1)}(\xi) \doteq \frac{\Delta^{n+1} f(x_0)}{(\Delta x)^{n+1}}$$

(*see* Formula 19.5). The remainder can then be written in the form

$$R_n \doteq \frac{\Delta^{n+1} y_0 (x - x_0)(x - x_1) \cdots (x - x_n)}{(\Delta x)^{n+1} \quad (n + 1)!}. \tag{25.1}$$

The accuracy of this approximation is increased as the size of Δx is decreased. It is also practical if the $(n + 1)$st differences are nearly constant.

For Newton's formula we have

$$x - x_i = h(u - i), \qquad (i = 0, \ldots, n),$$

so that

$$R_n \doteq \frac{\Delta^{n+1} y_0}{(n + 1)!} u(u - 1) \cdots (u - n)$$

$$= \Delta^{n+1} y_0 \binom{u}{n + 1}.$$

The choice of the form of

$$\frac{(z - x_0)(z - x_1) \cdots (z - x_n)}{(x - x_0)(x - x_1) \cdots (x - x_n)}$$

in the arbitrary function $F(z)$ is arbitrary and can be changed to suit the need as desired. By proper choice of this fraction and by observing the maximum derivative that can be made to vanish we are led to the remainder terms for each of our functions. We list them in summary form:

1. For Newton's formula (23.8)

$$R_n \doteq \Delta^{n+1} y_0 \binom{u}{n + 1}. \tag{25.2}$$

2. For Newton's formula (23.12)

$$R_n \doteq \Delta^{n+1} y_{-1} \binom{u + n}{n + 1}. \tag{25.3}$$

3. For Stirling's formula (23.17)

$$R_{2n} \doteq m_{2n+1} \binom{u + n}{2n + 1}. \tag{25.4}$$

4. For Bessel's formula (23.20)

$$R_{2n+1} \doteq m_{2n+2} \binom{u + n}{2n + 2}. \tag{25.5}$$

5. For Everett's formula (23.26)

$$R_{2n+2} \doteq \Delta^{2n+2}y_{-n-1}\binom{t+n+1}{2n+3} + \Delta^{2n+2}y_{-n}\binom{u+n+1}{2n+3}. \quad (25.6)$$

To evaluate any remainder term, it is necessary to be able to evaluate the appropriate higher order difference.

Example 3.8. Find the error committed by Stirling's formula if we stop with fourth differences in Example 3.5.

SOLUTION.

$$R_n \doteq m_5\binom{u+2}{5} = (.00120)(.006336)$$

$$= \boxed{.00000076}.$$

26.   EXERCISE III

1. Find the values of $f(153)$, $f(177)$, $f(181)$, $f(189)$ by linear interpolation in the table

x	150	160	170	180	190
$f(x)$	17609	20412	23045	25527	27875

2. Find the values of $f(153)$ and $f(189)$ by use of the appropriate Newton's formula in the table in Problem 1.

3. The following tabulated functions are given:

(a)		(b)	
x	y	x	y
0	1.00000	0	2.000000
.1	.95135	.2	1.042637
·2	.91817	.4	.132454
.3	.89747	.6	−.893670
.4	.88726	.8	−2.260301
.5	.88623	1.0	−4.000000
.6	.89352	1.2	−5.460275
.7	.90864	1.4	−4.506394
.8	.93138	1.6	3.644442
.9	.96177	1.8	28.022067
1.0	1.00000	2.0	84.000000

Find y at $x = .02, .93, .55, .72$, and $.13$ in (a).

Find y at $x = .1, 1.9, .82, 1.15$, and 1.32 in (b).

4. Find the inherent errors wherever possible in Problem 3.

5. By the use of a five-place table of tangents and cotangents find $\tan A$ if $\cot A = 1.0902$ without finding the angle A. Check by finding the angle A first and then $\tan A$.

6. Consider the four tabulated functions $y_i(i = 1, 2, 3, 4)$ in Problem 14, Exercise II.

(a) Find $y_3(.35)$ by Formulas 23.22, 23.8, and 23.17.

(b) Find $y_i(-.623)$ by Formulas 23.8, 23.17, and 23.21.

(c) Find $y_i(.3)$, using the difference table computed in Problem 14(c), Exercise II.

(d) Find $y_i(.3)$, using the difference table computed in Problem 14(d), Exercise II.

7. Write the first five terms of Bessel's interpolation formula with $u = v + \frac{1}{2}$.

8. In the function $F(z)$, used to find the inherent errors, let the fraction be

$$\frac{(z - x_0)(z - x_1)(z - x_{-1}) \cdots (z - x_n)(z - x_{-n})}{(x - x_0)(x - x_1)(x - x_{-1}) \cdots (x - x_n)(x - x_{-n})}.$$

Note that $F(z)$ vanishes at the $2n + 2$ values $z = x, x_i(i = -n, \ldots, 0, \ldots, n)$ and derive Formula 25.4.

9. Find N_{21} for $u = 1.665$ in Table III in the back of the book.

10. Using the tabulated functions given in Problem 14, Exercise II, choose nonlisted values of x in the interval $-2 \le x \le 2$ and find the corresponding values of y_i.

27.   INTERPOLATION WITH DIVIDED DIFFERENCES

The classical polynomial interpolating formulas derived so far have been limited to the case in which the intervals of the independent variable were equally spaced. To overcome this handicap, we now consider an interpolating polynomial which employs divided differences (see Section 17) and for which the spacing on the independent variable may be arbitrary. Let us again consider $y = f(x)$ whose $n + 1$ values, $y_i(i = 0, \ldots, n)$ are known at $x_i(i = 0, \ldots, n)$. The problem of interpolation is to obtain a value of y for a given value of x, which is not one of those tabulated. We seek a polynomial formula to accomplish this. Let us form the divided difference in the interval x to x_0 which from the definition (17.1) is

$$\Delta[x x_0] = \frac{y - y_0}{x - x_0}, \tag{27.1}$$

and on solving for y we obtain

$$y = y_0 + \Delta[xx_0](x - x_0). \tag{27.2}$$

Now

$$\Delta^2[xx_1] = \frac{\Delta[xx_0] - \Delta[x_0x_1]}{x - x_1},$$

from which we get

$$\Delta[xx_0] = \Delta[x_0x_1] + \Delta^2[xx_1](x - x_1). \tag{27.3}$$

Elimination of $\Delta[xx_0]$ between (27.2) and (27.3) yields

$$y = y_0 + \Delta[x_0x_1](x - x_0) + \Delta^2[xx_1](x - x_0)(x - x_1). \tag{27.4}$$

We can now define an expression for $\Delta^3[xx_2]$ by

$$\Delta^3[xx_2] = \frac{\Delta^2[xx_1] - \Delta^2[x_0x_2]}{x - x_2}$$

and solve this expression for $\Delta^2[xx_1]$ to substitute into (27.4). The result is

$$\begin{aligned}
y = y_0 &+ \Delta[x_0x_1](x - x_0) + \Delta^2[x_0x_2](x - x_0)(x - x_1) \\
&+ \Delta^3[xx_2](x - x_0)(x - x_1)(x - x_2).
\end{aligned} \tag{27.5}$$

A continuation of this procedure leads to a general formula:

$$\begin{aligned}
y(x) = y_0 &+ \Delta[x_0x_1](x - x_0) + \Delta^2[x_0x_2](x - x_0)(x - x_1) \\
&+ \Delta^3[x_0x_3](x - x_0)(x - x_1)(x - x_2) + \cdots \\
&+ \Delta^n[x_0x_n](x - x_0)(x - x_1)\cdots(x - x_{n-1}) \\
&+ \Delta^{n+1}[xx_n](x - x_0)(x - x_1)\cdots(x - x_n).
\end{aligned} \tag{27.6}$$

If we now let

$$\begin{aligned}
I(x) = y_0 &+ \Delta[x_0x_1](x - x_0) + \Delta^2[x_0x_2](x - x_0)(x - x_1) \\
&+ \Delta^3[x_0x_3](x - x_0)(x - x_1)(x - x_2) + \cdots \\
&+ \Delta^n[x_0x_n](x - x_0)(x - x_1)\cdots(x - x_{n-1})
\end{aligned} \tag{27.7}$$

and

$$R_n(x) = \Delta^{n+1}[xx_n](x - x_0)(x - x_1)\cdots(x - x_n), \tag{27.8}$$

Formula 27.6 becomes

$$y(x) = I(x) + R_n(x).$$

Formula 27.7 for $I(x)$ exhibits a polynomial of degree not more than n. If we let $x = x_i$, $(i = 0, \ldots, n)$, we obtain $R_n(x_i) = 0$ and

$$y(x_i) = I(x_i) = y_i, \qquad (i = 0, \ldots, n),$$

so that $I(x)$ satisfies the criteria for an interpolating polynomial and $R_n(x)$ becomes the remainder term or the inherent error. Thus $I(x)$, as given by (27.7), is the interpolating polynomial in terms of divided differences.

Example 3.9. Find $y(.3)$ from the table of values (x_i, y_i).

SOLUTION. Form the table of divided differences.

x	y	$\Delta[x_0 x_i]$	$\Delta^2[x_i x_k]$	$\Delta^3[x_i x_k]$	$\Delta^4[x_i x_k]$
0	-6.0000				
		.3			
		4.648	.03		
.2	-5.0704		-1.120	$-.003$	
		4.200		2.400	.0015
.4	-4.2304		.800		1.000
		4.680		3.400	
.8	-2.3584		3.520		
		6.792			
1.0	-1.0000				

Formula 27.7 is given in terms of the divided differences on the initial diagonal which have been "blocked off." Now compute the product

$$\prod_{i=0}^{k} (x - x_i) = (x - x_0)(x - x_1) \cdots (x - x_k), \quad (k = 0, 1, 2, 3),$$

and enter them directly above the difference by which it is multiplied in Formula 27.7. Note that the entries are easy to compute, since each succeeding one is obtained by multiplying the preceding one by $(x - x_i)$. Now calculate the sum of the products of the number in the blocks by the number directly above it.

$$y(.3) = -6.0000 + (4.648)(.3) + (-1.120)(.03)$$
$$+ (2.400)(-.003) + (1.000)(.0015)$$
$$= \boxed{-4.6449}.$$

If more than one value of the function is required, it is convenient to list the divided differences in a column and then to list the values of $\Pi(x - x_i)$ in adjacent columns.

Example 3.10. Find y for the following values of x: .3, .35, .5, .6, .7 in Example 3.9.

SOLUTION. Calculate the table

k	$\Delta^k[x_0x_k]$	$\prod_{i=0}^{k-1}(x-x_i)$				
		$x=.3$	$x=.35$	$x=.5$	$x=.6$	$x=.7$
0	-6.000	1	1	1	1	1
1	4.648	.3	.35	.5	.6	.7
2	-1.120	.03	.0525	.15	.24	.35
3	2.400	$-.003$	$-.002625$	.015	.048	.105
4	1.000	.0015	.001181	$-.0045$	$-.0096$	$-.0105$
	$y(x)=$	-4.6449	-4.4371	-3.8125	-3.3744	-2.8969

The values of $y(x)$ are found by calculating the sum of the products of the number in the second column times the number in the same row in the appropriate succeeding column.

The interpolating polynomial (27.7) employs the divided differences on the top diagonal line in the divided difference table. It is, of course, possible to use some other sequence of divided differences; in fact, for $n+1$ points there are 2^n different formulas. These formulas may be obtained by following a set of rules known as Sheppard's rules. For a given set of data calculate the divided difference table.

1. Start with any tabulated value of y_i.
2. The next term will be $\Delta[x_ix_j](x-x_i)$, where $j=i+1$ or $j=i-1$. Thus in the table we can move either upward or downward.
3. Move to successive divided differences by steps, each of which may be either upward or downward.
4. Each divided difference is multiplied by the product of factors of the form $(x-x_k)$ such that the product contains all the values x_k that were involved in the preceding difference.

It is thus possible to follow any "zigzag" path through the table of differences. If we introduce the notation

$$x-x_k=X_k,\tag{27.9}$$

the formulas are more easily written down and at the same time we can keep track of the coefficients of the difference. As an illustration, let us follow the path shown in the following table:

x	y	$\Delta[x_ix_j]$	$\Delta^2[x_ix_k]$	$\Delta^3[x_ix_k]$	$\Delta^4[x_ix_k]$	$\Delta^5[x_ix_k]$
x_0	y_0					
		$\Delta[x_0x_1]$				
x_1	y_1		$\Delta^2[x_0x_2]$			
		$\Delta[x_1x_2]$		$\Delta^3[x_0x_3]$		
x_2	y_2		$\Delta^2[x_1x_3]$		$\Delta^4[x_0x_4]$	
		$\Delta[x_2x_3]$		$\Delta^3[x_1x_4]$		$\Delta^5[x_0x_5]$
x_3	y_3		$\Delta^2[x_2x_4]$		$\Delta^4[x_1x_5]$	
		$\Delta[x_3x_4]$		$\Delta^3[x_2x_5]$		
x_4	y_4		$\Delta^2[x_3x_5]$			
		$\Delta[x_4x_5]$				
x_5	y_5					

Along this path we involve the subscripts on x_i in this order:

$$2, 1, 3, 4, 0, 5.$$

Consequently, the factor of the coefficients will enter in this order:

$$1, X_2, X_1, X_3, X_4, X_0,$$

and the formula is

$$I(x) = y_2 + X_2 \Delta[x_1x_2] + X_2X_1 \Delta^2[x_1x_3] + X_2X_1X_3 \Delta^3[x_1x_4]$$
$$+ X_2X_1X_3X_4 \Delta^4[x_0x_4] + X_2X_1X_3X_4X_0 \Delta^5[x_0x_5]. \tag{27.10}$$

28.   AITKEN'S REPEATED PROCESS

Formula 22.2 presents a method of linear interpolation that is convenient for machine calculations. As written, the formula interpolates in the interval from x_0 to x_1. It could also be written in a form to interpolate in the interval from x_0 to x_2; thus

$$I(x) = \frac{1}{x_2 - x_0} \begin{vmatrix} y_0 & x_0 - x \\ y_2 & x_2 - x \end{vmatrix}. \tag{28.1}$$

Some distinction in the notation $I(x)$ must be made in the expressions (22.2) and (28.1). To accomplish this in a logical manner let us order the values for the independent variable x in the sequence $x_0, x_1, x_2, \ldots, x_n$. Thus, if any entries in the original tabulation are omitted, those used are reordered so that we always have a sequence of consecutive integers in the subscripts. Furthermore, we shall always consider the beginning of the interval for interpolation to be at x_0. Then we may write

$$y_{11}(x) = I(x) \quad \text{in the interval } x_0 \text{ to } x_1,$$

$$y_{21}(x) = I(x) \quad \text{in the interval } x_0 \text{ to } x_2,$$

or, in general,

$$y_{i1}(x) = I(x) = \frac{1}{x_i - x_0} \begin{vmatrix} y_0 & x_0 - x \\ y_i & x_i - x \end{vmatrix} \tag{28.2}$$

denotes linear interpolation with the values (x_0, y_0) *and* (x_i, y_i). The function $y_{i1}(x)$ is a linear function of x. At $x = x_i$ we have

$$y_{i1}(x_i) = \frac{1}{x_i - x_0} [y_0(0) - y_i(x_0 - x_i)] = y_i \tag{28.3}$$

and, in particular, at $x = x_0$ we have

$$y_{i1}(x_0) = \frac{1}{x_i - x_0} [y_0(x_i - x_0) - 0] = y_0.$$

By changing the interval we can build up a set of values $y_{i1}(x), (i = 1, 2, \ldots, n)$. If linear interpolation is exact, these values will be alike. On the other hand, if the function $y = f(x)$ is not linear, they will differ by some amount. Let us list them together with the differences $x_i - x$ in the following manner:

$$
\begin{array}{lll}
x_0 & & \\
x_1 & y_{11}(x) & x_1 - x, \\
x_2 & y_{21}(x) & x_2 - x, \\
x_3 & y_{31}(x) & x_3 - x, \\
\vdots & & \\
x_i & y_{i1}(x) & x_i - x.
\end{array}
$$

We could then apply the linear interpolation formula to these entries. Thus

$$I(x) = \frac{1}{x_2 - x_1} \begin{vmatrix} y_{11}(x) & x_1 - x \\ y_{21}(x) & x_2 - x \end{vmatrix} = y_{22}(x). \tag{28.4}$$

If the determinant is expanded, we obtain

$$y_{11}(x)(x_2 - x) - y_{21}(x)(x_1 - x),$$

which is a second-degree polynomial in x, since $y_{i1}(x)$ are linear in x. Furthermore, at $x = x_0, x = x_1$, and $x = x_2$ we have by formula (28.3)

$$y_{22}(x_0) = \frac{1}{x_2 - x_1} \begin{vmatrix} y_0 & x_1 - x_0 \\ y_0 & x_2 - x_0 \end{vmatrix} = y_0 \left(\frac{x_2 - x_0 - x_1 + x_0}{x_2 - x_1} \right) = y_0,$$

$$y_{22}(x_1) = \frac{1}{x_2 - x_1} \begin{vmatrix} y_1 & x_1 - x_1 \\ y_1 & x_2 - x_1 \end{vmatrix} = y_1 \left(\frac{x_2 - x_1}{x_2 - x_1} \right) = y_1,$$

$$y_{22}(x_2) = \frac{1}{x_2 - x_1} \begin{vmatrix} y_2 & x_1 - x_2 \\ y_2 & x_2 - x_2 \end{vmatrix} = y_2 \left(-\frac{x_1 - x_2}{x_2 - x_1} \right) = y_2.$$

Thus $y_{22}(x)$ satisfies all the criteria for a second-degree interpolating polynomial. The process may be applied to the interval from x_1 to x_i so that, in general, we may write

$$y_{i2}(x) = \frac{1}{x_i - x_1} \begin{vmatrix} y_{11}(x) & x_1 - x \\ y_{i1}(x) & x_i - x \end{vmatrix}. \tag{28.5}$$

We now compute a set of values, $y_{i2}(x), (i = 2, \ldots, n)$, and form the table

$$x_2 \quad y_{22}(x) \quad x_2 - x,$$

$$x_3 \quad y_{32}(x) \quad x_3 - x,$$

$$\vdots$$

$$x_i \quad y_{i2}(x) \quad x_i - x.$$

Again applying the linear interpolation formula, we could obtain

$$y_{i3}(x) = \frac{1}{x_i - x_2} \begin{vmatrix} y_{22}(x) & x_2 - x \\ y_{i2}(x) & x_i - x \end{vmatrix}, \tag{28.6}$$

which yields a *third-degree interpolating polynomial*. The process can be repeated until all entries of the original table of values have been consumed. It is easily seen that the general formula is given by

$$y_{ik}(x) = \frac{1}{x_i - x_{k-1}} \begin{vmatrix} y_{k-1,k-1}(x) & x_{k-1} - x \\ y_{i,k-1}(x) & x_i - x \end{vmatrix} \tag{28.7}$$

in which k denotes the number of times linear interpolation has been applied and also the degree of the polynomial. The subscript i assumes the values $k, k + 1, \ldots, n$. The process is known as Aitken's method or, more appropriately, as *Aitken's repeated process*. It is a useful process, for the calculations are easily performed on a calculating machine; furthermore, it provides its own criterion of when the process has been carried far enough.

x_0	y_0				$x_0 - x$
x_1	y_1	$y_{11}(x)$			$x_1 - x$
x_2	y_2	$y_{21}(x)$	$y_{22}(x)$		$x_2 - x$
x_3	y_3	$y_{31}(x)$	$y_{32}(x)$	$y_{33}(x)$	$x_3 - x$
x_4	y_4	$y_{41}(x)$	$y_{42}(x)$	$y_{43}(x)$	$x_4 - x$

Computational Form for Aitken's Process

In accordance with our usual procedure, the calculations should be carried to one more decimal place to prevent rounding errors.

Example 3.11. Find $f(.53)$ in Example 3.3 by Aitken's method.

SOLUTION. Compute the following table of values:

x_i	y_i	$y_{i1}(x)$	$y_{i2}(x)$	$y_{i3}(x)$	$y_{i4}(x)$	$y_{i5}(x)$	$x_i - x$
.5	.34375						-3
.6	.87616	.503473					7
.7	1.47697	.513733	.496291				17
.8	2.17408	.526783	.495314	.497952			27
.9	3.00139	.543073	.494233	.498040	.497714		37
1.0	4.00000	.563125	.493034	.498137	.497702	.497758	47
1.1	5.21941	.587533	.491705	.498240	.497693	.497753	57

Thus to five figures we write $f(.53) = \boxed{.49775}$. In performing the calculation, a common factor is removed from $x_i - x$ and the divisor $x_i - x_{k-1}$ which eliminates the decimal point in these terms. Furthermore, any digits that become identical in the numbers in a column need not be used in the calculation of the next column. Thus the digits "49" in column $y_{i2}(x)$ need not be used in calculating column $y_{i3}(x)$; the results obtained from such calculation are then "attached to" .49 or simply recorded with .49 understood; the latter, however, is not recommended.

Because at the start of the problem it is not known how many $y_{ik}(x)$ need to be computed, the placing of the column $x_i - x$ on a work sheet becomes a problem. Consequently, it is often preferred to place this column immediately after the column "x." This may be done without changing the method of calculation *provided* $x - x_i$ is recorded in place of $x_i - x$, since it is well known from the theory of determinants that an interchange of two adjacent columns in the determinant changes the sign of the determinant.

Example 3.12. Find $f(.5)$ if the values of the function $y = f(x)$ are those given in the following table.

SOLUTION.

x_i	$x - x_i$	y_i	$y_{i1}(x)$	$y_{i2}(x)$	$y_{i3}(x)$	$y_{i4}(x)$
0	5	−6.0000				
.2	3	−5.0704	−3.676			
.4	1	−4.2304	−3.788	−3.844		
.8	−3	−2.3584	−3.724	−3.700	−3.808	
1.0	−5	−1.0000	−3.500	−3.610	−3.805	−3.8125
1.4	−9	3.6656	−2.548	−3.394	−3.799	−3.8125

Thus $f(.5) = \boxed{-3.8125}$.

29.   INVERSE INTERPOLATION

This subject matter deals with the *process* of finding the value of the *argument* corresponding to a given value of the function which is between two tabulated values. The reader was probably introduced to this process in a course in trigonometry at the time it became necessary to find an angle from its trigonometric function.

An easy method of doing inverse interpolation is Aitken's repeated process applied to the data after interchanging the roles of the dependent and independent variables.

Example 3.13. From the table of cos A in radians find A if cos A = .671178.

SOLUTION.

$y = \cos A$	$y_i - y_0$	$y_i - y_1$	$y - y_i$	A_i	$A_{i1}(y)$	$A_{i2}(y)$
.674876			−3698	.83		
.667463	−7413		3715	.84	834988	
.659983	−14893	−7480	11195	.85	66	834999
.652437	−22439	−15026	18741	.86	44	99

Thus $A = \boxed{.834999}$.

The denominators, $y_i - y_k$, by which the cross product must be divided, are fairly large numbers in inverse interpolation. The usual scheme for

Aitken's process is therefore augmented by columns of these divisors, and they are usually placed at the beginning of the scheme as shown in Example 3.13.

This method represents the inverse function $x = g(y)$ by means of an interpolating polynomial and therefore can be used only when this representation is sufficiently accurate.

A second method is one of *iteration* which uses the classical polynomial formulas. Let us consider Newton's formula (23.8) which can be written in the form

$$y = y_0 + u\,\Delta y_0 + \sum_{k=2}^{n} \binom{u}{k} \Delta^k y_0, \tag{29.1}$$

and upon solving for u we obtain

$$u = \frac{y - y_0}{\Delta y_0} - \frac{1}{\Delta y_0} \sum_{k=2}^{n} \binom{u}{k} \Delta^k y_0. \tag{29.2}$$

This is an iteration formula that expresses u explicitly in terms of a function of u. We may obtain a first approximation by letting

$$u_1 = \frac{y - y_0}{\Delta y_0}, \tag{29.3}$$

and by introducing

$$g(u) = \frac{1}{\Delta y_0} \sum_{k=2}^{n} \binom{u}{k} \Delta^k y_0$$

we can obtain a second approximation to u by substituting u_1 into $g(u)$:

$$u_2 = \frac{y - y_0}{\Delta y_0} - g(u_1).$$

A third approximation is obtained by substituting u_2 into $g(u)$ in Formula 29.2. The process may be repeated until there is no change in u_i.

Since all of the classical polynomial interpolating formulas may be solved for u, we can obtain an iteration formula from each of them. In the case of Stirling's formula (23.17) we have

$$y = y_0 + um_1 + \sum_{i=1}^{n} S_{2i}\Delta^{2i} y_{-i} + \sum_{i=2}^{n} S_{2i-1} m_{2i-1}$$

or

$$u = \frac{1}{m_1}[(y - y_0) - g_1(u) - g_2(u)]. \tag{29.4}$$

Example 3.14. What is the value of x for which $y = -3.7777$ in the data given below?

SOLUTION. Calculate the central difference table for the data.

x	y	Δy	$\Delta^2 y$	$\Delta^3 y$	$\Delta^4 y$
0	-6.0000				
		9296			
.2	-5.0704		-896		
		8400		1056	
.4	-4.2304	8480	160	1248	384
		8560		1440	
.6	-3.3744		1600		384
		10160		1824	
.8	-2.3584		3424		
		13584			
1.0	-1.0000				

Let $x_0 = .4$ and calculate m_1 and m_3, as shown in the table. We stop with the fourth difference so that Formula 29.4 reduces to

$$u = \frac{1}{m_1}(y - y_0 - S_2\Delta^2 y_{-1} - S_3 m_3 - S_4\Delta^4 y_{-2}),$$

with (see Formula 23.16)

$$S_2 = \tfrac{1}{2}u^2, \quad S_3 = \tfrac{1}{6}u(u^2 - 1), \quad S_4 = \tfrac{1}{4}uS_3.$$

The calculations in the iteration may be arranged in the following schematic:

	$y - y_0$	$\Delta^2 y_{-1}$	m_3	$\Delta^4 y_{-2}$	m_1
u_1		$S_2(u_1)$	$S_3(u_1)$	$S_4(u_1)$	
u_2		$S_2(u_2)$	$S_3(u_2)$	$S_4(u_2)$	
			etc.		

The problem is then completed by

	.4527	.0160	.1248	.0384	.8480
.533844		.142495	$-.063617$	$-.008490$	
.540903		.146288	$-.063775$	$-.008624$	
.540860		.146264	$-.063774$	$-.008623$	
.540860					

from which we get $u = .540860$ and

$$x = x_0 + hu = .4 + (.2)(.540860) = \boxed{.508172}.$$

The application of Lagrange's formula to inverse interpolation is discussed in Section 50C.

30.   MULTIPLE INTERPOLATION

In the preceding discussion we have applied interpolation to a function of a single variable. When we have functions of two or more variables, the interpolating formulas become complex, and the recommended procedure is to hold all variables constant except one, interpolate with respect to that variable for a set of values of those remaining, and repeat the procedure. It is better understood by referring to some examples.

Multiple interpolation is the process of finding a value of a function of more than one variable for given values of the independent variables which fall between those tabulated.

Example 3.15. Given the table of values for $t = f(E, A, r)$, find t at $E = 10°$, $A = 50°$, $r = 9.5$.

$$E = 20°$$

A \ r	4	8	12	16	20
0	.47	1.00	1.61	2.33	3.22
20	.47	1.00	1.61	2.33	3.20
40	.47	1.01	1.62	2.32	3.16
60	.48	1.02	1.62	2.30	3.08
80	.48	1.02	1.60	2.26	2.98

$$E = 0$$

0	.46	.99	1.60	2.31	3.18
20	.46	.99	1.60	2.31	3.17
40	.47	1.00	1.61	2.31	3.13
60	.48	1.01	1.61	2.28	3.05
80	.48	1.02	1.60	2.24	2.95

SOLUTION. Since there are only two entries for E, we are limited to linear interpolation with respect to this variable. The variation for A is small so that linear interpolation is sufficient here. Let us hold E and r "constant" and interpolate linearly with respect to A to obtain

$$A = 50°$$

E \ r	4	8	12	16	20
20°	.475	1.015	1.62	2.31	3.12
0°	.475	1.005	1.61	2.295	3.09

Now interpolating linearly with respect to E, we have

$$A = 50°, \ E = 10°$$

r	4	8	12	16	20
t	.475	1.010	1.615	2.3025	3.105

Let us apply Aitken's process to these values:

r_i	$r = r_i$	t_i	t_{i1}	t_{i2}	t_{i3}
4	5.5	.475			
8	1.5	1.010	1.210625		
12	−2.5	1.615	1.258750	1.228671	
16	−6.5	2.3025	1.312604	1.229746	1.227999
20	−10.5	3.105	1.379062	1.231679	1.227731

Thus $t(10°, 50°, 9.5) = \boxed{1.228}$.

For additional discussion of multiple interpolation see Chapter 5.

31.   TRIGONOMETRIC INTERPOLATION

If the data for the given function $y = f(x)$ indicate that the function may be periodic, then the interpolating formula should take this into account and trigonometric interpolation should be used. The classical formula for interpolating periodic functions is known as Hermite's formula.

$$I_H(x) = H_0(x)y_0 + H_1(x)y_1 + \cdots + H_n(x)y_n \qquad (31.1)$$

where

$$H_i(x) = \frac{\displaystyle\prod_{k=0}^{n} \sin(x - x_k)_{k \neq i}}{\displaystyle\prod_{k=0}^{n} \sin(x_i - x_k)_{k \neq i}}, \qquad (i = 0, \ldots, n), \qquad (31.2)$$

that is,

$$\prod_{k=0}^{n} \sin(x - x_k)_{k \neq i} = \sin(x - x_0) \cdots$$

$$\sin(x - x_{i-1})\sin(x - x_{i+1}) \cdots \sin(x - x_n).$$

The function $I_H(x)$ has the period 2π, since

$$\sin(x + 2\pi - x_k) = \sin(2\pi + x - x_k) = \sin(x - x_k).$$

Furthermore, at $x = x_0$ we have

$$H_0(x) = 1 \quad \text{and} \quad H_i(x) = 0 \quad \text{for} \quad i = 1, \ldots, n,$$

so that $I_H(x_0) = y_0$. In general, at $x = x_i$ we have $I_H(x_i) = y_i$, so that Formula 31.1 passes through the $n + 1$ points (x_i, y_i), which is the criterion for an interpolating function.

To apply Formula 31.1, compute the square array

$$\begin{vmatrix} \sin(x - x_0) & \sin(x_0 - x_1) & \sin(x_0 - x_2) & \cdots & \sin(x_0 - x_n) \\ \sin(x_1 - x_0) & \sin(x - x_1) & \sin(x_1 - x_2) & \cdots & \sin(x_1 - x_n) \\ \sin(x_2 - x_0) & \sin(x_2 - x_1) & \sin(x - x_2) & \cdots & \sin(x_2 - x_n) \\ \vdots & \vdots & \vdots & & \vdots \\ \sin(x_n - x_0) & \sin(x_n - x_1) & \sin(x_n - x_2) & \cdots & \sin(x - x_n) \end{vmatrix} \qquad (31.3)$$

The product of the elements of each row are the denominators of Formula 31.2 times $\sin(x - x_i)$. The product of the elements of the main diagonal is the numerator of Formula 31.2 times $\sin(x - x_i)$. Thus

$$H_i(x) = \frac{\Pi[\text{elements of the main diagonal of (31.3)}]}{\Pi[\text{elements of the } i\text{th row of (31.3)}]}$$

$$= \frac{N(x)}{D_i}. \qquad (31.4)$$

Now Formula 31.1 can be written

$$I_H(x) = \frac{y_0}{D_0} N(x) + \frac{y_1}{D_1} N(x) + \cdots + \frac{y_n}{D_n} N(x)$$

$$= [y_0 D_0^{-1} + y_1 D_1^{-1} + \cdots + y_n D_n^{-1}] N(x). \qquad (31.5)$$

Let us illustrate the procedure of calculation.

Example 3.16. Given the following table of values of x and y and assuming the function to be periodic, find the value of y at $x = .37$.

x	.2	.3	.4	.5	.6
y	.9801	.9553	.9211	.8776	.8253

SOLUTION. Calculate the square array (31.3) with

$x - x_0 = .17;$ $x_1 - x_0 = .1 = x_2 - x_1 = x_3 - x_2 = x_4 - x_3;$

$x - x_1 = .07;$ $x_2 - x_0 = .2 = x_3 - x_1 = x_4 - x_2;$

$x - x_2 = -.03;$ $x_3 - x_0 = .3 = x_4 - x_1;$

$x - x_3 = -.13;$ $x_4 - x_0 = .4.$

$x - x_4 = -.23;$

					$D_i \times 10^3$	$y_i D_i^{-1} \times 10^{-3}$
.16918	−.09983	−.19867	−.29552	−.38942	.386137	2.538218
.09983	.06994	−.09983	−.19867	−.29552	−.040923	−23.343840
.19867	.09983	.03000	−.09983	−.19867	−.011801	−78.052707
.29552	.19867	.09983	−.12963	−.09983	.075848	11.570509
.38942	.29552	.19867	.09983	−.22798	−.520350	−1.586047

$$N(x) = -.010491 \times 10^{-3} \qquad -88.873867 \times 10^3$$

$$y(.37) = N(x) \sum_{i=0}^{4} y_i D_i^{-1} = \boxed{.9324}.$$

There are many ways in which the trigonometric interpolating formula may be written. Thus Gauss's formula is identical to Formula 31.1 with the angles $(x - x_i)$ and $(x_i - x_k)$ replaced by half of the angles. Other variations can, of course, be made; however, it is believed that they offer little or no advantage over Formula 31.1 for trigonometric interpolation.

32.   LAGRANGE'S FORMULA

There is one more classical interpolating polynomial which is known as *Lagrange's formula*. This formula leads to so many applications that an entire chapter has been devoted to it. The complete discussion is given in Chapter 5.

33.   EXERCISE IV

1. Given the tables of values

(a)		(b)	
x	y	x	y
.2	−5.0704	1.5	48.09375
.6	−3.3744	1.6	65.53600
.8	−2.3584	1.7	87.69705
1.0	−1.0000	1.8	115.47360
1.4	3.6656	1.9	149.86915
1.6	7.5296	2.0	192.00000
2.0	20.0000	2.1	243.10125

find y at $x = .3, .7, .95$ in table (a) by the method of divided differences, find y at $x = 1.63, 1.91$ in table (b) by Aitken's process.

2. Find x for which $y = 100.00000$ in table (b).

3. Find x for which $y = 1$ in table (a), using Aitken's method.

4. The function $y = f(x)$ given in the following table is periodic:

x	0	.1	.2	.3	.4	.5	.6	.7	.8
y	.141	.158	.176	.194	.213	.231	.249	.268	.287

Find y if $x = .15, .52$,

5. Use the divided differences in Problem 14(b) of Exercise II to find $y_3(.35)$ and $y_i(-.623)$.

6. Replace the angles $(x - x_i)$ and $(x_i - x_k)$ by $\frac{1}{2}(x - x_i)$ and $\frac{1}{2}(x_i - x_k)$ in the array (31.3) and solve Example 3.16 by using the resulting values.

7. Solve Problem 4 with the technique in Problem 6.

4

Differentiation and Integration

34. INTRODUCTION

In this chapter we are concerned with numerical differentiation and integration. We shall derive formulas for the evaluation of the derivative of a function, even though that function may be defined only by a table of values at discrete points. We shall also derive formulas to find the value of a definite integral of such functions. For the present we limit our discussion to functions whose values are given for equidistant values of the independent variable. The more general case is considered in Chapter 5, in which this special case is also given a different treatment.

A table of values does not completely define a function and much less determine its differentiability. In fact, the function may not be differentiable anywhere. Furthermore, differentiation exaggerates any rounding errors or other irregularities. Thus it may be concluded that numerical differentiation is a process that should be viewed with much concern. On the other hand, if the data for the tabulated values are obtained from a physical system, it is reasonable to assume that the rate of change should be well defined and a differentiation may point to errors in the functional values.

Although differentiation exaggerates errors in a table of functional values, the process of integration to the contrary tends to smooth them out. This is understandable, since integration is a process of summation of many values, and errors in individual entries will be "averaged out."

In either process we approximate the function by an interpolation formula and derive from it a method for performing the process desired. In all cases in which the functions are defined by tabulated values we assume that they exist for all values of the independent variable in a given interval and that they are continuous in that interval.

35.   FIRST DERIVATIVES OF CLASSICAL INTERPOLATION FORMULAS

To obtain the values of the first derivative, we first derive a formula by differentiating any of the classical interpolation formulas. We recall from differential calculus that

$$\frac{dy}{dx} = \frac{dy}{du} \cdot \frac{du}{dx}.$$

Now $uh = x - x_0$, so that

$$\frac{du}{dx} = \frac{1}{h}$$

and

$$\frac{dy}{dx} = \frac{1}{h} \frac{dy}{du}. \tag{35.1}$$

Let us consider Newton's formula (23.8)

$$y = y_0 + u \, \Delta y_0 + \binom{u}{2} \Delta^2 y_0 + \cdots + \binom{u}{i} \Delta^i y_0 + \cdots + \binom{u}{n} \Delta^n y_0$$

and differentiate it with respect to x;

$$\frac{dy}{dx} = \frac{1}{h} [\Delta y_0 + D_2(u) \, \Delta^2 y_0 + \cdots$$
$$+ D_k(u) \, \Delta^k y_0 + \cdots + D_n(u) \, \Delta^n y_0], \tag{35.2}$$

where $D_k(u)$ is defined by Formula 3.27.

The coefficients of the differences may be evaluated by Formula 3.24, 3.25, or 3.26 with $x = u$. (See Section 3G.) However, for computational purposes, it is more convenient to use (3.28) and to arrange the calculations in the following schematic:

u	b	D
$u - 1$	$b_1(u)$	$D_1(u)$
$u - 2$	$b_2(u)$	$D_2(u)$
$u - 3$	$b_3(u)$	$D_3(u)$
$\vdots$	$\vdots$	$\vdots$
$u - i$	$b_i(u)$	$D_i(u)$
		$D_{i+1}(u)$

Example 4.1. Find the value of the derivative of $y = f(x)$ at $x = 1.03$ in Example 2.2.

SOLUTION. From the data we have $h = .1$, and at $x = 1.03$, $u = .3$. We now evaluate the derivatives $D_i(u)$ according to Formula 3.28 and the preceding schematic. At the same time we list the differences $\Delta^i y_0$ from Example 2.2. The value of the derivative is then the sum of the products of the entries in the last two columns divided by h. The work is arranged in the following calculation sheet:

$$b_{i+1} = \frac{1}{i+1} b_i(u - i + 1),$$

$$D_{i+1} = \frac{1}{i+1} [(u - i)D_i + (u - i + 1)b_i],$$

$$y' = \frac{1}{h} \sum D_i \Delta^i y_0.$$

i	$u - i$	b_i	D_i	$\Delta^i y_0$
0	.3			
1	$-.7$	1	1	1.37372
2	-1.7	.150000	$-.200000$	.40840
3	-2.7	$-.035000$	.078333	.10620
4	-3.7	.014875	$-.038000$	.02160
5			.020087	.00240

$$y' = \boxed{12.99586}.$$

One of the most important applications of numerical differentiation determines the value of the derivative at one of the tabulated points. This condition specializes the formula for the derivative considerably. Thus at $x = x_i$ we have

$$u = \frac{x_i - x_0}{h} = \frac{ih}{h} = i.$$

The derivatives that form the coefficients in Formula 35.2 can now be evaluated by 3.32 for $i < k$ and (3.31) for $i = k$. When $k < i$ we must use Formula 3.28. Formula 35.2 is derived from Newton's forward interpolation formula and thus is to be used at the *beginning* of a table of values. Consequently, we may tabulate the values of $D_k(i)$ for small values of i and k. For calculation purposes it is desirable to reduce Formula 35.2 to a sum of products of two numbers followed by a division. The values of $D_k(i)$ are reduced to a set of fractions with a lowest common denominator. If we limit the table to $k = 1, \ldots, 6$ and $i = 1, 2, 3, 4$, the lowest common denominator for the entire table is 60. The entries in Table 4.1 are the corresponding numerators.

TABLE 4.1. VALUES OF $D_k(i)$ = entry/60

i \ k	1	2	3	4	5	6
0	60	−30	20	−15	12	−10
1	60	30	−10	5	−3	2
2	60	90	20	−5	2	−1
3	60	150	110	15	−3	1
4	60	210	260	125	12	−2

By use of this table we may write the formulas for the value of the derivative at x_i up to the sixth difference. For example,

$$y'(x_2) = \frac{1}{60h}(60\,\Delta y_0 + 90\,\Delta^2 y_0 + 20\,\Delta^3 y_0$$
$$- 5\,\Delta^4 y_0 + 2\,\Delta^5 y_0 - \Delta^6 y_0). \tag{35.3}$$

Example 4.2. Find the value of the derivative of $y = f(x)$ at $x = 1.1$ in Example 2.2.

SOLUTION. From Table 4.1 and the differences from Example 2.2 we write

$D_k(1)$	60	30	−10	5	−3
$\Delta^k y_0$	1.37372	.40840	.10620	.02160	.00240

Since $h = .1$, we have

$$y'(1.1) = \tfrac{1}{6}\sum_{k=1}^{5} D_k(1)\Delta^k y_0 = \boxed{15.619}.$$

The reader may want to verify that in the same set of data we have $y'(1.0) = 12$, $y'(1.2) = 20.2$, $y'(1.3) = 25.947$, and $y'(1.4) = 33.088$.

Since differentiation is a troublesome process, as many differences as possible should be used. Table 4.2 gives the values of $D_k(i)$ in fractional form up to $k = 10$.

TABLE 4.2. VALUES OF $D_k(i)$

i \ k	1	2	3	4	5	6	7	8	9	10
0	1	$-\frac{1}{2}$	$\frac{1}{3}$	$-\frac{1}{4}$	$\frac{1}{5}$	$-\frac{1}{6}$	$\frac{1}{7}$	$-\frac{1}{8}$	$\frac{1}{9}$	$-\frac{1}{10}$
1	1	$\frac{1}{2}$	$-\frac{1}{6}$	$\frac{1}{12}$	$-\frac{1}{20}$	$\frac{1}{30}$	$-\frac{1}{42}$	$\frac{1}{56}$	$-\frac{1}{72}$	$\frac{1}{90}$
2	1	$\frac{3}{2}$	$\frac{1}{3}$	$-\frac{1}{12}$	$\frac{1}{30}$	$-\frac{1}{60}$	$\frac{1}{105}$	$-\frac{1}{168}$	$\frac{1}{252}$	$-\frac{1}{360}$
3	1	$\frac{5}{2}$	$\frac{11}{6}$	$\frac{1}{4}$	$-\frac{1}{20}$	$\frac{1}{60}$	$-\frac{1}{140}$	$\frac{1}{280}$	$-\frac{1}{504}$	$\frac{1}{840}$
4	1	$\frac{7}{2}$	$\frac{13}{3}$	$\frac{25}{12}$	$\frac{1}{5}$	$-\frac{1}{30}$	$\frac{1}{105}$	$-\frac{1}{280}$	$\frac{1}{630}$	$-\frac{1}{1260}$

If we differentiate the other classical polynomial interpolation formulas, we obtain a set of formulas from which we can evaluate the derivatives of tabulated functions. Each formula has its own usefulness and is used under the same conditions for which the original interpolation function was devised. In the derivation of the formulas particular attention is paid to the forms assumed by the derivatives of the coefficients of the differences. We shall now list the general formulas and some special cases that are frequently used. The reader should have no difficulty in verifying the particular forms displayed.

From Newton's backward interpolation formula (23.12) we have

$$y'(x) = \frac{1}{h}[D_1^*(u)\,\Delta y_{n-1} + D_2^*(u)\,\Delta^2 y_{n-2} + D_3^*(u)\,\Delta^3 y_{n-3}$$
$$+ \cdots + D_k^*(u)\,\Delta^k y_{n-k}], \tag{35.4}$$

where

$$D_1^*(u) = 1,$$

$$D_2^*(u) = \frac{1}{2}(2u + 1),$$

$$D_3^*(u) = \frac{1}{3}[(u + 2)\,D_2^*(u) + (u + 1)\,b_2^*(u)], \tag{35.5}$$

$$\vdots$$

$$D_k^*(u) = \frac{1}{k}[(u + k - 1)\,D_{k-1}^*(u) + (u + k - 2)\,b_{k-1}^*(u)],$$

and

$$b_i^*(u) = \frac{1}{i}(u + i - 2)\, b_{i-1}^*(u), \qquad (b_1^* = 1; i = 2, 3, \ldots);$$

as a special case at $x = x_n$, we have $u = 0$ and (35.4) reduces to

$$y'(x_n) = \frac{1}{h}\left(\Delta y_{n-1} + \frac{1}{2}\Delta^2 y_{n-2} + \frac{1}{3}\Delta^3 y_{n-3} + \frac{1}{4}\Delta^4 y_{n-4}\right.$$
$$\left. + \cdots + \frac{1}{k}\Delta^k y_{n-k}\right). \tag{35.6}$$

Example 4.3. Find the value of $y'(2)$ in Example 2.2.

   SOLUTION. From Example 2.2 we obtain the values of $\Delta^i y_{n-i}$ and

$$y'(2) = [10.98932 + \tfrac{1}{2}(1.99720) + \tfrac{1}{3}(.30780) + \tfrac{1}{4}(.03600) + \tfrac{1}{5}(.00240)]10$$
$$= \tfrac{1}{6}[60(10.98932) + 30(1.99720) + 20(.30780) + 15(.03600) + 12(.00240)]$$
$$= \boxed{121.00}.$$

From Stirling's formula (23.17) and Bessel's formula (23.20) we obtain

$$y'(x) = \frac{1}{h}(S_1' m_1 + S_2' \Delta^2 y_{-1} + S_3' m_3 + S_4' \Delta^4 y_{-2} + \cdots$$
$$+ S_{2n-1}' m_{2n-1} + S_{2n}' \Delta^{2n} y_{-n}) \tag{35.7}$$

and

$$y'(x) = \frac{1}{h}(B_1' \Delta y_0 + B_2' m_2 + B_3' \Delta^3 y_{-1} + B_4' m_4 + \cdots$$
$$+ B_{2n}' m_{2n} + B_{2n+1}' \Delta^{2n+1} y_{-n}), \tag{35.8}$$

where S_k' and B_k' are given by

k	S_k'	B_k'
1	1	1
2	u	$\frac{1}{2}(2u - 1)$
3	$\frac{1}{3}(uS_2' + S_2 - \frac{1}{2}S_1')$	$\frac{1}{3}(B_1 B_2' + B_1' B_2)$
4	$\frac{1}{4}(uS_3' + S_3)$	$\frac{1}{4}[(u - 2)S_3' + S_3]$
5	$\frac{1}{5}(uS_4' + S_4 - S_3')$	$\frac{1}{5}(B_1' B_4 + B_1 B_4')$
6	$\frac{1}{6}(uS_5' + S_5)$	$\frac{1}{6}[(u - 3)S_5' + S_5]$

$$\tag{35.9}$$

k	S'_k	B'_k
7	$\frac{1}{7}(uS'_6 + S_6 \cdot \cdot \frac{3}{2}S'_5)$	$\frac{1}{7}(B'_1 B_6 + B_1 B'_6)$
$\vdots$		
$2i-1$	$\dfrac{1}{2i-1}[uS'_{2i-2} + S_{2i-2}$ $-\frac{1}{2}(i-1)S'_{2i-3}]$	
$2i$	$\dfrac{1}{2i}(uS'_{2i-1} + S_{2i-1})$	$\dfrac{1}{2i}[(u-i)S'_{2i-1} + S_{2i-1}]$
$2i+1$		$\dfrac{1}{2i+1}(B'_1 B_{2i} + B_1 B'_{2i})$

$$(35.9)$$

The formulas in (35.9) for the coefficients of the differences in the formulas for the derivative are given in recursion form; that is, those succeeding are given in terms of those preceding. They can, of course, be written out in terms of u by continuous substitution. This method is advantageous for calculation purposes; however, the formulas in (35.9) necessitate the evaluation of S_k and B_k as well as the derivatives of these quantities. Furthermore, B'_k is given in terms of S_k and S'_k, which is undesirable. Nevertheless, since S_k and B_k may be evaluated from recursion formulas, the calculations still proceed quite rapidly.

A special application of Formula 35.7 determines the derivative at $x = x_0$, in which case $u = 0$ and the formula reduces to

$$y'(x_0) = \frac{1}{h}\left(m_1 - \frac{1}{6}m_3 + \frac{1}{30}m_5 - \frac{1}{140}m_7 + \frac{1}{630}m_9 + \cdots\right). \qquad (35.10)$$

A special application of Formula 35.8 determines the derivative at $x = x_{\frac{1}{2}}$, in which case $u = \frac{1}{2}$ and the formula reduces to

$$y'(x_{\frac{1}{2}}) = \frac{1}{h}\left(\Delta y_0 - \frac{1}{24}\Delta^3 y_{-1} + \frac{3}{640}\Delta^5 y_{-2} + \cdots\right). \qquad (35.11)$$

Example 4.4. Given the table of values (x_i, y_i), find the values of the first derivative at $x = 1.80, 1.85, 1.90, 2.80$.

SOLUTION. First calculate the augmented central difference table; then for

$$x = 1.80 \quad \text{use Formula 35.10,}$$
$$x = 1.85 \quad \text{use Formula 35.7,}$$
$$x = 1.90 \quad \text{use Formula 35.11,}$$
$$x = 2.80 \quad \text{use Formula 35.6.}$$

The work is arranged on a calculating sheet:

$$h = .2$$

x	y	Δy	$\Delta^2 y$	$\Delta^3 y$	$\Delta^4 y$	$\Delta^5 y$
1.0	−2.00000					
		75584				
1.2	−1.24416		11200			
		86784		−31680		
1.4	−.37632		−20480		3840	
		66304		−27840		7680
1.6	.28672		−48320		11520	
		17984		−16320		7680
1.8	.46656	−14336	−64640	−6720	19200	7680
		−46656		2880		7680
2.0	.00000		−61760		26880	
		−108416		29760		7680
2.2	−1.08416		−32000		34560	
		−140416		64320		7680
2.4	−2.48832		32320		42240	
		−108096		106560		
2.6	−3.56928		138880			
		30784				
2.8	−3.26144					

At $x = 1.80$: $x_0 = 1.80$, $u = 0$.

$$y'(1.80) = \tfrac{1}{6}(30m_1 - 5m_3 + m_5) = \boxed{-.64800}.$$

At $x = 1.85$: $x_0 = 1.80$, $u = .25$.

k	1	2	3	4	5
S_k		.03125	−.039063	−.002441	.007691
S_k'	1	.25	−.135417	−.018229	.025684

$$y'(1.85) = \boxed{-1.48694}.$$

The values for S_k are obtained from Table IV on p. 356.

At $x = 1.90$: $x_0 = 1.80$, $u = \frac{1}{2}$.

$$y'(1.90) = \tfrac{1}{384}(1920\Delta y_0 - 80\Delta^3 y_{-1} + 9\Delta^5 y_{-2}) = \boxed{-2.33700}.$$

At $x = 2.80$: $x_n = 2.8$; $u = 0$.

$$y'(2.80) = \tfrac{1}{12}(60\Delta y_{n-1} + 30\Delta^2 y_{n-2} + 20\Delta^3 y_{n-3} + 15\Delta^4 y_{n-4} + 12\Delta^5 y_{n-5})$$
$$= \boxed{7.39200}.$$

Before differentiating Everett's formula (23.26) let us note that

$$\frac{dy}{dx} = \frac{1}{h}\frac{dy}{du} = \frac{1}{h}\frac{dy}{dt}\frac{dt}{du} = \frac{1}{h}\frac{dy}{dt}(-1) = -\frac{1}{h}\frac{dy}{dt}.$$

The differentiation thus yields

$$y'(x) = \frac{1}{h}[-E'_{00}(t)y_0 - E'_{10}(t)\Delta^2 y_{-1} - E'_{20}(t)\Delta^4 y_{-2} - \cdots$$
$$\qquad\qquad + E'_{01}(u)y_1 + E'_{11}(u)\Delta^2 y_0 + E'_{21}(u)\Delta^4 y_{-1} + \cdots]. \tag{35.12}$$

Now the form of $E_{i0}(t)$ and $E_{i1}(u)$ are identical for the same $i > 1$ so that the forms of their derivatives are identical. We list the first four:

$$E'_{01}(u) = 1,$$
$$E'_{11}(u) = \tfrac{1}{6}[u(u-1) + (u-1)(u+1) + (u+1)u],$$
$$E'_{21}(u) = \tfrac{1}{20}[(u^2 - 4)E'_{11}(u) + 2u\,E_{11}(u)], \tag{35.13}$$
$$E'_{31}(u) = \tfrac{1}{42}[(u^2 - 9)E'_{21}(u) + 2u\,E_{21}(u)],$$

and $E'_{i0}(t)$ are identical with u replaced by t. There are two special forms:

1. $u = 0$ and $t = 1$ then

$$y'(x) = \frac{1}{h}\left(-y_0 - \frac{1}{3}\Delta^2 y_{-1} + \frac{1}{20}\Delta^4 y_{-2} - \frac{1}{105}\Delta^6 y_{-3}\right.$$
$$\left. + \cdots + y_1 - \frac{1}{6}\Delta^2 y_0 + \frac{1}{30}\Delta^4 y_{-1} - \frac{1}{140}\Delta^6 y_{-2} + \cdots\right). \tag{35.14}$$

2. $u = 1$ and $t = 0$, then

$$y'(x) = \frac{1}{h}\left(-y_0 + \frac{1}{6}\Delta^2 y_{-1} - \frac{1}{30}\Delta^4 y_{-2} + \frac{1}{140}\Delta^6 y_{-2}\right.$$
$$\left. - \cdots + y_1 + \frac{1}{3}\Delta^2 y_0 - \frac{1}{20}\Delta^4 y_{-1} + \frac{1}{105}\Delta^6 y_{-1} - \cdots\right). \tag{35.15}$$

Example 4.5. Find the value of the first derivative at $x = 1.80$, 1.90, and 2.00 for the data in Example 4.4, using Everett's formula.

SOLUTION. We have $h = .2$.

(a) At $x = 1.80$ we use $x_0 = 1.80$; thus $u = 0$ and $t = 1$, and we apply Formula 35.14:

$$y'(1.80) = \tfrac{1}{12}[-60(.46656) - 20(-.64640) + 3(.19200)$$
$$+ 60(.00000) - 10(-.61760) + 2(.26880)]$$
$$= \boxed{-.64800}.$$

(b) At $x = 1.90$ we use $x_0 = 1.80$; thus $u = t = \tfrac{1}{2}$, and we apply Formula 35.12:

i	$+E'_{i0}(t)$	$\Delta^{2i}y_{-i}$	$E'_{i1}(u)$	$\Delta^{2i}y_{i-1}$	$E_{i0}(t) = E_{i1}(u)$
0	-1	.46656	1	0	.5
1	.041667	$-.64640$	$-.041667$	$-.61760$	$-.0625$
2	$-.004688$	.19200	.004688	.26880	

$$y'(1.90) = \boxed{-2.33700}.$$

The values of $E_{i0}(t)$ and $E_{i1}(u)$ may be obtained from Table V, p. 358.

(c) If we take $x_0 = 1.8$ at $x = 2.00$, then $u = 1$ and $t = 0$, so that we may apply Formula 35.15.

$$y'(x) = \tfrac{1}{12}[-60(.46656) + 10(-.64640) - 2(.19200)$$
$$+ 60(.00000) + 20(-.61760) - 3(.26880)]$$
$$= \boxed{-4.00000}.$$

The first derivative of Lagrange's formula is discussed in Chapter 5.

36.   HIGHER DERIVATIVES OF CLASSICAL INTERPOLATION FORMULAS

The extension to higher derivatives is straightforward. The formulas derived in the last section could be differentiated again to yield the second derivative, which in turn could be differentiated again to yield the third derivative, etc. We shall not display all of the formulas that would result from this operation. We shall instead concentrate on a few special cases.

Let us consider the formulas that would result from differentiation of Newton's forward formula. The second derivative is obtained by differentiating Formula 35.2.

$$y''(x) = \frac{1}{h^2} [D_2^2(u)\Delta^2 y_0 + D_3^2(u)\Delta^3 y_0 + \cdots + D_k^2(u)\Delta^k y_0 + \cdots], \quad (36.1)$$

where, from Formula 3.35, we have

$$D_{i+1}^2(u) = \frac{1}{i+1}[2D_i(u) + (u-i)D_i^2(u)], \quad (i = 2, 3, \ldots) \quad (36.2)$$

and, in particular,

$$D_2^2(u) = 1.$$

We can easily generalize to the kth derivative;

$$y^{(k)}(x) = \frac{1}{h^k}[D_k^k(u)\Delta^k y_0 + D_{k+1}^k(u)\Delta^{k+1} y_0 + \cdots] \quad (36.3)$$

and

$$D_{i+1}^{(k)}(u) = \frac{1}{i+1}[k D_i^{(k-1)}(u) + (u-i)D_i^{(k)}(u)]. \quad (36.4)$$

These formulas are used at the beginning of a table of values. It is therefore especially interesting to reduce the formulas at $x = x_0$ and $x = x_1$ or, in other words, at $u = 0$ and $u = 1$. The values of $D_i^{(k)}(0)$ may be put in tabular form and reduced to the lowest common denominator for an appropriate number of differences.

TABLE 4.3.   VALUES OF $D_i{}^k(0)$ = entry/L.C.D.

k \ i	1	2	3	4	5	6	L.C.D.
1	60	−30	20	−15	12	−10	60
2		180	−180	165	−150	137	180
4			8	−12	14	−15	8
3				6	−12	17	6
5					2	−5	2
6						1	1

TABLE 4.4. VALUES OF $D_i{}^k(1)$ = entry/L.C.D.

k \ i	1	2	3	4	5	6	L.C.D.
1	60	30	−10	5	−3	2	60
2		180	0	−15	15	−13	180
3			8	−4	2	−1	8
4				6	−6	5	6
5					2	−3	2
6						1	1

From these tables we can write, for example,

$$y''(x_0) = \frac{1}{180h^2}(180\Delta^2 y_0 - 180\Delta^3 y_0 + 165\Delta^4 y_0 - 150\Delta^5 y_0 + 137\Delta^6 y_0)$$

or

$$y'''(x_1) = \frac{1}{8h^3}(8\Delta^3 y_0 - 4\Delta^4 y_0 + 2\Delta^5 y_0 - \Delta^6 y_0).$$

Example 4.6. Find $y''(1)$ from the data in Example 4.4.

SOLUTION.

$$y''(1) = \frac{1}{7.2}[180(.11200) - 180(-.31680) + 165(.03840) - 150(.07680)]$$

$$= \boxed{10}.$$

We emphasize again that numerical differentiation of empirical data is not precise, and unless the data are extremely well fitted by the interpolation polynomials it is a fantasy to attempt to find derivatives of large orders. We recommend the use of all the differences available and present the fractional form of $D_i^k(0)$ for $i = 1, \ldots, 10$ and $k = 1, \ldots, 6$. See Table 4.5.

The values of the higher derivatives at $x = x_n$ may be obtained by repeated differentiation of Newton's backward formula, and a table of coefficients similar to Table 4.3 may be calculated. This is left as an exercise for the reader.

Another set of formulas of special interest are those that may be used to evaluate the higher derivatives of a function at $x = x_0$, where x_0 is the central

TABLE 4.5. VALUES OF $D_i{}^k(0)$

k \\ i	1	2	3	4	5	6	7	8	9	10
1	1	$-\frac{1}{2}$	$\frac{1}{3}$	$-\frac{1}{4}$	$\frac{1}{5}$	$-\frac{1}{6}$	$\frac{1}{7}$	$-\frac{1}{8}$	$\frac{1}{9}$	$-\frac{1}{10}$
2		1	-1	$\frac{11}{12}$	$-\frac{5}{6}$	$\frac{137}{180}$	$-\frac{7}{10}$	$\frac{363}{560}$	$-\frac{761}{1260}$	$\frac{7129}{12600}$
3			1	$-\frac{3}{2}$	$\frac{7}{4}$	$-\frac{15}{8}$	$\frac{29}{15}$	$-\frac{469}{240}$	$\frac{29531}{15120}$	$-\frac{1303}{672}$
4				1	-2	$\frac{17}{6}$	$-\frac{7}{2}$	$\frac{967}{240}$	$-\frac{547}{144}$	$\frac{635039}{151200}$
5					1	$-\frac{5}{2}$	$\frac{25}{6}$	$-\frac{35}{6}$	$\frac{1069}{144}$	$-\frac{3089}{360}$
6						1	-3	$\frac{23}{4}$	-9	$\frac{3013}{240}$

value in a central difference table. To derive such a set, we obtain the successive derivatives of Stirling's formula and evaluate the coefficients at $x = x_0$; that is, $u = 0$.

From Formula 35.7 we obtain by a differentiation

$$y''(x) = \frac{1}{h^2}(S_2'' \Delta^2 y_{-1} + S_3'' m_3 + S_4'' \Delta^4 y_{-2} + S_5'' m_5 + \cdots) \qquad (36.5)$$

and

$$y'''(x) = \frac{1}{h^3}(S_3''' m_3 + S_4''' \Delta^4 y_{-2} + S_5''' m_5 + S_6''' \Delta^6 y_{-3} + \cdots), \qquad (36.6)$$

where

$S_2'' = 1$	
$S_3'' = u$	$S_3''' = 1$
$S_4'' = \frac{1}{4}(uS_3'' + 2S_3')$	$S_4''' = u$
$S_5'' = \frac{1}{5}(uS_4'' + 2S_4' - S_3'')$	$S_5''' = \frac{1}{5}(uS_4''' + 3S_4'' - S_3''')$
$S_6'' = \frac{1}{6}(uS_5'' + 2S_5')$	$S_6''' = \frac{1}{6}(uS_5''' + 3S_5'')$
etc.	etc.

The process may, of course, be continued for higher derivatives. The evaluation of $S_i^{(k)}(u)$ at $u = 0$ is an easy matter, and again we may put the results in tabular form.

TABLE 4.6. VALUES OF $S_i^{(k)}(0)$

k \ i	1	2	3	4	5	6	7	8	9	10
1	1	0	$-\frac{1}{6}$	0	$\frac{1}{30}$	0	$-\frac{1}{140}$	0	$\frac{115}{72576}$	0
2		1	0	$-\frac{1}{12}$	0	$\frac{1}{90}$	0	$-\frac{1}{560}$	0	$\frac{23}{72576}$
3			1	0	$-\frac{1}{4}$	0	$\frac{5}{84}$	0	$-\frac{209}{15120}$	0
4				1	0	$-\frac{1}{6}$	0	$\frac{5}{168}$	0	$-\frac{209}{29400}$
5					1	0	$-\frac{1}{3}$	0	$\frac{137}{1512}$	0
6						1	0	$-\frac{1}{4}$	0	$\frac{137}{2520}$
7							1	0	$-\frac{5}{12}$	0
8								1	0	$-\frac{1}{3}$
9									1	0
10										1

Example 4.7. Find $y''(2)$ from the data in Example 4.4.

SOLUTION.

$$y''(2) = \frac{1}{7.2}[180(-.61760) - 15(.26880)] = -16.$$

The higher derivatives of Lagrange's formula are discussed in Chapter 5.

37.   MAXIMUM AND MINIMUM VALUES OF TABULATED FUNCTIONS

The maximum and minimum values of a function are obtained by setting its first derivative equal to zero and solving for the variable. The process may be applied to a tabulated function. We may equate any one of the general formulas for the first derivative derived in Section 35 equal to zero and solve for u. Then the value of x may be found from $x = x_0 + hu$. Let us consider Stirling's formula (35.7) and for simplicity terminate it after the sixth difference. We have

$$y'(u) = m_1 + S'_2 \Delta^2 y_{-1} + S'_3 m_3 + S'_4 \Delta^4 y_{-2} + S'_5 m_5 + S'_6 \Delta^6 y_{-3}, \quad (37.1)$$

where

$$S'_2 = u,$$

$$S'_3 = \tfrac{1}{2}u^2 - \tfrac{1}{6},$$

$$S'_4 = \tfrac{1}{6}u^3 - \tfrac{1}{12}u, \quad (37.2)$$

$$S'_5 = \tfrac{1}{24}u^4 - \tfrac{1}{8}u^2 + \tfrac{1}{30},$$

$$S'_6 = \tfrac{1}{120}u^5 - \tfrac{1}{36}u^3 + \tfrac{1}{90}u.$$

By substituting the values in (37.2) into Formula 37.1 and writing the result as a polynomial in u we obtain

$$y'(u) = a_5 u^5 + a_4 u^4 + a_3 u^3 + a_2 u^2 + a_1 u + a_0, \quad (37.3)$$

where

$$a_5 = \tfrac{1}{120}\Delta^6 y_{-3},$$

$$a_4 = \tfrac{1}{24}m_5,$$

$$a_3 = \tfrac{1}{36}(6\Delta^4 y_{-2} - \Delta^6 y_{-3}),$$

$$a_2 = \tfrac{1}{8}(4m_3 - m_5), \quad (37.4)$$

$$a_1 = \tfrac{1}{180}(180\Delta^2 y_{-1} - 15\Delta^4 y_{-2} + 2\Delta^6 y_{-3}),$$

$$a_0 = \tfrac{1}{30}(30m_1 - 5m_3 + m_5).$$

In solving the equation obtained by setting Formula 37.3 equal to zero, we may be faced with the problem of finding the roots of an algebraic equation whose coefficients are approximate numbers. Methods for working this problem are discussed in Chapter 6.

Example 4.8. Find the maximum and minimum values of the function

x	0	1	2	3	4	5
y	0	.25	0	2.25	16.00	56.25

SOLUTION. Calculate a central difference table:

z	y	Δy	$\Delta^2 y$	$\Delta^3 y$	$\Delta^4 y$
0	0				
		.25			
1	.25		$-.50$		
		$-.25$		3	
2	0	1.00	2.50	6	6
		2.25		9	
3	2.25		11.50		6
		13.75		15	
4	16.00		26.50		
		40.25			
5	56.25				

Let $x_0 = 2$; then, since $\Delta^5 y = \Delta^6 y = 0$,

$$y'(u) = a_3 u^3 + a_2 u^2 + a_1 u + a_0$$
$$= \tfrac{1}{6}(6)u^3 + \tfrac{1}{2}(6)u^2 + \tfrac{1}{12}(24)u + \tfrac{1}{30}(0)$$
$$= u^3 + 3u^2 + 2u.$$

The solutions of $y'(u) = 0$ are $u = 0, -1, -2$. Then, since $h = 1$ there are maxima and minima at

$$x = x_0 + u = 2 + u_i = \boxed{2, 1, 0}.$$

The values of the function can now be read out of the table.

To determine whether there is a maximum or a minimum at the resulting value of x, inspect the table of values. It is not necessary to be concerned with the second derivative. Thus in the foregoing example it is easily seen that the values at $x = 0$ and $x = 2$ are minima values.

38.   EXERCISE V

1. Given the data of Problem 3(a) in Exercise III, find the value of the first derivative at $x = 0$, .15, .50, .52, .55, 1.0.

2. Given the data of Problem 3(b) in Exercise III, find the value of the third derivative at $x = .2$ and $x = 1$.

3. Express the first derivative of Newton's forward formula terminated after the sixth differences as a polynomial in u. [*Hint.* Write each $\binom{u}{i}$ as a polynomial before differentiating.]

4. Find the maxima and minima values of

x	-2	-1	0	1	2	3	4
y	2	$-.25$	0	$-.25$	2	15.75	56

5. Using the data of Problem 14 in Exercise II find
(a) $y_i^{(k)}(-2)$ for $k = 1, 2, 3, 4$ and $i = 1, 2, 3, 4$;
(b) $y_i^{(k)}(-1)$ for $k = 1, 2, 3, 4$ and $i = 1, 2, 3, 4$;
(c) $y_i^{(k)}(0)$ for $k = 1, 2, 3, 4$ and $i = 1, 2, 3, 4$.

6. Differentiate Formula 37.1 and find expressions for S_i'', $(i = 2, 3, 4, 5, 6)$. Write the result as a polynomial in u.

7. Differentiate Formula 37.3 and compare the answer with that found in Problem 6.

8. Given the function $y = 3x^4 - 7x^3$, tabulate the function for $0 \le x \le 2$ with $x = h = .1$. Use the tabular values to find $y'''(1)$ and check the answer by calculating the exact value.

9. Terminate Formula 23.21 after six terms, write as a polynomial in u, and differentiate. Apply the resulting formulas to Problem 5(c).

10. Let $n = 4$ in Formula 37.1; differentiate and write a formula for the first derivative of $I_H(x)$.

11. Investigate the form of $H_i M_i$ (see answer to Problem 10 for definition of M_i) if x equals x_i, one of the tabulated values of x.

12. Apply the formulas found in Problems 10 and 11 to find $y'(.3)$ for Example 3.16.

39.   NUMERICAL INTEGRATION—INTRODUCTION

Numerical integration is the process of calculating the value of a definite integral from the tabulated values of the integrand. The student of calculus was introduced to this subject at the time he studied the trapezoidal rule and Simpson's rule. The process is frequently called mechanical quadrature if it is applied to the integration of a function of one variable.

The solution to the problem of numerical integration may be obtained by replacing the integrand by an interpolation function and integrating this function between the desired limits. Thus, if we integrate the interpolation formulas in Chapter 3, we obtain quadrature formulas for the integration of a function whose values are given in tabular form. In carrying out this calculation, we must be aware that we are replacing the given integrand by an interpolating function, usually a polynomial, and then integrating this function. The accuracy of the result depends on the ability of the interpolating function to represent the integrand over the interval of integration. It is frequently desirable to investigate this fact before embarking on extensive numerical integration.

It is possible to derive a large number of quadrature formulas but quite impractical to exhibit them all. We shall concentrate our efforts on those that are readily adapted to calculating machines and that have proven to be sufficiently accurate for most applications. The particular formulas obtained by integrating Lagrange's interpolation function are discussed in Chapter 5.

40.   QUADRATURE FORMULA FOR EQUIDISTANT VALUES

Let us first consider a function whose values are given at equally spaced intervals of the independent variables. In this case we have

$$x = x_0 + hu \tag{40.1}$$

so that

$$dx = h\,du \tag{40.2}$$

and

$$\int_{x_1}^{x_2} y(x)\,dx = h \int_{u_1}^{u_2} y(u)\,du. \tag{40.3}$$

Let us consider Newton's forward Formula 23.8

$$y(x) = y_0 + u\,\Delta y_0 + \binom{u}{2}\Delta^2 y_0 + \binom{u}{3}\Delta^3 y_0 + \cdots + \binom{u}{i}\Delta^i y_0 + \cdots$$

and integrate it between the limits x_0 and x_n which establishes the limits on u from 0 to n.

$$\int_{x_0}^{x_n} y(x)\,dx = h \int_0^n \left(y_0 + u\,\Delta y_0 + \binom{u}{2}\Delta^2 y_0 + \cdots \right) du \tag{40.4}$$

$$= h[a_0 y_0 + a_1 \Delta y_0 + a_2 \Delta^2 y_0 + \cdots + a_k \Delta^k y_0 + \cdots],$$

where

$$a_0 = \int_0^n du = u \Big|_0^n = n,$$

$$a_1 = \int_0^n u\, du = \frac{1}{2} u^2 \Big|_0^n = \frac{1}{2} n^2,$$

$$a_2 = \int_0^n \binom{u}{2} du = \frac{1}{6} u^3 - \frac{1}{4} u^2 \Big|_0^n = \frac{1}{6} n^3 - \frac{1}{4} n^2,$$

$$a_k = \int_0^n \binom{u}{k} du = \frac{1}{k!} \int_0^n \prod_{j=0}^{k-1} (u - j)\, du.$$

By the use of Stirling's numbers we may write a_k as polynomials in n. They are of degree $k + 1$ and terminate with n^2. A lowest common denominator for the coefficients may be found and factored out. Thus we obtain the coefficients of the various powers of n in Table 4.7.

TABLE 4.7. COEFFICIENTS OF n^i IN a_k

k	L.C.D.	n^{10}	n^9	n^8	n^7	n^6	n^5	n^4	n^3	n^2
1	2									1
2	12								2	−3
3	24							1	−4	4
4	720						6	−45	110	−90
5	1440					2	−24	105	−200	144
6	60480				12	−210	1428	−4725	7672	−5040
7	120960			3	−72	700	−3528	9744	−14112	8640
8	3628800		10	−315	4140	−29400	121842	−295470	392040	−226800
9	7257600	2	−80	1365	−12960	74830	−269136	590620	−730560	403200

If we specify n, the polynomials may be evaluated and the a_k become constants; their values may then be tabulated for given values of n. There are better formulas, however, and such tabulation is not worthwhile.

41.   SPECIAL RULES

It is well known from the study of integral calculus that

$$\int_0^6 y\, dx = \int_0^2 y\, dx + \int_2^4 y\, dx + \int_4^6 y\, dx. \tag{41.1}$$

Let us now divide the set of points (x_i, y_i) into groups of three (x_0, x_1, x_2),

(x_2, x_3, x_4), (x_4, x_5, x_6), etc. For each group there are no differences beyond the second, so that in Formula 40.4 $n = 2$, and it becomes

$$\int_{x_0}^{x_2} y\, dx \doteq h[2y_0 + 2\Delta y_0 + (\tfrac{8}{6} - \tfrac{4}{4})\Delta^2 y_0]$$

$$= h[2y_0 + 2(y_1 - y_0) + \tfrac{1}{3}(y_2 - 2y_1 + y_0)] \tag{41.2}$$

$$= \tfrac{1}{3}h[y_0 + 4y_1 + y_2].$$

For the interval from x_2 to x_4 we obtain

$$\int_{x_2}^{x_4} y\, dx \doteq h(2y_2 + 2\Delta y_2 + \tfrac{1}{3}\Delta^2 y_2)$$

$$= \tfrac{1}{3}h(y_2 + 4y_3 + y_4). \tag{41.3}$$

We may continue this process and then add them all together. Thus, if n is *even*, we obtain

$$\int_{x_0}^{x_n} y\, dx \doteq \frac{h}{3}(y_0 + 4y_1 + 2y_2 + 4y_3 + 2y_4 + \cdots + 4y_{n-1} + y_n)$$

$$= \frac{h}{3}\sum_{i=0}^{n} c_i y_i \tag{41.4}$$

where

i	0	1	2	3	4	5	$\cdots$	$n-2$	$n-1$	n
c_i	1	4	2	4	2	4	$\cdots$	2	4	1

This is the well-known Simpson's rule and is the easiest of the quadrature formulas to apply. In its application there must be an *odd number of points*, and it is quite accurate for small values of h.

The data may be divided into groups of seven points $(x_0, \ldots, x_6)$ for which $n = 6$, and by Formula 40.4 we have

$$\int_{x_0}^{x_6} y\, dx \doteq h(6y_0 + 18\Delta y_0 + 27\Delta^2 y_0 + 24\Delta^3 y_0 + \tfrac{123}{10}\Delta^4 y_0$$

$$+ \tfrac{33}{10}\Delta^5 y_0 + \tfrac{41}{140}\Delta^6 y_0). \tag{41.5}$$

If we replace $\tfrac{41}{140}h\Delta^6 y_0$ by $\tfrac{3}{10}h\Delta^6 y_0$, we will be committing an error of $h\Delta^6 y_0/140$, which may be tolerated provided h and $\Delta^6 y_0$ are sufficiently small. Making this substitution and replacing all the differences by their values in terms of the given values of y reduces Formula 41.5 to

$$\int_{z_0}^{z_6} y \, dx \doteq .3h(y_0 + 5y_1 + y_2 + 6y_3 + y_4 + 5y_5 + y_6).$$ (41.6)

The same procedure is now applied to the points for x_6 and x_{12} to obtain

$$\int_{x_6}^{x_{12}} y \, dx \doteq .3h(y_6 + 5y_7 + y_8 + 6y_9 + y_{10} + 5y_{11} + y_{12}).$$ (41.7)

By continuing the process and adding the results, we obtain

$$\int_{x_0}^{x_n} y \, dx \doteq .3h(y_0 + 5y_1 + y_2 + 6y_3 + y_4 + 5y_5$$
$$+ 2y_6 + 5y_7 + y_8 + 6y_9 + y_{10} + 5y_{11}$$
$$+ \cdots$$
$$+ 2y_{n-6} + 5y_{n-5} + y_{n-4} + 6y_{n-3} + y_{n-2}$$
$$+ 5y_{n-1} + y_n)$$
$$= .3h \sum_{i=0}^{n} c_i y_i,$$ (41.8)

where

i	0	1	2	3	4	5	6	7	8	9	10	11	$\cdots$	n
c_i	1	5	1	6	1	5	2	5	1	6	1	5		1

The coefficients may best be remembered in groups of six:

First group	1, 5, 1, 6, 1, 5
All interior groups	2, 5, 1, 6, 1, 5
Last group	2, 5, 1, 6, 1, 5, 1

This is known as Weddle's rule. It requires at least seven consecutive values of the function and uses them in multiples of *six* if more than the first seven are required. In general it is more accurate than Simpson's rule.

In the application of these rules it is recommended that the multipliers c_i be recorded adjacent to the values of the function they multiply.

Example 4.9. Find the value of $\int_0^6 y \, dx$ for the function tabulated.

SOLUTION. We shall find the value by using both of the foregoing rules. In this case we have $h = 1$.

x	y	$c_i(S)$	$c_i(W)$
0	0	1	1
1	-45	4	5
2	-496	2	1
3	-2541	4	6
4	-8184	2	1
5	-19525	4	5
6	-37320	1	1

$$I_S = \tfrac{1}{3} \sum c_i(S) y_i = \boxed{-47708.0}$$

$$I_W = .3 \sum c_i(W) y_i = \boxed{-47728.8}$$

This is a tabulation of the function

$$y(x) = x^6 - 9x^5 - 9x^4 - 9x^3 - 9x^2 - 10x,$$

and the integral from $x = 0$ to $x = 6$ correct to one decimal place is $\boxed{-47733.9}$. Thus Simpson's rule gives a value that is in error by $.054\%$ and Weddle's rule gives a value that is in error by $.011\%$.

42. INTEGRATION FORMULAS BASED ON CENTRAL DIFFERENCES

In this section we shall integrate Stirling's and Bessel's interpolation formulas. First let us integrate Stirling's formula (23.17) from $x_0 - h$ to $x_0 + h$; that is $u = -1$ to $u = 1$. We have

$$\int_{-1}^{1} y \, du \doteq \int_{-1}^{1} (y_0 + S_1 m_1 + S_2 \Delta^2 y_{-1} + S_3 m_3$$

$$+ S_4 \Delta^4 y_{-2} + \cdots) \, du \tag{42.1}$$

$$= s_0 y_0 + s_1 m_1 + s_2 \Delta^2 y_{-1} + s_3 m_3 + s_4 \Delta^4 y_{-2} + \cdots,$$

where

$$s_0 = u \Big|_{-1}^{1} = 2,$$

$$s_1 = \frac{1}{2} u^2 \Big|_{-1}^{1} = 0,$$

$$s_2 = \frac{1}{6} u^3 \Big|_{-1}^{1} = \frac{1}{3},$$

$$s_3 = \frac{1}{24} (u^4 - 2u^2) \Big|_{-1}^{1} = 0,$$

$$s_4 = \frac{1}{24} \frac{u^5}{5} - \frac{u^3}{3} \Big|_{-1}^{1} = -\frac{1}{90},$$

etc.

We note that the coefficients of m_i contain only even powers of u and consequently are zero when integrated from $u = -1$ and $u = 1$. There remain, then, only the even differences, and we write

$$\int_{-1}^{1} y \, du \doteq 2y_0 + \tfrac{1}{3} \Delta^2 y_{-1} - \tfrac{1}{90} \Delta^4 y_{-2} + \tfrac{1}{756} \Delta^6 y_{-3} - \cdots. \qquad (42.2)$$

Since we can order x_0 at any interior point of a central difference table, the value of the integral from $u = 0$ to $u = 2$ is identical in form to Formula 42.2, with the subscripts on the y's advanced by one unit. Thus

$$\int_{0}^{2} y \, du \doteq 2y_1 + \tfrac{1}{3} \Delta^2 y_0 - \tfrac{1}{90} \Delta^4 y_{-1} + \tfrac{1}{756} \Delta^6 y_{-2} - \cdots. \qquad (42.3)$$

If we continue by finding the integrals from 2 to 4, 4 to 6, etc., and then add them all together, we obtain for an even value of n

$$\int_{x_0}^{x_n} y \, dx \doteq h[2(y_1 + y_3 + y_5 + \cdots + y_{n-1})$$
$$+ \tfrac{1}{3}(\Delta^2 y_0 + \Delta^2 y_2 + \Delta^2 y_4 + \cdots + \Delta^2 y_{n-2})$$
$$- \tfrac{1}{90}(\Delta^4 y_{-1} + \Delta^4 y_1 + \Delta^4 y_3 + \cdots + \Delta^4 y_{n-3}) \qquad (42.4)$$
$$+ \tfrac{1}{756}(\Delta^6 y_{-2} + \Delta^6 y_0 + \Delta^6 y_2 + \cdots + \Delta^6 y_{n-4})$$
$$+ \cdots].$$

For machine calculation the formula should be reduced to least-common-denominator form before doing the calculation.

Let us now integrate Bessel's formula (23.20) from x_0 to x_1; that is, $u = 0$ to 1. The coefficients of the result are

$$b_0 = u \Big|_0^1 = 1,$$

$$b_1 = \frac{1}{2}(u^2 - u) \Big|_0^1 = 0,$$

$$b_2 = \frac{1}{12}(2u^3 - 3u^2) \Big|_0^1 = -\frac{1}{12},$$

$$b_3 = \frac{1}{24}(u^4 - 2u^3 + u^2) \Big|_0^1 = 0,$$

$$b_4 = \frac{11}{720},$$

$$b_5 = 0,$$

$$b_6 = -\frac{191}{60480},$$

etc.,

so that we have

$$\int_{x_0}^{x_1} y \, dx \doteq h\left(m_0 - \frac{1}{12}m_2 + \frac{11}{720}m_4 - \frac{191}{60480}m_6 + \cdots\right). \qquad (42.5)$$

If we now proceed as we have in the past and integrate from x_1 to x_2, then x_2 to x_3, etc., we can obtain in each case a formula similar to (42.5) involving the arithmetic mean of the even differences on the lines through $x_{\frac{3}{2}}, x_{\frac{5}{2}}$, etc. In order to employ the notation m_k, it is necessary to use a double subscript on m. Let the first subscript denote the line on which the arithmetic means of the even differences are calculated, so that between x_{j-1} and x_j we write $m_{j, 2i}, (j = 1, \ldots, n)$. Then the general formula is

$$\int_{x_{j-1}}^x y \, dx \doteq h\left(m_{j0} - \frac{1}{12}m_{j2} + \frac{11}{720}m_{j4} - \frac{191}{60480}m_{j6} + \cdots\right). \qquad (42.6)$$

If we now add all of these terms together, we obtain

$$\int_{x_0}^{x_n} y \, dx \doteq h\left(\sum_{j=1}^n m_{j0} - \frac{1}{12}\sum_{j=1}^n m_{j2} + \frac{11}{720}\sum_{j=1}^n m_{j4} - \cdots\right). \qquad (42.7)$$

The evaluation of this formula requires a length calculation which may be somewhat simplified. From the definition we have

$$\sum_{j=1}^{n} m_{j0} = \tfrac{1}{2}[(y_0 + y_1) + (y_1 + y_2) + (y_2 + y_3) + \cdots + (y_{n-1} + y_n)]$$

$$= \tfrac{1}{2}y_0 + y_1 + y_2 + y_3 + \cdots + \tfrac{1}{2}y_n,$$

$$\sum_{j=1}^{n} m_{j2} = \tfrac{1}{2}[(\Delta^2 y_{-1} + \Delta^2 y_0) + (\Delta^2 y_0 + \Delta^2 y_1) + \cdots$$

$$+ (\Delta^2 y_{n-2} + \Delta^2 y_{n-1})]$$

$$= \tfrac{1}{2}(\Delta^2 y_{-1} + 2\Delta^2 y_0 + 2\Delta^2 y_1 + 2\Delta^2 y_2 + 2\Delta^2 y_3 + \cdots$$

$$2 + \Delta^2 y_{n-2} + \Delta^2 y_{n-1})$$

$$= \tfrac{1}{2}(\Delta y_0 - \Delta y_{-1} + 2\Delta y_1 - 2\Delta y_0 + 2\Delta y_2 - 2\Delta y_1 + 2\Delta y_3$$

$$- 2\Delta y_2 + \cdots \Delta y_n - \Delta y_{n-1})$$

$$= \tfrac{1}{2}(-\Delta y_{-1} - \Delta y_0 + \Delta y_{n-1} + \Delta y_n)$$

$$= \tfrac{1}{2}[\Delta y_n + \Delta y_{n-1} - (\Delta y_{-1} + \Delta y_0)]$$

$$= (m_{n1} - m_{01}).$$

The cancellation of the center terms when the even-order differences are reduced to the next lower odd-order differences holds for the rest of the terms in Formula 42.7, which then reduces to

$$\int_{x_0}^{x_n} y \, dx \doteq h\left[\left(\frac{1}{2}y_0 + y_1 + y_2 + y_3 + \cdots + \frac{1}{2}y_n\right)\right.$$

$$- \frac{1}{12}(m_{n1} - m_{01}) + \frac{11}{720}(m_{n-1,3} - m_{03}) \qquad (42.8)$$

$$\left. - \frac{191}{60480}(m_{n-2,5} - m_{0,5}) + \cdots\right].$$

In this case n may be even or odd. To arrive at a better understanding of Formula 42.8, let us indicate clearly in a central difference table which elements are used; they have been blocked off in Table 4.8.

Example 4.10. Find the value of the integral from $x = 3$ to $x = 6$ of the function

x	0	1	2	3	4	5	6	7
y	0	−45	−496	−2541	−8184	−19525	−37320	−58821

TABLE 4.8. ELEMENTS FOR FORMULA 42.8

x	y	Δy	$\Delta^2 y$	$\Delta^3 y$	$\Delta^4 y$	$\Delta^5 y$	$\Delta^6 y$	$\Delta^7 y$	$\Delta^8 y$
x_{-4}	y_{-4}								
		Δy_{-4}							
x_{-3}	y_{-3}		$\Delta^2 y_{-4}$						
		Δy_{-3}		$\Delta^3 y_{-4}$					
x_{-2}	y_{-2}		$\Delta^2 y_{-3}$		$\Delta^4 y_{-4}$				
		Δy_{-2}		$\Delta^3 y_{-3}$		$\Delta^5 y_{-4}$			
x_{-1}	y_{-1}		$\Delta^2 y_{-2}$		$\Delta^4 y_{-3}$		$\Delta^6 y_{-4}$		
		Δy_{-1}		$\Delta^3 y_{-2}$		$\Delta^5 y_{-3}$		$\Delta^7 y_{-4}$	
x_0	y_0	$\boxed{m_{01}}$	$\Delta^2 y_{-1}$	$\boxed{m_{03}}$	$\Delta^4 y_{-2}$	$\boxed{m_{05}}$	$\Delta^6 y_{-3}$	$\boxed{m_{07}}$	$\Delta^8 y_{-4}$
		Δy_0		$\Delta^3 y_{-1}$		$\Delta^5 y_{-2}$		$\Delta^7 y_{-3}$	
x_1	y_1	m_{11}	$\Delta^2 y_0$	m_{13}	$\Delta^4 y_{-1}$	m_{15}	$\Delta^6 y_{-2}$	$\boxed{m_{17}}$	$\Delta^8 y_{-3}$
		Δy_1		$\Delta^3 y_0$		$\Delta^5 y_{-1}$		$\Delta^7 y_{-2}$	
x_2	y_2	m_{21}	$\Delta^2 y_1$	m_{23}	$\Delta^4 y_0$	$\boxed{m_{25}}$	$\Delta^6 y_{-1}$		
		Δy_2		$\Delta^3 y_1$		$\Delta^5 y_0$			
x_3	y_3	m_{31}	$\Delta^2 y_2$	$\boxed{m_{33}}$	$\Delta^4 y_1$				
		Δy_3		$\Delta^3 y_2$					
x_4	y_4	$\boxed{m_{41}}$	$\Delta^2 y_3$						
		Δy_4							
x_5	y_5								

SOLUTION. Calculate the difference table and let $x_0 = 3$.

x	y	Δy	$\Delta^2 y$	$\Delta^3 y$	$\Delta^4 y$	$\Delta^5 y$	$\Delta^6 y$
0	0						
		-45					
1	-45		-406				
		-451		-1188			
2	-496		-1594		-816		
		-2045		-2004		720	
3	-2541	$\boxed{-3844}$	-3598	$\boxed{-2052}$	-96	$\boxed{1080}$	720
		-5643		-2100		1440	
4	-8184		-5698		1344	$\boxed{1800}$	720
		-11341		-756		2160	
5	-19525		-6454	$\boxed{996}$	3504		
		-17795		2748			
6	-37320	$\boxed{-19648}$	-3706				
		-21501					
7	-58821						

By applying Formula 42.8 with $h = 1$ we have

$$\int_3^6 y\, dx \doteq -47639.5 - \frac{1}{12}(-15804) + \frac{11}{720}(3048) - \frac{191}{60480}(720)$$

$$= -47639.5 + 1317 + 46.566667 - 2.273809$$

$$= \boxed{-46278.2}\,.$$

To perform the calculations on a calculating machine, write the formula over the least common denominator; thus

$$\int_3^6 y\, dx \doteq \frac{1}{60480}[30240(-2541) + 60480(-8184)$$

$$+ 60480(-19525) + 30240(-37320)$$

$$- 5040(-19648) + 5040(-3844) + 924(996)$$

$$- 924(-2052)$$

$$- 191(1800) + 191(1080)]$$

$$= \boxed{-46278.2}\,.$$

Although Formulas 42.4 and 42.8 have a classical interest, they are seldom used in practice. For more applicable formulas to find the value of an integral for tabulated functions, see Chapter 5.

43.   GAUSS'S FORMULA FOR NUMERICAL INTEGRATION

An accurate quadrature formula for finding the value of the definite integral

$$I = \int_a^b f(x)\, dx,$$

where $f(x)$ is a known function but whose integral is either not easily evaluated or cannot be conveniently expressed in closed form, was derived by Gauss and is based on Legendre polynomials. [See Section 3H.] The principle is to obtain the best subdivision of the interval (a, b), the value of the function at these points, and the coefficients to multiply the functional values to yield the value of the definite integral.

In the first step we transform the interval (a, b) to the interval $(-1, 1)$,[1] which is accomplished by letting

$$x = \tfrac{1}{2}(b - a)v + \tfrac{1}{2}(a + b). \tag{43.1}$$

[1]Some authors have transformed to the interval $(-\tfrac{1}{2}, \tfrac{1}{2})$ or $(0, 1)$ and care must be exercised when using tables of values for the coefficients.

Then at $x = a$ we have

$$= \frac{2a - a - b}{b - a} = -1,$$

and at $x = b$ we have

$$v = \frac{2b - a - b}{b - a} = 1.$$

The new form of $f(x)$ is

$$f(x) = f[\tfrac{1}{2}(b - a)v + \tfrac{1}{2}(a + b)] = \varphi(v) \qquad (43.2)$$

and

$$dx = \tfrac{1}{2}(b - a)\,dv,$$

so that

$$\int_a^b f(x)\,dx = \frac{b - a}{2} \int_{-1}^1 \varphi(v)\,dv. \qquad (43.3)$$

Now it is desired to have a formula

$$\int_{-1}^1 \varphi(v)\,dv \doteq g_1\varphi(v_1) + g_2\varphi(v_2) + g_3\varphi(v_3) + \cdots + g_n\varphi(v_n), \qquad (43.4)$$

which is a good evaluation of the integral when $\varphi(v)$ is any polynomial of as high a degree as possible and $v_i, (i = 1, \ldots, n)$, are the points of subdivision of the interval $(-1, 1)$. This is Gauss's mechanical quadrature formula. It is clear that we need to determine both the $g_i, (i = 1, \ldots, n)$, and the $v_i, (i = 1, \ldots, n)$; thus $2n$ relations are necessary, and the highest degree of the polynomials $\varphi(v)$ will probably be $2n - 1$. Let us therefore write

$$\varphi(v) = a_0 + a_1v + a_2v^2 + a_3v^3 + \cdots + a_{2n-1}v^{2n-1}, \qquad (43.5)$$

from which is obtained

$$\int_{-1}^1 \varphi(v)\,dv \doteq \left(a_0v + \tfrac{1}{2}a_1v^2 + \tfrac{1}{3}a_2v^3 + \cdots + \frac{1}{2n}a_{2n-1}v^{2n}\right)_{-1}^1 \qquad (43.6)$$

$$= 2a_0 + \tfrac{2}{3}a_2 + \tfrac{2}{5}a_4 + \cdots.$$

Substitution of $v_i, (i = 1, \ldots, n)$, into the polynomial (43.5) yields the n values

$$\varphi(v_i) = a_0 + a_1v_i + a_2v_i^2 + a_3v_i^3 + \cdots + a_{2n-1}v_i^{2n-1}. \qquad (43.7)$$

Formula 43.4 then becomes

$$\int_{-1}^{1} \varphi(v)\, dv \doteq g_1(a_0 + a_1v_1 + a_2v_1^2 + a_3v_1^3 + \cdots + a_{2n-1}v_1^{2n-1})$$

$$+ g_2(a_0 + a_1v_2 + a_2v_2^2 + a_3v_2^3 + \cdots + a_{2n-1}v_2^{2n-1})$$

$$+ g_3(a_0 + a_1v_3 + a_2v_3^2 + a_3v_3^3 + \cdots + a_{2n-1}v_3^{2n-1})$$

$$\vdots$$

$$+ g_n(a_0 + a_1v_n + a_2v_n^2 + a_3v_n^3 + \cdots + a_{2n-1}v_n^{2n-1}) \quad (43.8)$$

$$= a_0(g_1 + g_2 + g_3 + \cdots + g_n)$$

$$+ a_1(g_1v_1 + g_2v_2 + g_3v_3 + \cdots + g_nv_n)$$

$$+ a_2(g_1v_1^2 + g_2v_2^2 + g_3v_3^2 + \cdots + g_nv_n^2)$$

$$\vdots$$

$$+ a_{2n-1}(g_1v_1^{2n-1} + g_2v_2^{2n-1} + \cdots + g_nv_n^{2n-1}).$$

Since Formulas 43.6 and 43.8 must be identical for *all* values of a_i, the co-efficients of a_i must be equal. Thus we obtain the $2n$ equations

$$
\begin{aligned}
g_1 + g_2 + g_3 + \cdots + g_n &= 2 \\
g_1v_1 + g_2v_2 + g_3v_3 + \cdots + g_nv_n &= 0 \\
g_1v_1^2 + g_2v_2^2 + g_3v_3^2 + \cdots + g_nv_n^2 &= \tfrac{2}{3} \qquad (43.9) \\
g_1v_1^3 + g_2v_2^3 + g_3v_3^3 + \cdots + g_nv_n^3 &= 0 \\
\vdots \\
g_1v_1^{2n-1} + g_2v_2^{2n-1} + \cdots + g_nv_n^{2n-1} &= 0
\end{aligned}
$$

The solution of this system of nonlinear equations would be quite difficult. However, it can be reduced to a system of linear equations in g_i if we choose as values for v_i the zeros of the Legendre polynomials which are known to be real and distinct. These zeros have been calculated and tabulated, and the corresponding values of g_i have also been evaluated. They are listed in Table VII, p. 361, to ten significant digits. Since the v_i are negatively symmetrical, that is, $v_i = -v_{-i}$, and $g_i = g_{-i}$, only half plus one need be recorded.

To illustrate the use of Gauss's formula, let us consider an example.

Example 4.11. Calculate the value of

$$I = \int_{2}^{8} \frac{dx}{x}.$$

SOLUTION. Let

$$x = \tfrac{1}{2}(b - a)v + \tfrac{1}{2}(b + a)$$
$$= \tfrac{1}{2}(8 - 2)v + \tfrac{1}{2}(8 + 2)$$
$$= 3v + 5;$$

then

$$f(x) = \frac{1}{x} = \frac{1}{3v + 5} = \varphi(v).$$

Choose $n = 7$ and evaluate $\varphi(v_i)$ by obtaining the v_i from Table VII and arranging the work as follows:

i	v_i	$\varphi(v_i)$	g_i
-3	$-.9491079123$	$.4645380344$	$.1294849662$
3	$.9491079123$	$.1274319798$	$.1294849662$
-2	$-.7415311856$	$.3603075875$	$.2797053915$
2	$.7415311856$	$.1384160911$	$.2797053915$
-1	$-.4058451514$	$.2643778911$	$.3818300505$
1	$.4058451514$	$.1608354318$	$.3818300505$
0	0	$.2000000000$	$.4179591837$

The value of the integral is then

$$I = \frac{b - a}{2} \sum g_i \varphi(v_i)$$
$$= 3(.4620981736)$$
$$= \boxed{1.386294521}.$$

The true value of the integral is

$$I = \int_2^8 \frac{dx}{x} = \ln\frac{8}{2} = \ln 4 = 1.386294361.$$

Thus the error is

$$E_G = -.000000160.$$

In practice the values of v_i and g_i are not recorded, for they may be taken directly out of the table. Furthermore, since $g_i = g_{-i}$, we have

$$g_{-i}\varphi(v_{-i}) + g_i\varphi(v_i) = g_i[\varphi(v_{-i}) + \varphi(v_i)],$$

and therefore the sum

$$\varphi(v_{-i}) + \varphi(v_i)$$

could be computed and recorded to cut the recording nearly in half.

Both Lobatto and Tchebycheff have made variations on Gauss's formula, Lobatto to include the end values and Tchebycheff to make the coefficients of the g's equal. Such formulas offer advantages only in special cases.

44.   NUMERICAL DOUBLE INTEGRATION

The process of calculating the value of a definite double integral of a function of two variables is called *numerical double integration* and also *mechanical cubature*. A formula for this process may be derived by first obtaining an interpolation function in terms of the differences of a function of two variables. However, this is unnecessary, since mechanical cubature may be performed by a double application of a quadrature formula.

Let $z = f(x, y)$ be a function of two independent variables x and y and let its values be given at equally spaced intervals, $x_i, (i = 0, \ldots, n)$, of length h and $y_i, (i = 0, \ldots, m)$, of length k. Then since $dx = h\,du$ and $dy = k\,dv$, we have

$$I = \int_{x_0}^{x_n} \int_{y_0}^{y_m} Z(x, y)\,dy\,dx = hk \int_0^n \int_0^m z(u, v)\,dv\,du. \qquad (44.1)$$

If the values of $Z_{ij}(x_i, y_i)$ are exhibited in a rectangular array (see Table 2.5), then the value of I in Formula 44.1 may be found by applying the following rule:

Rule. *The value of the double integral may be found by applying to each horizontal row (or to each vertical column) any quadrature formula employing equidistant ordinates. Then, to the results thus obtained for the rows (or columns), again apply a similar formula.*

The value of the double integral can thus be found by repeated application of Simpson's rule, Weddle's rule, or any other quadrature formula.

Example 4.12. Find the value of the integral by numerical integration:

$$I = \int_1^{2.2} \int_1^{2.2} \frac{dx\,dy}{xy}.$$

SOLUTION. Let the values of the integrand be given as shown in the following table which has $h = .3$ and $k = .2$:

y \ x	1.0	1.2	1.4	1.6	1.8	2.0	2.2	A_x	$c_i(S)$
1.0	1.00000	.83333	.71429	.62500	.55556	.50000	.45455	.788463	1
1.3	.76923	.64103	.54945	.48077	.42735	.38462	.34965	.606513	4
1.6	.62500	.52083	.44643	.39063	.34722	.31250	.28409	.492790	2
1.9	.52632	.43860	.37594	.32895	.29240	.26316	.23923	.414983	4
2.2	.45455	.37879	.32468	.28409	.25253	.22727	.20661	.358393	1
$c_i(W)$	1	5	1	6	1	5	1		

$$\boxed{I \doteq .62184}.$$

Apply Weddle's rule to each row to obtain

$$A_x = (.06)\Sigma[c_i(W)](\text{entry}),$$

which have been entered in a column for each x. Then apply Simpson's rule to the column of A_x to obtain

$$I \doteq .1\Sigma[c_i(s)]A_x = .62184.$$

The true value of the integral is

$$J = (\ln 2.2)(\ln 2.2) = .62167.$$

Thus the error is $-.00017$.

45.   ACCURACY OF NUMERICAL INTEGRATION

The formulas derived in this chapter for finding the value of a definite integral are approximate, and thus there is an inherent error associated with each. It is desirable to be able to evaluate this error, and it is possible to derive expressions for the errors.

Consider first Simpson's rule and let $f(x)$ be a well-behaved function so that it is continuous in the interval under consideration and has as many continuous derivatives as required. Then we may write

$$F(x) = \int_a^x f(x)\,dx, \qquad F'(x) = f(x), \qquad F''(x) = f'(x), \text{ etc.}$$

The definite integral from $x_0 - h$ to $x_0 + h$ is

$$I = \int_{x_0-h}^{x_0+h} f(x)\, dx = F(x_0 + h) - F(x_0 - h). \tag{45.1}$$

Simpson's rule yields

$$I_s = \frac{h}{3}[f(x_0 - h) + 4f(x_0) + f(x_0 + h)] \tag{45.2}$$

and the difference between them is the inherent error

$$E_s = I - I_s = F(x_0 + h) - F(x_0 - h) - \tfrac{1}{3}h[f(x_0 - h) \\ + 4f(x_0) + f(x_0 + h)]. \tag{45.3}$$

This expression may now be transformed by expanding each term of the right-hand side in a Taylor's series; that is,

$$F(x_0 + h) = F(x_0) + hf(x_0) + \frac{1}{2}h^2 f'(x_0) + \frac{1}{3!}h^3 f''(x_0) + \cdots,$$

$$F(x_0 - h) = F(x_0) - hf(x_0) + \frac{1}{2}h^2 f'(x_0) - \frac{1}{3!}h^3 f''(x_0) + \cdots,$$

$$f(x_0 + h) = f(x_0) + hf'(x_0) + \frac{1}{2}h^2 f''(x_0) + \frac{1}{3!}h^3 f'''(x_0) + \cdots, \tag{45.4}$$

$$f(x_0 - h) = f(x_0) - hf'(x_0) + \frac{1}{2}h^2 f''(x_0) - \frac{1}{3!}h^3 f'''(x_0) + \cdots,$$

and substituting into (45.3) we see that the terms up to the fourth derivative subtract out.

$$F(x_0) - F(x_0) = 0,$$

$$hf(x_0) + hf(x_0) - \frac{1}{3}h[f(x_0) + 4f(x_0) + f(x_0)] = 0,$$

$$\frac{1}{2}h^2 f'(x_0) - \frac{1}{2}h^2 f'(x_0) - \frac{1}{3}h[hf'(x_0) - hf'(x_0)] = 0,$$

$$\vdots$$

$$\left[\frac{1}{5!}f^{iv}(x_0) + \frac{1}{5!}f^{iv}(x_0)\right]h^5 - \frac{1}{3}h\left[\frac{1}{4!}h^4 f^{iv}(x_0) + \frac{1}{4!}h^4 f^{iv}(x_0)\right]$$

$$= \left(\frac{2}{5!} - \frac{1}{3}\frac{2}{4!}\right)h^5 f^{iv}(x_0).$$

Thus

$$E_s = -\tfrac{1}{90}h^5 f^{iv}(x_0) + \cdots \tag{45.5}$$

is an expression for the error over the interval from $x_0 - h$ to $x_0 + h$. If we change the interval to be from $x_1 - h$ to $x_1 + h$, $f^{iv}(x_0)$ is replaced by $f^{iv}(x_1)$ in Formula 45.5. The entire interval from a to b can now be subdivided into subintervals x_0 to x_2, x_2 to x_4, etc., so that the total error is

$$E_s = -\tfrac{1}{90}h^5 [f^{iv}(x_1) + f^{iv}(x_3) + f^{iv}(x_5) + \cdots + f^{iv}(x_{n-1})] - \cdots. \tag{45.6}$$

If we ignore all the terms above the fourth derivative and let $f^{iv}(x_k)$ be the largest value of any of the $f^{iv}(x_i)$, we may replace each by $f^{iv}(x_k)$ and add the $\tfrac{1}{2}n$ quantities to yield the approximation

$$E_s \doteq -\frac{nh^5}{180} f^{iv}(x_k) = -\frac{b-a}{180} h^4 f^{iv}(x_k), \tag{45.7}$$

since

$$b - a = nh.$$

This gives us an estimate for the error in Simpson's rule.

Since the fourth derivative is zero if $f(x)$ is a polynomial of degree no larger than the third, it is seen that Simpson's rule gives the exact value of the integral for these polynomials.

The foregoing error formula is expressed in terms of the fourth derivative which may not always be conveniently evaluated. It is therefore desirable to replace it by the equivalent differences and then to replace those by their values in terms of the given ordinates. The first part can be done by using Formula 19.5 to write the approximation

$$f^{iv}(x_i) \doteq \frac{\Delta^4 y_{i-2}}{h^4},$$

so that we have

$$E_s \doteq -\frac{h}{90}(\Delta^4 y_{-1} + \Delta^4 y_1 + \Delta^4 y_3 + \cdots + \Delta^4 y_{n-3}). \tag{45.8}$$

To carry the transformation further, we use Formula 11.6 to write the differences in terms of the given ordinates:

$$\Delta^4 y_{-1} = y_3 - 4y_2 + 6y_1 - 4y_0 + y_{-1},$$
$$\Delta^4 y_1 = y_5 - 4y_4 + 6y_3 - 4y_2 + y_1,$$
$$\vdots$$
$$\Delta^4 y_{n-3} = y_{n+1} - 4y_n + 6y_{n-1} - 4y_{n-2} + y_{n-3},$$

and on substituting them into Formula 45.8 we have, after collecting terms,

$$E_s \doteq -\frac{h}{90}[y_{-1} + y_{n+1} - 4(y_0 + y_n) + 7(y_1 + y_{n-1})$$

$$-8(y_2 + y_4 + \cdots + y_{n-2}) + 8(y_3 + y_5 + \cdots + y_{n-3})] \qquad (45.9)$$

for $n \geq 6$.

For n less than six some of the y_i will not exist. Since n must be even for Simpson's rule, we have the following two special forms:

$n = 2$:

$$E_s \doteq -\frac{h}{90}[y_{-1} + y_3 - 4(y_0 + y_2) + 6y_1]. \qquad (45.10)$$

$n = 4$:

$$E_s \doteq -\frac{h}{90}[y_{-1} + y_5 - 4(y_0 + y_4) + 7(y_1 + y_3) - 8y_2]. \qquad (45.11)$$

It is to be noted that these formulas utilize two values, y_{-1} and y_{n+1}, which are outside the interval of integration. In order to obtain them it may be necessary to extrapolate by using Newton's forward and backward interpolation formulas.

Example 4.13. Find the approximate error committed by Simpson's rule in Example 4.9.

SOLUTION. In this case $h = 1$, $n = 6$, and, since $y = f(x)$ is a known polynomial, we may evaluate y_{-1} and y_7: $y_{-1} = 11$ and $y_7 = -58821$.

$$E_s \doteq -\tfrac{1}{90}[11 - 58821 - 4(0 - 37320) + 7(-45 - 19525)$$

$$-8(-496 - 8184) + 8(-2541)]$$

$$= \boxed{-28.8}.$$

This compares favorably with the true error, which is $\boxed{-25.9}$.

The principal part of the error in Weddle's rule stems from the fact that we omitted the quantity

$$E_W = -\frac{h}{140}\Delta^6 y_0 \doteq -\frac{h^7}{140}f^{vi}(x). \qquad (45.12)$$

We may therefore use this quantity as an approximate expression of the error. In so doing we are neglecting only the differences of an order higher than the sixth, and thus Weddle's rule gives an exact result for polynomials of degree five or less.

By again employing Formula 11.6 we may write

$$E_W \doteq -\frac{h}{140}[y_6 - 6y_5 + 15y_4 - 20y_3 + 15y_2 - 6y_1 + y_0]. \quad (45.13)$$

Example 4.14. Find the approximate error committed by Weddle's rule in Example 4.9.

SOLUTION.

$$E_W \doteq -\tfrac{1}{90}[-37320 - 6(-19525) + 15(-8184) - 20(-2541)$$

$$+ 15(-496) - 6(-45) + 0]$$

$$= \boxed{-8}.$$

The true error is $-47733.9 - (-47728.8) = -5.1$

As we can see from the last two examples, the true error is usually numerically less than or equal to the computed error, which adds assurance to the original calculations.

The inherent error in Gauss's quadrature formula is dependent on the theory of Legendre polynomials, and the derivation of an error formula is beyond the scope of this book. It is, however, possible to state a rule for approximating the error. First of all, it is dependent on being able to expand $\varphi(v)$ in a power series:

$$\varphi(v) = c_0 + c_1 u + c_2 u^2 + \cdots + c_n u^n + \cdots. \quad (45.14)$$

If this is possible, we approximate the error by

$$E_G = \frac{b - a}{(2n + 1)2^{2n}}\left[\frac{n!}{1 \cdot 3 \cdot 5 \cdots (2n - 1)}\right]^2$$

$$\times \left\{c_{2n} + \frac{c_{2n+2}}{8}\left[\frac{(n + 1)(n + 2)}{2n + 3} + \frac{n(n - 1)}{2n - 1}\right]\right\}. \quad (45.15)$$

The evaluation of this formula is quite cumbersome, and in practice it is used only when absolutely necessary. The accuracy of Gauss's formula can, of course, be improved by increasing the number of points.

46.   EXERCISE VI

1. Given the following data

x	y	x	y
0	0	2.2	166.769856
.2	.949696	2.4	215.660544
.4	2.375424	2.6	268.026304
.6	4.703424	2.8	319.393536
.8	8.605696	3.0	363.000000
1.0	15.000000	3.2	389.287936
1.2	25.003776	3.4	385.351104
1.4	39.841984	3.6	334.335744
1.6	60.708864	3.8	214.795456
1.8	88.583616	4.0	0
2.0	124.000000		

and using Simpson's rule find

(a) $\int_0^{1.2} y\,dx$;   (b) $\int_0^{3.6} y\,dx$;   (c) $\int_0^{4.0} y\,dx$;   (d) $\int_1^{3} y\,dx$;

using Weddle's rule find

(e) $\int_0^{1.2} y\,dx$;   (f) $\int_0^{3.6} y\,dx$;   (g) $\int_1^{3.4} y\,dx$.

2. Find a sufficient number of differences for the data in Problem 1 to evaluate the integral from $x = 2$ to $x = 3$ by Formula 42.8.

3. Find $\int_0^1 x\,dx$ by using $n = 7$ in Gauss's quadrature formula.

4. Find $\int_1^2 \dfrac{dx}{x\sqrt{x+1}}$ by using $n = 5$ in Gauss's quadrature formula.

5. Find an expression involving the first five terms for the integral of Newton's backward interpolation formula between the limits $x = x_{n-1}$ and $x = x_n$.

6. Find $\int_1^7 (7x^6 + 6x^5 + 5x^4 + 4x^3 + 3x^2 + 2x + 1)\,dx$ by   Simpson's and Weddle's rules.

7. Using the data on Problem 14 in Exercise II, find

(a) $\int_{-1\cdot0}^{0\cdot8} y_i\,dx$, $(i = 1, 2, 3, 4)$

by Simpson's and Weddle's rules.

(b) $\int_{-1}^{1} y_i \, dx$, $(i = 1, 2, 4)$ by Formula 42.8.

8. Find $\int_{0}^{1} \sqrt{x} \sin x \, dx$, using $n = 5$ in Gauss's formula.

9. Let $n = 4$ in Formula 31.1; then derive a formula for $\int_{x_0}^{x_4} I_H(x) \, dx$ by considering the sum of integrals over one interval at a time.

10. Apply the formula derived in Problem 9 to the data of Example 3.16. Integrate the data by Simpson's rule and compare the answers.

5

Lagrangian Formulas

47.   INTRODUCTION

The derivation and discussion of formulas based on the idea of passing an nth degree polynomial through $(n + 1)$ given points has been deferred to this chapter in order that this concept may be presented as a unit. The basic formula is credited to Lagrange and is usually referred to as Lagrange's interpolation formula, since its primary use was for interpolation problems. This formula, however, may be used as the basis for many other numerical analysis problems, and in the special cases tables of coefficients may be calculated which reduce the problem simply to one of obtaining the sums of products. The formulas are not limited to equally spaced intervals but may be applied to this special case.

Because we are fitting the data or replacing a function by a polynomial, the formulas should be used only whenever this is possible, and checks should be made to discover any irregularities.

48.   THE FUNDAMENTAL FORMULA

Let the values of the ordinates $y_0, y_1, \ldots, y_n$ of the function $y = f(x)$ be given at the $(n + 1)$ points $x_0, x_1, \ldots, x_n$. The polynomial of the nth degree through these points may be written as

$$
\begin{aligned}
L(x) = {} & \frac{(x - x_1)(x - x_2) \cdots (x - x_n)}{(x_0 - x_1)(x_0 - x_2) \cdots (x_0 - x_n)} y_0 \\
& + \frac{(x - x_0)(x - x_2) \cdots (x - x_n)}{(x_1 - x_0)(x_1 - x_2) \cdots (x_1 - x_n)} y_1 \\
& \vdots \\
& + \frac{(x - x_0) \cdots (x - x_{i-1}) \, (x - x_{i+1}) \cdots (x - x_n)}{(x_i - x_0) \cdots (x_i - x_{i-1})(x_i - x_{i+1}) \cdots (x_i - x_n)} y_i \\
& \vdots \\
& + \frac{(x - x_0)(x - x_1) \cdots (x - x_{n-1})}{(x_n - x_0)(x_n - x_1) \cdots (x_n - x_{n-1})} y_n.
\end{aligned}
\tag{48.1}
$$

If we let

$$
P(x) = (x - x_0)(x - x_1) \cdots (x - x_n) = \prod_{j=0}^{n} (x - x_j) \tag{48.2}
$$

and

$$
P_i(x) = (x - x_i)^{-1} P(x) = (x - x_i)^{-1} \prod_{j=0}^{n} (x - x_j), \tag{48.3}
$$

then Formula 48.1 becomes

$$
L(x) = \frac{P_0(x)}{P_0(x_0)} y_0 + \frac{P_1(x)}{P_1(x_1)} y_1 + \cdots + \frac{P_n(x)}{P_n(x_n)} y_n. \tag{48.4}
$$

It is easily seen that

$$
P_r(x_i) = 0 \quad \text{if} \quad i \neq r,
$$

so that

$$
L(x_r) = \frac{P_r(x_r)}{P_r(x_r)} y_r = y_r, \qquad (r = 0, \ldots, n), \tag{48.5}
$$

and the polynomial given by (48.1) is one that passes through the $(n + 1)$ points $(x_r, y_r), (r = 0, \ldots, n)$. In general, $P_i(x)$ is a polynomial of degree n; that is,

$$
P_i(x) = a_{i,n} x^n + a_{i,n-1} x^{n-1} + \cdots + a_{i,0} \quad \text{with} \quad a_{i,n} = 1 \tag{48.6}
$$

and

$$
P_i(x_i) = a_{i,n} x_i^n + a_{i,n-1} x_i^{n-1} + \cdots + a_{i,0} = k_i. \tag{48.7}
$$

Let $L(x)$ approximate the function $f(x)$; that is,

$$f(x) = L(x) + R(x),\tag{48.8}$$

where the remainder $R(x)$ is such that

$$R(x_i) = 0 \quad \text{for} \quad (i = 0, 1, \ldots, n).\tag{48.9}$$

Furthermore, if we let

$$R(x) = P(x)\,Q(x)$$

and consider an arbitrary function $\varphi(z)$, defined over the same domain as that of $f(x)$ and having the form

$$\varphi(z) = f(z) - L(z) - P(z)\,Q(x),\tag{48.10}$$

with the property that

$$\varphi(x_i) = 0 \quad \text{when} \quad z = x_i,$$
$$\varphi(x) = 0 \quad \text{when} \quad z = \text{some } x \ne x_i,$$

for all $i = 0, 1, \ldots, n$, then $\varphi(z)$ vanishes at $n + 2$ points. By repeated application of Rolle's theorem $\varphi^{n+1}(\xi)$ vanishes where $x_0 \le \xi \le x_n$. However

$$L^{n+1}(z) = 0 \quad \text{and} \quad P^{n+1}(z) = (n + 1)!$$

so that on differentiating (48.10) to the order $n + 1$ we have

$$0 = f^{n+1}(\xi) - (n + 1)!\,Q(x)$$

or

$$Q(x) = \frac{1}{(n + 1)!} f^{n+1}(\xi),$$

and at $z = x$ (48.10) yields

$$f(x) = L(x) + \frac{P(x)f^{n+1}(\xi)}{(n + 1)!}.\tag{48.11}$$

Thus we may write

$$f(x) = \sum_{i=0}^{n} \frac{P_i(x)}{P_i(x_i)} y_i + \frac{P(x)}{(n + 1)!} f^{n+1}(\xi),\tag{48.12}$$

where ξ lies in the interval $[x_0, x_n]$.

The last term of Formula 48.12 is in a sense a remainder term and is a measure of the accuracy of the fit of the polynomial $L(x)$.

Formula 48.4 has the useful property that *it is invariant under a linear transformation.* This can be easily shown. Let us make the transformation.

$$x = hu + a, \qquad x_i = hu_i + a;$$

then

$$
\begin{aligned}
P_i(x) &= (x - x_i)^{-1} P(x) \\
&= (x - x_i)^{-1}(x - x_0)(x - x_1) \cdots (x - x_n) \\
&= (hu + a - hu_i - a)^{-1}(hu + a - hu_0 - a) \\
&\qquad\qquad (hu + a - hu_1 - a) \cdots (hu + a - hu_n - a) \\
&= h^{-1}(u - u_i)^{-1} h^{n+1}(u - u_0)(u - u_1) \cdots (u - u_n) \\
&= h^n(u - u_i)^{-1} P(u) \\
&= h^n P_i(u);
\end{aligned}
$$

$$
\begin{aligned}
P_i(x_i) &= (x_i - x_0)(x_i - x_1) \cdots (x_i - x_{i-1})(x_i - x_{i+1}) \cdots (x_i - x_n) \\
&= (hu_i + a - hu_0 - a) \cdots (hu_i + a - hu_{i-1} - a) \\
&\qquad\qquad (hu_i + a - hu_{i+1} - a) \cdots (hu_i + a - hu_n - a) \\
&= h^n(u_i - u_0)(u_i - u_1) \cdots (u_i - u_{i-1})(u_i - u_{i+1}) \cdots (u_i - u_n) \\
&= h^n P_i(u_i).
\end{aligned}
$$

Therefore

$$L(x) = \sum_{i=0}^{n} \frac{P_i(x)}{P_i(x_i)} y_i = \sum_{i=0}^{n} \frac{P_i(u)}{P_i(u_i)} y_i = L(u).$$

49.   EQUALLY SPACED INTERVALS

If the values of x_i, $(i = 0, \ldots, n)$, are given at equally spaced intervals, we have

$$x_i = x_0 + ih, \tag{49.1}$$

where

$$h = \Delta x = x_1 - x_0 = x_r - x_{r-1}, \qquad (r = 1, \ldots, n),$$

we also let

$$u = \frac{x - x_0}{h} \quad \text{or} \quad x = x_0 + uh. \tag{49.2}$$

The polynomial $P_i(x)$ now takes a special form:

$$P_i(x) = (x - x_i)^{-1} \prod_{j=0}^{n} (x - x_j)$$

$$= (x_0 + uh - x_0 - ih)^{-1} \prod_{j=0}^{n} (x_0 + uh - x_0 - jh)$$

$$= h^{-1}(u - i)^{-1} \prod_{j=0}^{n} h(u - j) \tag{49.3}$$

$$= h^n(u - i)^{-1} \prod_{j=0}^{n} (u - j).$$

Now

$$\prod_{j=0}^{n} (u - j) = u(u - 1) \cdots (u - n) \tag{49.4}$$
$$= S_0^{n+1} u^{n+1} + S_1^{n+1} u^n + \cdots + S_n^{n+1} u,$$

where

$S_i^{n+1}, (i = 0, \ldots, n)$, are Stirling's numbers of the first kind.

For equally spaced intervals we have

$$P_i(x_i) = \prod_{j=0}^{n} (x_i - x_j)_{j \neq i} = h^n \prod_{j=0}^{n} (i - j)_{j \neq i} \tag{49.5}$$
$$= h^n i!(n - i)!(-1)^{n-i},$$

so that

$$\frac{P_i(x)}{P_i(x_i)} = \frac{h^n \prod_{j=0}^{n} (u - j)_{j \neq i}}{h^n i!(n - i)!} (-1)^{n-1} \tag{49.6}$$

$$= (-1)^{n-i} [i!(n - i)!]^{-1} \prod_{j=0}^{n} (u - j)_{j \neq i}$$

and

$$L(x) = L_0(u)y_0 + L_1(u)y_1 + \cdots + L_n(u)y_n, \tag{49.7}$$

where $L_i(u)$ is given by (49.6).

Since $L_i(u)$ are functions of n and u, it is possible to compute tables of these coefficients, and thus the value of $L(x)$ for a specified x can be computed by a sum of products. In order to cut down the range of values on u for such a table, a shift to a "center" value is made which changes the notation some-what. Let us number the $n + 1$ points $x_0, \ldots, x_n$.

Case 1. Even number points; $n + 1 = 2r$. We could number the points

$$x_{-r}, x_{-r+1}, \ldots, x_{-2}, x_{-1}, x_1, x_2, \ldots, x_r,$$

and we are faced with a choice of x_{-1} or x_1 as the "center" value. The general practice is to pick x_{-1} as the "center" point and to call it x_0. The numbering then becomes

$$x_{-r+1}, x_{-r+2}, \ldots, x_{-1}, x_0, x_1, x_2, \ldots, x_r.$$

For example, if we are given six points, they are numbered

$$x_{-2}, x_{-1}, x_0, x_1, x_2, x_3.$$

Formula 49.1 now takes the form

$$x_i = x_0 + ih, \quad (i = -r + 1, \ldots, -1, 1, \ldots, r),$$

and since we have shifted to a central value we shall replace u by p and define p by

$$x = x_0 + ph \quad \text{or} \quad p = (x - x_0)h^{-1}.$$

With these changes, Formula 49.3 becomes

$$P_i(x) = (x - x_i)^{-1} \prod_{j=0}^{n} (x - x_j)$$

$$= h^{-1}(p - i)^{-1} \prod_{j=-r+1}^{r} (x_0 + ph - x_0 - jh) \qquad (49.8)$$

$$= h^{2r-1}(p - i)^{-1} \prod_{j=-r+1}^{r} (p - j).$$

For greater clarity we exhibit the last product,

$$\prod_{j=-r+1}^{r} (p - j) = (p + r - 1)(p + r - 2) \cdots (p + 1)p(p - 1) \cdots (p - r).$$

Furthermore,

$$P_i(x_i) = \prod_{j=0}^{n} (x_i - x_j)_{j \neq i} = h^{2r-1} \prod_{j=-r+1}^{r} (i - j)_{i \neq j}$$

$$= h^{2r-1}[(i + r - 1)(i + r - 2) \cdots (i + 1)(i) \qquad (49.9)$$

$$\cdots (1)(-1)(-2) \cdots (r - i)]$$

$$= h^{2r-1}[(i + r - 1)!(r - i)!](-1)^{r-i}$$

and the coefficients of y_i become

$$A_i(p) = (-1)^{r-i}[(i + r - 1)!(r - i)!]^{-1} \prod_{j=-r+1}^{r} (p - j)_{j \neq i}. \qquad (49.10)$$

In the tabulation of these coefficients the following property is useful:

$$A_i(p) = A_{1-i}(1-p). \tag{49.11}$$

Case 2. Odd number of points; $n + 1 = 2r + 1$. The points are numbered

$$x_{-r}, x_{-r+1}, \ldots, x_{-1}, x_0, x_1, \ldots, x_r$$

and

$$A_i(p) = (-1)^{r-i}[(i+r)!(r-i)!]^{-1} \prod_{j=-r}^{r} (p-j)_{j \neq i} \tag{49.12}$$

with the property

$$A_i(p) = A_{-i}(-p). \tag{49.13}$$

Let us consider five points as an example, and let $p = .7$. Now let us find A_{-2}, A_{-1}, A_0, A_1, A_2. Substituting into Formula 49.12, we obtain

$$A_{-2}(.7) = (-1)^{2+2}[(-2+2)!(2+2)!]^{-1}(.7+1)(.7+0)(.7-1)(.7-2)$$
$$= (-1)^4[(4)!]^{-1}[(1.7)(.7)(-.3)(-1.3)]$$
$$= \tfrac{1}{24}(.4641)$$
$$= .0193375.$$

$$A_{-1}(.7) = (-1)^{2+1}[(-1+2)!(2+1)!]^{-1}[(.7+2)(.7+0)(.7-1)(.7-2)$$
$$= -(3!)^{-1}[(2.7)(.7)(-.3)(-1.3)]$$
$$= -.12285$$

$$A_0(.7) = (-1)^2[(2!)(2!)]^{-1}[(.7+2)(.7+1)(.7-1)(.7-2)]$$
$$= .447525.$$

$$A_1(.7) = (-1)^1[(3!)(1!)]^{-1}(.7+2)(.7+1)(.7+0)(.7-2)$$
$$= .69615$$

$$A_2(.7) = (-1)^0[4!(0!)]^{-1}(.7+2)(.7+1)(.7+0)(.7-1)$$
$$= -.0401625.$$

Extensive tables of these coefficients have been published by the National Bureau of Standards. A limited list for five points is given in Table VIII, p. 362.

50.   INTERPOLATION

One of the prime applications of Lagrange's formula is in interpolation. The problem is to find a value of a function at a point x which falls between tabulated values at points $x_0, x_1, \ldots$.

A. Equally Spaced Intervals

The simplest case is that in which the tabulated values are given at equally spaced intervals; then Formula 49.7 produces the desired results. Furthermore, the coefficients may be tabulated, and the problem is reduced to one of finding the sum of the products of two numbers and is easily performed as one operation on a calculating machine. For this purpose the coefficients are tabulated about a "midpoint" and we have

$$f(x) \doteq A_{-r}y_{-r} + A_{-r+1}y_{-r+1} + \cdots + A_0 y_0 + A_1 y_1 + \cdots + A_r y_r. \quad (50.1)$$

The procedure is explained by an example.

Example 5.1. Find $f(1.77)$ by a five-point Lagrangian formula from the table of values:

x_i	1.5	1.6	1.7	1.8	1.9	2.0
y_i	48.09375	65.53600	87.69705	115.47360	149.86915	192.00000
$A_i(.7)$	.0193375	$-.1228500$	.4475250	.6961500	$-.0401625$	
$A_i(-.3)$		$-.0261625$	.2541500	.8895250	$-.1368500$	.0193375

SOLUTION. Let $x_0 = 1.7$; then

$$p = \frac{x - x_0}{h} = \frac{1.77 - 1.7}{.1} = .7.$$

The Lagrangian coefficients $A_i(.7)$ were taken from Table VIII, p. 363.

$$f(1.77) \doteq \sum_{i=-2}^{2} A_i(.7)y_i = \boxed{106.49336}.$$

If we let $x_0 = 1.8$,

$$p = \frac{1.77 - 1.8}{.1} = -.3$$

we obtain

$$f(1.77) \doteq \sum_{i=-2}^{2} A_i(-.3)y_i = \boxed{106.49348}.$$

B. Unequally Spaced Intervals

The case of unequally spaced intervals makes the method more difficult to handle but increases its importance because fewer methods are available. It now becomes necessary to return to Formula 48.4. A schematic may be devised which greatly aids the computation. First, a linear transformation is made on the given $x_i, (i = 0, \ldots, n)$, in order to obtain small integers insofar as possible.

Form the square array

$$
\begin{array}{ccccc}
x - x_0 & x_0 - x_1 & x_0 - x_2 & \cdots & x_0 - x_n \\
x_1 - x_0 & x - x_1 & x_1 - x_2 & \cdots & x_1 - x_n \\
x_2 - x_0 & x_2 - x_1 & x - x_2 & \cdots & x_2 - x_n \\
\vdots & & & & \\
x_n - x_0 & x_n - x_1 & x_n - x_2 & \cdots & x - x_n
\end{array}
\tag{50.2}
$$

We note that the product of the principal diagonal is

$$
P(x) = (x - x_0)(x - x_1) \cdots (x - x_n). \tag{50.3}
$$

The products of the elements in each row yield

$$
\begin{aligned}
R_i &= (x_i - x_0) \cdots (x - x_i) \cdots (x_i - x_n), \\
&= (x - x_i)P_i(x_i).
\end{aligned}
\tag{50.4}
$$

Thus

$$
\frac{P_i(x)}{P_i(x_i)} = \frac{(x - x_i)^{-1} P(x)}{(x - x_i)^{-1} R_i} = \frac{P(x)}{R_i} \tag{50.5}
$$

and

$$
\begin{aligned}
y \doteq L(x) &= \frac{P(x)}{R_0} y_0 + \frac{P(x)}{R_1} y_1 + \frac{P(x)}{R_2} y_2 + \cdots + \frac{P(x)}{R_n} y_n \\
&= P(x)\left(\frac{y_0}{R_0} + \frac{y_1}{R_1} + \cdots + \frac{y_n}{R_n}\right).
\end{aligned}
\tag{50.6}
$$

The square array in (50.2) may now be augmented by the two columns R_i and y_i/R_i (for speedy operation R_i need not be recorded). The sum of the last column multiplied by the product of the terms of the main diagonal yields the desired result.

Example 5.2. Given the values

x	0	3	9	12	15	21	27
y	150	108	0	−54	−100	−144	−84

find y at $x = 18$.

SOLUTION. We first make the transformation $x = 3s$; then

s_i	0	1	3	4	5	7	9

and $s = 6$. The array of $s - s_i$ and $s_i - s_j$ after being augmented by R_i and y_i/R_i becomes

$s_i - s_0$	$s_i - s_1$	$s_i - s_2$	$s_i - s_3$	$s_i - s_4$	$s_i - s_5$	$s_i - s_6$	R_i	y_i/R_i
6	−1	−3	−4	−5	−7	−9	22680	.006613757
1	5	−2	−3	−4	−6	−8	−5760	−.01875
3	2	3	−1	−2	−4	−6	864	0
4	3	1	2	−1	−3	−5	−360	.150
5	4	2	1	1	−2	−4	320	−.3125
7	6	4	3	2	−1	−2	2016	−.071428571
9	8	6	5	4	2	−3	−51840	.001620370

The product of terms in principal diagonal, $P(s) = 540$.   Sum = −.244444444

$$y \doteq (540)(-.244444444) = -132.$$

C. Inverse Interpolation

Lagrange's formula adapts itself nicely to inverse interpolation; Formula 48.4 is simply a relation between two variables, either of which may be considered the independent variable. Thus we can write x as a function of y:

$$L(y) = \frac{P_0(y)}{P_0(y_0)}x_0 + \frac{P_1(y)}{P_1(y_1)}x_1 + \cdots + \frac{P_n(y)}{P_n(y_n)}x_n. \tag{50.7}$$

Normally the values of y_i are unequally spaced and the method just described must, in general, be employed. Furthermore, it is more difficult to find a linear transformation that will reduce the size of the numbers. Let us consider an example.

Example 5.3. From a five-place table of natural sines we have

x	30	31	33	34	36
y	.50000	.51504	.54464	.55919	.58779

Find x when $y = .52992$.

SOLUTION. Let $y = .1s$; then determine the value at $s = 5.2992$.

s_i	5.0000	5.1504	5.4464	5.5919	5.8779	5.2992

The computational form is

$s_i - s_0$	$s_i - s_1$	$s_i - s_2$	$s_i - s_3$	$s_i - s_4$	R_i	x_i/R_i
.2992	$-.1504$	$-.4464$	$-.5919$	$-.8779$	.010438234	2874.049
.1504	.1488	$-.2960$	$-.4415$	$-.7275$	$-.002127679$	-14569.867
.4464	.2960	$-1472.$	$-.1455$	$-.4315$	$-.001221146$	-27023.796
.5919	.4415	.1455	$-.2927$	$-.2860$	.003182957	10681.891
.8779	.7275	.4315	.2860	$-5787.$	$-.045611921$	-789.267

$$P(s) = \prod (s - s_i) = -.001110065. \qquad\qquad \sum \frac{x_i}{R_i} = -28826.990$$

$$x \doteq (-.001110065)(-28826.99) = 31.9998.$$

To five-place accuracy $\boxed{x = 32}$.

D. Multiple Interpolation

Interpolation in tables of multiple arguments is a laborious procedure and is usually accomplished by repeated application of interpolation on a single variable. Repeated application of Lagrange's formula can best be illustrated by example. We shall limit our attention to equally spaced intervals; for unequally spaced intervals the technique in Section 50B must be employed.

Consider $y = f(x, r)$ and assume that the table of values is arranged as follows:

r \ x	r_0	r_1	r_2	r_3	r_4	r_5
x_0	y_{00}	y_{01}	y_{02}	y_{03}	y_{04}	y_{05}
x_1	y_{10}	y_{11}	y_{12}	y_{13}	y_{14}	y_{15}
x_2	y_{20}	y_{21}	y_{22}	y_{23}	y_{24}	y_{25}
x_3	y_{30}	y_{31}	y_{32}	y_{33}	y_{34}	y_{35}
x_4	y_{40}	y_{41}	y_{42}	y_{43}	y_{44}	y_{45}
x_5	y_{50}	y_{51}	y_{52}	y_{53}	y_{54}	y_{55}

Find a value of $y(x, r)$ where $x_2 < x < x_3$ and $r_1 < r < r_2$ by a three-point Lagrangian formula.

We obtain

$$p_x = \frac{x - x_2}{\Delta_x} \quad \text{and} \quad p_r = \frac{r - r_1}{\Delta r}$$

and utilize the points x_1, x_r, x_3 and r_0, r_2, denoting the Lagrangian coefficient by A^x_{-1}, A^x_0, A^x_1 and A^r_{-1}, A^r_0, A^r_1. If we interpolate first with respect to x at each $r_i (i = 0, 1, 2)$, we have

$$y_{x0} = A^x_{-1} y_{10} + A^x_0 y_{20} + A^x_1 y_{30},$$
$$y_{x1} = A^x_{-1} y_{11} + A^x_0 y_{21} + A^x_1 y_{31}, \tag{50.8}$$
$$y_{x2} = A^x_{-1} y_{12} + A^x_0 y_{22} + A^x_1 y_{32}.$$

Then interpolation with respect to r yields

$$
\begin{aligned}
y(x, r) &= A^r_{-1} y_{x0} + A^r_0 y_{x1} + A^r y_{x2} \\
&= A^r_{-1}[A^x_{-1} y_{10} + A^x_0 y_{20} + A^x_1 y_{30}] \\
&\quad + A^r_0[A^x_{-1} y_{11} + A^x_0 y_{21} + A^x_1 y_{31}] \\
&\quad + A^r_1[A^x_{-1} y_{12} + A^x_0 y_{22} + A^x_1 y_{32}] \tag{50.9} \\
&= A^r_{-1} A^x_1 y_{10} + A^r_{-1} A^x_0 y_{20} + A^r_{-1} A^x_1 y_{30} \\
&\quad + A^r_0 A^x_{-1} y_{11} + A^r_0 A^x_0 y_{21} + A^r_0 A^x_1 y_{31} \\
&\quad + A^r_1 A^x_{-1} y_{12} + A^r_1 A^x_0 y_{22} + A^r_1 A^x_1 y_{32}.
\end{aligned}
$$

It is seen that nothing is gained by attempting to use the last expression, for this would require the recording of the nine products $A^r_i A^x_j (i, j = -1, 0, 1)$, whereas in the use of the first expression only four recordings are necessary. The second method would have application only in the special case in which p_x and p_r remain constant for a large number of interpolations. The most expeditious method, therefore, is to compute the three $y_{xi} (i = 0, 1, 2)$, then

$$y(x, r) \doteq A^r_{-1} y_{x0} + A^r_0 y_{x1} + A^r_1 y_{x2}. \tag{50.10}$$

Example 5.4. Given a function of two variables, $y = f(r, \beta)$, in tabulated form,

r \ β	80°	81°	82°	83°	84°
5	.17519	.18085	.18721	.19447	.20288
6	.21023	.21702	.22466	.23336	.24346
7	.24526	.25319	.26210	.27226	.28403
8	.28030	.28936	.29954	.21115	.32461
9	.31534	.32553	.33699	.35004	.36519
10	.35038	.36170	.37443	.38894	.40576

find $f(7.3, 81°.25)$.

SOLUTION. First hold β constant and interpolate with respect to r using the five-point formula with $r_0 = 7$, $u = .3$, and $A_i(.3)$ from Table VIII, p. 362, to obtain

β	80°	81°	82°	83°	84°
$f(7.3, \beta)$	.255771	.264041	.273332	.283928	.296203

Now, by using the five-point formula with $\beta_0 = 82$, $u = -.75$ and $A_i(-.75)$, from Table VIII, p. 363, we get

$$f(7.3, 81°.25) \doteq \boxed{.26626}.$$

51.   DIFFERENTIATION

Lagrange's formula may be used to find the derivative of a function $y = f(x)$ which is known only at discrete values $x_i(i = 0, \ldots, n)$. From Formula 8 we have

$$f(x) = L(x) + R(x),$$

so that

$$\frac{dy}{dx} = f'(x) = L'(x) + R'(x). \tag{51.1}$$

Since, by Formula 48.11,

$$R(x) = \frac{P(x) f^{(n+1)}(\xi)}{(n+1)!},$$

$$R'(x) = \frac{P'(x) f^{(n+1)}(\xi)}{(n+1)!} + \frac{P(x) f^{(n+2)}(\xi)}{(n+1)!}.$$

(51.2)

The second term of this expression is difficult to find even if it is known that $f^{(n+2)}(x)$ exists. However, if it is evaluated at a given point, x_i, then $P(x_i) = 0$ and only the first term remains. In practice, the remainder term is used only to check the accuracy.

The derivative of $L'(x)$ is given by

$$L'(x) = L_0'(x) y_0 + L_1'(x) y_1 + \cdots + L_n'(x) y_n$$

(51.3)

and

$$L_i'(x) = \frac{1}{P_i(x_i)} \frac{d}{dx} P_i(x)$$

$$= \frac{1}{P_i(x_i)} [(x - x_0) \cdots (x - x_{i-1})(x - x_{i+1}) \cdots$$

$$(x - x_n)] \left(\frac{1}{x - x_0} + \cdots + \frac{1}{x - x_{i-1}} \right.$$

$$\left. + \frac{1}{x - x_{i+1}} + \cdots + \frac{1}{x - x_n} \right),$$

(51.4)

or

$$L_i'(x) = \frac{1}{P_i(x_i)} \left[\prod_{j=0}^{n} (x - x_j)_{j \neq i} \right] \left(\sum_{j=0}^{n} \frac{1}{x - x_j} \right)_{j \neq i}$$

$$= \frac{P_i(x)}{P_i(x_i)} \left(\sum_{j=0}^{n} \frac{1}{x - x_j} \right)_{j \neq i}.$$

(51.5)

Formula 51.3 contains an expression for finding the derivative of a function at a general value of x. The computation of the coefficients of $y_i (i = 0, \ldots, n)$, namely, $L_i'(x)$, as given by Formula 51.5, may be performed by calculating the square array in (50.2) and using Formula 50.5. Furthermore, if we let

$$\sigma_i = \sum_{j=0}^{n} (x - x_j)_{j \neq i}^{-1},$$

Formula 51.3 can be written in the form

$$L'(x) = P(x) \sum_{i=0}^{n} y_i \sigma_i R_i^{-1}.$$

Example 5.5. Given the values

x	0	1	3	4	5	7	9
y	150	108	0	-54	-100	-144	-84

find the value of the derivative of y at $x = 6$.

SOLUTION. The square array for $x_i - x_j$ is identical to that in Example 5.2, so $P(6) = 540$ and we may start with the R_i values. If we leave the values in fractional form, the calculations for this example may be performed without the use of a calculating machine.

R_i	σ_i	$y_i \sigma_i R_i^{-1}$
22680	$\frac{7}{10}$	$\frac{1}{216}$
-5760	$\frac{2}{3}$	$-\frac{1}{80}$
864	$\frac{8}{15}$	0
-360	$\frac{11}{30}$	$\frac{11}{200}$
320	$-\frac{2}{15}$	$\frac{1}{24}$
2016	$\frac{28}{15}$	$-\frac{2}{15}$
-41840	$\frac{6}{5}$	$\frac{7}{360}$

$$y'(6) \doteq P(6) \sum_{i=0}^{n} y_i \sigma_i R_i^{-1} = 540\left(-\tfrac{23}{540}\right) = -23.$$

A. The Derivative at x_k for Unequally Spaced Intervals

Of special interest is the derivative evaluated at one of the given points, $x_k(i = 0, \ldots, n)$. Formula 51.5 takes on two forms:

(a) $k \neq i$. In this case the product $\prod_{j=0}^{n} (x - x_j)_{j \neq i} = 0$, except when it is multiplied by $(x_k - x_k)^{-1}$. Thus

$$L'_i(x_k) = \frac{1}{P_i(x_i)}\left[\prod_{j=0}^{n}(x_k - x_j)_{\substack{j \neq i \\ j \neq k}}\right]$$

$$= \frac{1}{P_i(x_i)}[(x_k - x_0)\cdots(x_k - x_{k-1})(x_k - x_{k+1})\cdots$$

$$(x_k - x_{i-1})(x_k - x_{i+1})\cdots(x_k - x_n)] \quad (51.6)$$

$$= \frac{1}{P_i(x_i)}\frac{[(x_k - x_0)\cdots(x_k - x_{k-1})(x_k - x_{k+1})\cdots(x_k - x_n)]}{x_k - x_i}$$

$$= \frac{1}{P_i(x_i)}\prod_{j=0}^{n}(x_k - x_j)_{j \neq k}(x_k - x_i)^{-1}.$$

If we let

$$D_{ik} = (x_k - x_i)P_i(x_i), \qquad (i \neq k), \tag{51.7}$$

we have

$$L'_i(x) = \frac{1}{D_{ik}}\prod_{j=0}^{n}(x_k - x_j)_{j \neq k}. \tag{51.8}$$

(b) $k = i$. In this case we have

$$\prod(x_i - x_j)_{j \neq i} = P_i(x_i) \tag{51.9}$$

and

$$L'_i(x_i) = \frac{P_i(x_i)}{P_i(x_i)}\sum_{\substack{j=0 \\ j \neq i}}^{n}\frac{1}{x_i - x_j}$$

$$= \sum_{j=0, \neq i}^{n}(x_i - x_j)^{-1}. \tag{51.10}$$

Thus the complete expression for $L'(x_k)$ becomes

$$L'(x_k) = L'_0(x_k)y_0 + \cdots + L'_k(x_k)y_k + \cdots + L'_n(x_k)y_n$$

$$= \frac{y_0}{D_{0k}}\prod_{j=0}^{n}(x_k - x_j)_{j \neq k} + \frac{y_1}{D_{1k}}\prod_{j=0}^{n}(x_k - x_j)_{j \neq k}$$

$$+ \cdots + y_k\sum_{j=0}^{n}(x_k - x_j)^{-1}_k + \cdots + \frac{y_n}{D_{nk}}\prod_{j=0}^{n}(x_k - x_j)_{j \neq k} \quad (51.11)$$

$$= \prod_{j=0}^{n}(x_k - x_j)_{j \neq k}\left(\frac{y_0}{D_{0k}} + \frac{y_1}{D_{1k}} + \cdots + \frac{y_n}{D_{nk}}\right)$$

$$+ y_k\sum_{j=0}^{n}(x_k - x_j)^{-1}_{j \neq k}$$

or

$$L'(x_k) = \prod_{j=0}^{n} (x_k - x_j)_{j \neq k} \left(\sum_{i=0}^{n} y_i D_{ik}^{-1} \right)_{i \neq k} + y_k \sum_{j=0}^{n} (x_k - x_j)_{j \neq k}^{-1}. \qquad (51.12)$$

This formula for the derivative of $y = f(x)$ at $x = x_k$ can be found by the use of a schematic similar to that given in 50B. Form the square array

$$\begin{vmatrix} & x_0 - x_1 & x_0 - x_2 & \cdots & x_0 - x_k & \cdots & x_0 - x_n \\ x_1 - x_0 & & x_1 - x_2 & \cdots & x_1 - x_k & \cdots & x_1 - x_n \\ x_2 - x_0 & x_2 - x_1 & & \cdots & x_2 - x_k & \cdots & x_2 - x_n \\ \vdots & & & & & & \\ x_k - x_0 & x_k - x_1 & x_k - x_2 & \cdots & & \cdots & x_k - x_n \\ \vdots & & & & & & \\ x_n - x_0 & x_n - x_1 & x_n - x_2 & \cdots & x_n - x_k & \cdots & \end{vmatrix}$$

Note that no element appears on the main diagonal. Now the product of the elements of each row is $P_i(x_i)$. If this is again multiplied by $(x_i - x_k)$, we have $- D_{ik}$. Thus we can augment this array by two columns, D_{ik} and $y_i D_{ik}^{-1}$; the first being obtained by multiplying the product of each row by the element in the kth column (i.e., this element twice in the product) and changing sign. There will be no entry in the $(i = k)$ row. The product $\prod_{j=0}^{n} (x_k = x_j)_{j \neq k}$ $= \prod_{j=0}^{n} [-(x_j - x_k)]_{j \neq k}$ is obtained by multiplying the negative of the elements in the kth column.

The elements of the second augmented column are now summed and multiplied by this product to yield the first term of Formula 51.12. The second term is obtained by summing the negative reciprocals of the terms in the kth column, as can be easily seen from its expression. The final value of the derivative is then given by Formula 51.12. Let us illustrate the procedure with an example.

Example 5.6. Let us consider the example V.2 given in 50B, and let it be desired to obtain the derivative at $s_i = 5$; i.e., $x = 15$.

SOLUTION. At $s_i = 5$ we have $k = 4$.

	$s_i - s_0$	$s_i - s_1$	$s_i - s_2$	$*$ $s_i - s_3$	$s_i - s_4$	$s_i - s_5$	$s_i - s_6$	D_{i4}	$y_i D_{i4}^{-1}$
		-1	-3	-4	-5	-7	-9	18900	.007936507
	1		-2	-3	-4	-6	-8	-4608	$-.023437500$
	3	2		-1	-2	-4	-6	576	0
	4	3	1		-1	-3	-5	-180	.300000000
	5	4	2	1		-2	-4		
	7	6	4	3	2		-2	4032	$-.035714285$
	9	8	6	5	4	2		-69120	.001215278

$$\prod (s_4 - s_i) = 320. \qquad\qquad\qquad .250$$

$$\sum (s_4 - s_i)^{-1} = \tfrac{1}{5} + \tfrac{1}{4} + \tfrac{1}{2} + \tfrac{1}{1} - \tfrac{1}{2} - \tfrac{1}{4} = \tfrac{1}{5} + 1 = \tfrac{6}{5} = 1.2000$$

$$L'(s) = (320)(.25) + (1.2)(-100) = \boxed{-40}.$$

To find the derivative of y with respect to x, we must consider the transformation $x = 3s$. Since

$$\frac{dy}{dx} = \frac{dy}{ds}\frac{ds}{dx} \quad \text{and} \quad \frac{ds}{dx} = \frac{1}{3},$$

we have

$$y'(15) \doteq \frac{1}{3}L'(s) = \frac{1}{3}(-40) = -\frac{40}{3}.$$

B. The Derivative at x_k for Equally Spaced Intervals

If the values of the independent variable are given at equally spaced intervals, we have from (49.7)

$$L(x) = L_0(u)y_0 + L_1(u)y_1 + \cdots + L_n(u)y_n, \tag{51.13}$$

where

$$L_i(u) = (-1)^{n-i}[i!(n-i)!]^{-1} \prod_{j=0}^{n} (u-j)_{j \neq i}. \tag{51.14}$$

Since $x = uh + x_0$, we have

$$\frac{dy}{dx} = \frac{dy}{du}\frac{du}{dx} = \frac{1}{h}\frac{dy}{du},$$

$$y' \doteq L'(x) = \frac{1}{h} \sum_{i=0}^{n} L_i'(u)y_i \tag{51.15}$$

and

$$L_i'(u) = (-1)^{n-i}[i!(n-i)!]^{-1}\frac{d}{du}\prod_{j=0}^{n}(u-j)_{j\neq i}. \tag{51.16}$$

Furthermore (see Formula 51.5),

$$\frac{d}{du}\prod_{j=0}^{n}(u-j)_{j\neq i} = \left[\prod_{j=0}^{n}(u-j)_{j\neq i}\right]\left[\sum_{j=0}^{n}(u-j)_{j\neq i}^{-1}\right]. \tag{51.17}$$

When $x = x_k$, we have

$$u = \frac{x-x_0}{h} = \frac{x_k-x_0}{h} = k, \tag{51.18}$$

so that at this point Formula 51.17 takes on two special forms:

(a) $k \neq i$. Here we have

$$\frac{d}{du}\prod_{j=0}^{n}(u-j)_{j\neq i} = [u(u-1)\cdots(u-k+1)(u-k-1)\cdots$$

$$(u-i+1)(u-i-1)\cdots(u-n)]$$

$$= k(k-1)\cdots 1(-1)\cdots \tag{51.19}$$

$$(k-i+1)(k-i-1)\cdots(k-n)$$

$$= (k-i)^{-1}k!(n-k)!(-1)^{n-k}$$

and

$$L_i'(u) = (-1)^{n-i}[i!(n-i)!]^{-1}(k-i)^{-1}k!(n-k)!(-1)^{n-k}$$

$$= (-1)^{i+k}\frac{k!(n-k)!}{i!(n-i)!(k-i)}. \tag{51.20}$$

Note: $(-1)^{2n-i-k} = (-1)^{2n}(-1)^{-(i+k)} = (-1)^{i+k}.$

(b) $k = i$. For this case we have

$$\frac{d}{du}\prod_{j=0}^{n}(u-j)_{j\neq i} = [i(i-1)\cdots(2)(1)(-1)(-2)\cdots(i-n)]$$

$$\left(\frac{1}{i}+\frac{1}{i-1}+\cdots\frac{1}{1}-\frac{1}{1}+\cdots+\frac{1}{i-n}\right) \tag{51.21}$$

$$= i!(n-i)!(-1)^{n-i}\sum_{j=0}^{n}\frac{1}{i-j}\bigg|_{j\neq i},$$

so that

$$L'_i(u) = (-1)^{n-i} \frac{i!(n-i)!(-1)^{n-i}}{i!(n-i)!} \left(\sum_{j=0}^{n} \frac{1}{i-j} \right)_{j \neq i}$$

$$= \frac{1}{i} + \frac{1}{i-1} + \cdots + \frac{1}{2} + \frac{1}{1} - \frac{1}{1} - \frac{1}{2} - \cdots - \frac{1}{n-i}$$

$$= \sum_{j=1}^{i} \frac{1}{j} - \sum_{j=1}^{n-i} \frac{1}{j} \tag{51.22}$$

$$= - \sum_{j=i+1}^{n-i} \frac{1}{j} \quad \text{if} \quad 2i \leq n-1$$

$$= \sum_{j=n-i+1}^{i} \frac{1}{j} \quad \text{if} \quad 2i > n-1.$$

Thus the coefficients of $y_i (i = 0, \ldots, n)$ are functions of n, k, and i and may be computed once and for all and tabulated. Furthermore, the table of coefficients is "negatively symmetric" about the "midpoint," so that it is necessary to tabulate only half of them. Let the coefficients be denoted by A'_{ki}; then for equally spaced intervals

$$y'(x_k) \doteq L'(x_k) = \frac{1}{h} (A'_{k0} y_0 + A'_{k1} y_1 + \cdots + A'_{kn} y_n), \tag{51.23}$$

and A'_{ki} are given for Formulas 51.20 and 51.22.

Now for $k > m$, where $m = \frac{1}{2}n + 1$ if n is even and $m = \frac{1}{2}(n+1)$ if n is odd, we have

$$A'_{ki} = -A'_{n-k,n-i}.$$

By Formula 51.20 we have for $k \neq i$

$$A'_{ki} = (-1)^{i+k} \frac{k!(n-k)!}{i!(n-i)!(k-i)}$$

and

$$A'_{n-k,n-i} = (-1)^{(n-k)+(n-i)} \frac{(n-k)![n(nk)]!}{(n-i)![n-(n-i)]![n-k-(n-i)]}$$

$$= (-1)^{k+i} \frac{(n-k)!(k!)}{(n-i)!(i)!(i-k)}$$

$$= (-1)^{k+i-1} \frac{(n-k)!k!}{(n-i)!(i)!(k-i)};$$

thus

$$A'_{ki} = -A'_{n-k,n-i}.$$

For $k = i$ we have by Formula 51.22

$$A'_{kk} = \sum_{j=n-k+1}^{k} \frac{1}{j} \quad \text{and} \quad A'_{n-k,n-k} = -\sum_{j=n-k+1}^{n-n+k} \frac{1}{j},$$

so that

$$A'_{kk} = -A'_{n-k,n-k}.$$

The tabulation of A'_{ki} can be made in two ways. The first is to obtain the lowest common denominator for the A'_{ki} of each n and tabulate the coefficients of y_i as integers with a final division to obtain the derivative. Thus

$$y'(x_k) \doteq \frac{1}{hD_n} \sum_{i=0}^{n} a'_{ki} y_i,$$

where

$$a'_{ki} = A'_{ki} D_n$$

and D_n is the lowest common denominator of A'_{ki}. Table IX, p. 366, gives the values of D_n and a'_{ki} for 10 points. The second method is to publish A'_{ki} in decimal form see Table X, p. 368.

Example 5.7. Find dy/dx at $x = 1.7$ in the data given in Example 5.1.

SOLUTION. Here $u = \dfrac{1.7 - 1.5}{.1} = 2 = k; n = 5; h = .1.$

From Tables IX, p. 366 ($D_n = 60$), and X, p. 368, we have

y_i	48.09375	65.53600	87.69705	115.47360	149.86915	192.00000
a'_{2i}	3	-30	-20	60	-15	2
A'_{2i}	.050000	$-.500000$	$-.333333$	1.000000	$-.250000$	.033333

$$y'_2 \doteq 10 \frac{\left(\displaystyle\sum_{i=0}^{5} a'_{2i} y_i \right)}{60} = \boxed{248.10650}.$$

$$y'_2 \doteq 10 \left(\sum_{i=0}^{5} A'_{2i} y_i \right) = \boxed{248.10652}.$$

The formulas derived in this section may be used as the basis for obtaining methods of solving differential equations. These are discussed in Chapter 7.

52.   HIGHER DERIVATIVES

The higher derivatives are obtained by repeated differentiation of (51.3). Thus

$$L''(x) = L_0''(x)y_0 + L_1''(x)y_1 + \cdots + L_n''(x)y_n, \tag{52.1}$$

where

$$L_i''(x) = \frac{1}{P_i(x_i)} \frac{d^2}{dx^2}[P_i(x)]. \tag{52.2}$$

Although a notation and schematic can be devised for the general case, it is very unwieldy. Consequently we shall develop only the special case of equally spaced intervals. From (51.15) we have

$$y'(x) = \frac{1}{h} \sum_{i=0}^{n} L_i'(u)y_i, \tag{52.3}$$

so that

$$y''(x) = \frac{1}{h^2} \sum_{i=0}^{n} L_i''(u)y_i. \tag{52.4}$$

Now

$$L_i(u) = (-1)^{n-i} \frac{n!}{i!(n-i)!} (u-i)^{-1} \binom{u}{n},$$

where $\binom{u}{n}$ is the binomial coefficient notation.

Let

$$b_i = \frac{(-1)^{n-i}}{i!(n-i)!}; \tag{52.5}$$

then

$$L_i'(u) = b_i \frac{d}{du} \left[\prod_{j=0}^{n} (u-j)_{j \neq i} \right],$$

and

$$L_i''(u) = b_i \frac{d^2}{du} \left[\prod_{j=0}^{n} (u-j)_{j \neq i} \right]. \tag{52.6}$$

These derivatives may be evaluated at $u = 0, 1, 2, 3, \ldots, n$ to yield the values of the derivatives at $x = x_0, x_1, \ldots, x_n$. Thus we can write

$$y''(x_k) \doteq L''(x_k)$$

$$= \frac{1}{h^2}(A_{k0}''y_0 + A_{k1}''y_1 + A_{k2}''y_2 + \cdots + A_{kn}''y_n), \tag{52.7}$$

where
$$A''_{ki} = L''_i(k),$$

which may be computed once and for all and have been tabulated in Table XI, p. 370.

The continuation to higher derivatives is immediate. The third derivative is given by

$$y'''(x_k) \doteq L'''(x_k) = \frac{1}{h^3}(A'''_{k0}y_0 + A'''_{k1}y_1 + \cdots + A'''_{kn}y_n), \qquad (52.8)$$

and the values for A'''_{ki} have been tabulated in Table XII, p. 371.

Example 5.8. Find the first, second, and third derivatives at $x = 1$ of the function whose values are

x	-2	-1	0	1	2	3	4
y	104	17	0	-1	8	69	272

SOLUTION. Using Tables IX, XI, XII, at the back of the book, with $n = 6$, $h = 1$, $x_3 = 1$, $u = 3$, we write

$$y'(1) = \tfrac{1}{60}[-1(104) + 9(17) - 45(0) + 0(-1) + 45(8) - 9(69) + 1(272)]$$
$$= \boxed{1}.$$

$$y''(1) = \tfrac{1}{180}[2(104) - 27(17) + 270(0) - 490(-1) + 270(8) - 27(69) + 2(272)]$$
$$= \boxed{6}.$$

$$y'''(1) = \tfrac{1}{24}[3(104) - 24(17) + 39(0) + 0(-1) - 39(8) + 24(69) - 3(272)]$$
$$= \boxed{18}.$$

53.   INTEGRATION

As in the case of differentiation, Lagrange's formula may also be used to find the integral of a function $f(x)$ which is known only at discrete values $x_i (i = 0, \ldots, n)$. The integral of $L(x)$ is a good approximation of the integral of $f(x)$, so that we may write

$$\int_a^b f(x)\, dx \doteq \alpha_0 y_0 + \alpha_1 y_1 + \cdots + \alpha_n y_n + R, \qquad (53.1)$$

where (see Formula 48.12)

$$\alpha_i = \frac{1}{P_i(x_i)} \int_a^b P_i(x) \, dx, \qquad (i = 0, \ldots, n), \tag{53.2}$$

and

$$R = \frac{f^{(n+1)}(\xi)}{(n+1)!} \int_a^b P(x) \, dx. \tag{53.3}$$

The problem of finding the integral of $f(x)$ then reduces to the evaluation of the coefficients α_i and the sum of products. The coefficients α_i depend on the $n+1$ points, x_i, and the limits of integration (a, b). If we write $P_i(x)$ as a polynomial in descending powers of x

$$P_i(x) = x^n + a_{i,n-1} x^{n-1} + \cdots + a_{i,1} x + a_{i,0}, \tag{53.4}$$

the integral may be written in the form

$$\int P_i(x) \, dx = b_{i,n+1} x^{n+1} + b_{i,n} x^n + \cdots + b_{i,1} x + b_{i,0}, \tag{53.5}$$

where

$$b_{i,n+1} = \frac{1}{n+1} \qquad (i = 0, \ldots, n),$$

$$b_{i,j} = \frac{1}{j}(a_{i,j-1}) \qquad (i = 0, \ldots, n; j = 1, \ldots, n), \tag{53.6}$$

$$b_{i,0} = \text{constants of integraiton.}$$

The coefficients b_{ij} may be tabulated and augmented by a row of the constants $P_i(x_i)$. It is not necessary to write b_{i0}, since they will disappear when the limits of integration are inserted. Thus

x^{n+1}	x^n	x^{n-1}	$\ldots$	x^2	x	$P_i(x_i)$
$b_{0,n+1}$	$b_{0,n}$	$b_{0,n-1}$	$\cdots$	$b_{0,2}$	$b_{0,1}$	$P_0(x_0)$
$\cdot$	$\cdot$	$\cdot$		$\cdot$	$\cdot$	$\cdot$
$\cdot$	$\cdot$	$\cdot$	$\cdots$	$\cdot$	$\cdot$	$\cdot$
$\cdot$	$\cdot$	$\cdot$		$\cdot$	$\cdot$	$\cdot$
$b_{n,n+1}$	$b_{n,n}$	$b_{n,n-1}$	$\cdots$	$b_{n,2}$	$b_{n,1}$	$P_n(x_n)$

There remains only the range of integration to consider. If this range changes so that many integrals are required, the values for α_i may be tabulated in the following manner:

i	$x_0 - x_1$	$x_0 - x_2$	...	$x_1 - x_5$	...	$x_3 - x_9$	...
0	α_0	α_0	...	α_0	...	α_0	...
1	α_1	α_1	...	α_1	...	α_1	...
2	α_2	α_2	...	α_2	...	α_2	...
.	.	.	...	.	...	.	...
.	.	.	...	.	...	.	...
.	.	.		.		.	
n	α_n	α_n	...	α_n	...	α_n	...

For equally spaced intervals

$$P_i(x) = P_i(u) = u(u-1)\cdots(u-i+1)(u-i-1)\cdots(u-n)$$
$$= \sum_{j=0}^{n} a_{i,j} u^j \tag{53.7}$$

and, since $dx = h\,du$,

$$\int P_i(x)\,dx = h \int P_i(u)\,du. \tag{53.8}$$

The values of a_{ij} may be found easily by use of Stirling's numbers of the first kind. Consider, for example, the case of four points:

$$P_0(u) = (u-1)(u-2)(u-3) = u^3 - 6u^2 + 11u - 6,$$
$$P_1(u) = u(u-2)(u-3) = u^3 - 5u^2 + 6u,$$
$$P_2(u) = u(u-1)(u-3) = u^3 - 4u^2 + 3u.$$
$$P_3(u) = u(u-1)(u-2) = u^3 - 3u^2 + 2u.$$

If we note that

$$P_i(u) = \frac{P(u)}{u-i}, \tag{53.9}$$

the polynomial $P(u)$ has for its coefficients the Stirling numbers of the first kind and from which we remove the factor $(u-i)$. This can be done by a synthetic division and easily put into a schematic. The removal of $(u-0)$ does not change the numbers. The first polynomial has the Stirling numbers of the first kind as coefficients.

	u^3	u^2	u	u^0	DIVISION
a_{0j}	1	-6	11	-6	0
		1	-5		
a_{1j}	1	-5	6		1
		2	-8		
a_{2j}	1	-4	3		2
		$+3$	-9		
a_{3j}	1	-3	2		3

The coefficients b_{ij} are now easily written down:

	u^4	u^3	u^2	u	$P_i(u_i)$	L.C.D.
b_{0j}	$\frac{1}{4}$	$-\frac{6}{3}$	$\frac{11}{2}$	$-\frac{6}{1}$	-6	12
b_{1j}	$\frac{1}{4}$	$-\frac{5}{3}$	$\frac{6}{2}$		2	12
b_{2j}	$\frac{1}{4}$	$-\frac{4}{3}$	$\frac{3}{2}$		-2	12
b_{3j}	$\frac{1}{4}$	$-\frac{3}{3}$	$\frac{2}{2}$		6	12

$P_i(u_i)$ are found by the formula

$$P_i(u_i) = i!(n - i)!(-1)^{n-i} \tag{53.10}$$

and, realizing that $P_0(u_0) = a_{00}$, they then alternate in sign. A column for the lowest common denominator (L.C.D.) is included for factoring out the denominator; it is to be recalled that $P_i(u_i)$ is a denominator.

Let us now consider a specific integral, say

$$\int_0^2 f(x)\,dx$$

for four points. We have

$$\alpha_0 = \frac{h}{P_0(u_0)} \int_0^2 P(u)$$

$$= \frac{h}{P_0(u_0)} (b_{04}u^4 + b_{03}u^3 + b_{02}u^2 + b_{01}u)\Big|_0^2$$

$$= \frac{h}{-6}\left[\frac{1}{4}(2)^4 - \frac{6}{3}(2)^3 + \frac{11}{2}(2)^2 - 6(2)\right]$$

$$= -\frac{h}{6}\left(\frac{1}{12}\right)[(3)(2)^4 - 24(2)^3 + 66(2)^2 - 72(2)]$$

$$= -\frac{h}{72}(48 - 192 + 264 - 144)$$

$$= -\frac{h}{72}(-24)$$

$$= \frac{2}{6}h.$$

The following schematic eases the computation

	$2^4 = 16$	$2^3 = 8$	$2^2 = 4$	2	L.C.D.	$P_i(u_i)$	$\alpha_i h^{-1}$
b_{0j}	3	-24	66	-72	12	-6	$\frac{1}{3}$
b_{1j}	3	-20	36		12	2	$\frac{4}{3}$
b_{2j}	3	-16	18		12	-2	$\frac{1}{3}$
b_{3j}	3	-12	12		12	6	0

$$\int_0^2 f(x)\,dx \doteq \frac{h}{3}(y_0 + 4y_1 + y_2 + 0y_3).$$

For equally spaced intervals the values of α_i can be tabulated for the range of integration 0–1, 0–2, etc. The value of an integral between other integral limits can be found by recalling that

$$\int_2^4 f(x)\,dx = \int_0^4 f(x)\,dx - \int_0^2 f(x)\,dx.$$

Values of α_i are given in Table XIII, p. 372, and their use can be illustrated by an example.[1]

Example 5.9. Find the $\displaystyle\int_{1.5}^{1.8} y\,dx$, given the table

x_i	1.5	1.6	1.7	1.8	1.9	2.0
y_i	48.09375	65.53600	87.69705	115.47360	149.86915	192

SOLUTION.

$$\int_{1.5}^{1.8} f(x)\,dx = h\int_0^3 f(u)\,du$$

$$\doteq h\left[\sum_{i=0}^{5} \alpha_i(0\text{–}3)y_i\right].$$

From Table XIII, p. 372, for six points in the interval 0–3 we have

α_i	.31875	1.36875	.71250	.71250	−.13125	.01875

and, since $h = .1$,

$$\int_{1.5}^{1.8} y\,dx = .1(233.721045) = 23.372104.$$

54.　ACCURACY OF LAGRANGIAN FORMULAS

All of the formulas derived in this chapter are based on the assumption that the given data can be fitted by a polynomial in the region under discussion, and this initial assumption should frequently be checked. The inherent error in the Lagrangian formulas is exhibited in the remainder term of (48.12)

$$R_n = \frac{f^{(n-1)}(\xi)}{(n+1)!}P(x),$$

where ξ is an arbitrary point in the interval $(0, n)$. This remainder term may be carried throughout all of the derivations of the formulas and is a measure

[1]Values of α_i may also be computed around a "central value." See *Journal of Mathematics and Physics* **24**, 1, 1–21 (1945).

of their accuracy. Thus in Formula 51.23 for the derivative there should be added the remainder (51.2) which at $x = x_k$ reduces to

$$\frac{h^n}{(n+1)!} y^{(n+1)}(\xi).$$

For the integrals we have the expression in (53.3). The accuracy should always be tested whenever possible.

55.   LAGRANGIAN MULTIPLIER[2]

Although the Lagrangian multiplier is not directly associated with the Lagrangian formulas discussed so far, it still seems appropriate to include it here because it is concerned with the finding of an extremum of a function that is constrained by some additional condition. In the principle of least squares, which is so often used in numerical analysis, we are concerned with the problem of minimizing the sum of the squares of the residuals of the analytical expression and the values found by substitution of the known points. If an additional constraint is imposed on the parameters in the analytical expression, the problem can be solved by use of the Lagrangian multiplier.

Let us consider a function of two variables, $f(x, y)$, and let us find the maximum and minimum values of this function if, in addition, x and y are related by $g(x, y) = 0$.

The necessary condition for an extremum is that the total differential vanish. Thus for the function $f(x, y)$

$$\frac{\partial f}{\partial x} dx + \frac{\partial f}{\partial y} dy = 0. \tag{55.1}$$

The total differential of the contrained relation is

$$\frac{\partial g}{\partial x} dx + \frac{\partial g}{\partial y} dy = 0. \tag{55.2}$$

If (55.2) is multiplied by an undetermined multiplier, λ, and added to (55.1), we have

$$\left(\frac{\partial f}{\partial x} + \lambda \frac{\partial g}{\partial x}\right) dx + \left(\frac{\partial f}{\partial y} + \lambda \frac{\partial g}{\partial y}\right) dy = 0. \tag{55.3}$$

[2]For a more detailed discussion see John M. H. Olmsted, *Advanced Calculus*. New York: Appleton-Century-Crofts, 1961, pp. 317–319.

Equation 55.3 would be satisfied if λ were determined so that

$$\frac{\partial f}{\partial x} + \lambda \frac{\partial g}{\partial x} = 0,$$

$$\frac{\partial f}{\partial y} + \lambda \frac{\partial g}{\partial y} = 0, \qquad (55.4)$$

$$g(x, y) = 0.$$

The multiplier λ is called the *Lagrangian multiplier*.

Example 5.10. Find the dimensions of a rectangular box, without a top, having maximum volume and whose surface is 66 in².

SOLUTION. Let the dimensions of the box be x, y, and z. The volume function to be maximized is

$$V(x, y, z) = xyz,$$

subject to the constraint

$$xy + 2xz + 2yz = 66.$$

The system (55.4) for this problem is

$$yz + \lambda(y + 2z) = 0,$$

$$xz + \lambda(x + 2z) = 0,$$

$$xy + \lambda(2x + 2y) = 0,$$

$$xy + 2xz + 2yz = 66.$$

By multiplying the first equation by x, the second by y, the third by z, and adding, we obtain

$$3xyz + 2\lambda(xy + 2xz + 2yz) = 0.$$

By substituting the last equation into this result, we obtain

$$3xyz + 132\lambda = 0 \quad \text{or} \quad \lambda = -\frac{xyz}{44}.$$

The first three equations of the system now take the form

$$\frac{yz}{44}(44 - xy - 2xz) = 0,$$

$$\frac{xz}{44}(44 - xy - 2yz) = 0,$$

$$\frac{xy}{44}(44 - 2xz - 2yz) = 0.$$

The solutions are $x = y = \sqrt{22}, z = \dfrac{11}{\sqrt{22}}$.

Another example is discussed in Chapter 8.

56.   EXERCISE VII

In the following exercises employ the Lagrangian formulas.

1. In the data of Exercise 3.3(a) find y at $x = .55$ and $x = .72$.

2. In the data of Exercise 3.3(b) find y at $x = .82$, 1.15, and 1.32.

3. Solve Example 3.12, using Lagrange's formula.

4. Apply Lagrange's formula to the last step of Example 3.15.

5. Solve Problem 1(a) at $x = .7$ and 1(b) at $x = 1.91$ of Exercise IV.

6. Solve Problem 1 of Exercise V by the methods of this chapter.

7. Solve Problem 2 of Exercise V by the methods of this chapter.

8. Solve Problem 1 of Exercise VI by the methods of this chapter.

9. Solve Problem 5 of Exercise V, with $k < 4$, by the methods of this chapter.

10. Solve Problem 7 of Exercise VI by the methods of this chapter.

11. Divide the interval $(0, 1)$ into 10 equal parts and find $\int_0^1 x \, dx$ by the methods of this chapter. Compare the answer with that found in Problem 3 of Exercise VI.

12. Find the dimensions of a closed cylinder having a maximum volume and a total surface of 20π in^2.

6

Elementary Equations and Systems

57.   INTRODUCTION

The solution of algebraic equations is thoroughly discussed in a course in algebra. There, however, one is primarily concerned with the existence of solutions and expressing the solution in closed form. Whenever approximate solutions are desired, they are obtained either by graphical methods or perhaps by Horner's method. Trigonometric equations are discussed in books on trigonometry, but very little, if anything, is said about combinations of algebraic and transcendental equations.

It is the purpose of this chapter to present methods of finding the roots of any elementary equation; by "elementary" we shall mean algebraic or transcendental or a combination of these equations. Systems of equations are also discussed.

58.   SOME FUNDAMENTAL CONCEPTS

Before proceeding to the detailed methods let us review some of the fundamental concepts of algebra. The existence of roots of an algebraic equation is based on a number of theorems, all of which are quite important. Since they are adequately developed in a number of books, it is necessary only to list them here. Let us consider a polynomial $y = f(x)$ of the nth degree. If this is set equal to zero, $f(x) = 0$, we have an equation, and its solutions are called the *roots* of the equation or the *zeros* of the function $f(x)$. If n is a positive integer, $f(x) = 0$ is said to be a *rational integral equation*. We now state some important theorems.

Remainder Theorem. If a polynomial $f(x)$ is divided by $(x - r)$ until a remainder independent of x is obtained, this remainder is equal to $f(r)$.

Factor Theorem. If r is a zero of the polynomial $f(x)$, then $(x - r)$ is a factor of $f(x)$.

Fundamental Theorem of Algebra. Every rational integral equation, $f(x) = 0$, of the nth degree has n and only n roots.

Rational Roots. If a rational number, b/c, a fraction in its lowest form, is a root of the rational integral equation

$$a_0x^n + a_1x^{n-1} + \cdots + a_{n-1}x + a_n = 0,$$

with integral coefficients, then b is a factor of a_n and c is a factor of a_0.

Complex Roots. Complex roots of a rational integral equation with real coefficients occur in conjugate pairs; that is, $r_1 = a + bi$ and $r_2 = a - bi$. The same is true of quadratic surds.

Other Root Theorems. For the rational integral equation with real coefficients, $f(x) = 0$:

1. Every such equation of an odd degree with $a_0 > 0$ has at least one real root whose sign is opposite to that of its last term.
2. Every such equation of an even degree with $a_0 > 0$ and a negative last term has at least two real roots, one positive and one negative.
3. If the equation $f(x) = 0$ has k roots equal to x_0, then $f'(x)$ will have $k - 1$ zeros equal to x_0.
4. If $a, b, c, \ldots, k$ are the roots of the equation $f(x) = 0$, then

$$f'(x) = \frac{f(x)}{x - a} + \frac{f(x)}{x - b} + \frac{f(x)}{x - c} + \cdots + \frac{f(x)}{x - k}.$$

Reducing the Degree of the Equation. Once a root of an equation has been found, it may be "divided out," leaving a quotient of degree one less than the original equation. Further investigation may then be applied to this quotient.

Descartes' Rule of Signs. The number of positive roots of an equation $f(x) = 0$ with real coefficients cannot exceed the number of variations in sign in the polynomial $f(x)$ and the number of negative roots cannot exceed the number of variations in sign in $f(-x)$.

Location Principle. If $f(x)$ is continuous from $x = a$ to $x = b$ and if $f(a)$ and $f(b)$ have opposite signs, then $f(x) = 0$ has an odd number of roots between a and b; if $f(a)$ and $f(b)$ have like signs, then $f(x) = 0$ either has no roots or an even number of roots between a and b.

Rules of Transformation

1. *To form an equation each of whose roots is k times the corresponding roots of the given equation, multiply the coefficients a_0 by 1, a_1 by k, a_2 by k^2, ... a_i by k_i, ..., a_n by k^n.*

2. *To form an equation each of whose roots is equal to the negative of the corresponding roots of the given equation, change the signs of the odd-degree terms.*

3. *To form an equation each of whose roots is less by h than a corresponding root of a given equation, divide $f(x)$ and each successive quotient by $(x - h)$ until n divisions have been performed. The remainders obtained in each division form the coefficients of the new equation in ascending order.*

SPECIAL TRANSFORMATIONS

EQUATION	TRANSFORMED TO	BY
$x^3 + bx^2 + cx + d = 0$	$y^3 + py + q = 0$	$x = y - \frac{1}{3}b$
$x^4 + bx^3 + cx^2 + dx + e = 0$	$y^4 + qy^2 + ry + s = 0$	$x = y - \frac{1}{4}b$

The Relationship of Roots and Coefficients. In any rational integral equation of the nth degree,

$$a_0 x^n + a_1 x^{n-1} + a_2 x^{n-2} + \cdots + a_n = 0,$$

$\dfrac{a_1}{a_0} = -\text{(the sum of the roots)},$

$\dfrac{a_2}{a_0} = \text{the sum of the products of the roots taken two at a time},$

$\dfrac{a_3}{a_0} = -\text{ (the sum of the products of the roots taken three at a time)},$

$\vdots$

$\dfrac{a_n}{a_0} = (-1)^n \text{(the product of all the roots)}.$

Splitting the Equation.   The roots of an equation may be found by obtaining the abscissas of the points of intersection of two functions into which the original function has been decomposed. For example, the solution of $(x - \cos x = 0)$ is the value of x for which $y_1 = x$ intersects $y_2 = \cos x$.

Graphing.   Many clues to the solutions of equations may be obtained from the plots of their functions, and the value of a graph cannot be over-emphasized.

59.   ONE EQUATION IN ONE UNKNOWN

Most numerical methods for the solution of ordinary equations are based on the method of successive approximations. The problem is then one of finding a recurrence relation that permits the calculation of a sequence of numbers $x_0, x_1, x_2, \ldots$ which converges to the desired root, r. For the equation

$$y = f(x) = 0 \tag{59.1}$$

the common recurrence relation is

$$x_{i+1} = x_i - \frac{f(x_i)}{g(x_i)}, \tag{59.2}$$

in which $g(x_i)$ may be the slope of an appropriate line. The correct value for $g(x_i)$ would be the slope of the line from (x_i, y_i) to $(r, 0)$, for then

$$g(x_i) = \frac{y_i - 0}{x_i - r}$$

and

$$x_{i+1} = x_i - \frac{y_i}{(y_i)/(x_i - r)} = \frac{[y_i x_i - y_i(x_i - r)]}{y_i} = r.$$

The most classical form of $g(x_i)$ is the value of the derivative of $f(x)$ at x_i, $f'(x_i)$. Formula 59.2 then becomes

$$x_{i+1} = x_i - \frac{f(x_i)}{f'(x_i)}. \tag{59.3}$$

This is known as the *Newton-Raphson method* or, more popularly, as Newton's method.

Other common forms of $g(x_i)$ are

(a) the slope of the chord joining two points already calculated,

$$g(x_i) = \frac{y_k - y_i}{x_k - x_i};$$ (59.4)

(b) the constant slope between two points (x_1, y_1) and (x_2, y_2) for which $f(x_1)$ and $f(x_2)$ have unlike signs,

$$g(x_i) = \frac{y_1 - y_2}{x_1 - x_2};$$ (59.5)

(c) the constant value of the derivative at a chosen point, x_0,

$$g(x_i) = f'(x_0);$$

(d) an arithmetic mean between (b) and (c)

$$g(x_i) = \frac{1}{2}\left[f'(x_0) + \frac{y_1 - y_2}{x_1 - x_2} \right].$$ (59.6)

The most popular is the Newton-Raphson method, provided it is not too difficult to calculate the value of the derivative.

Example 6.1. Find the real root of

$$2x - \cos x - 1 = 0.$$

SOLUTION. Find the first approximation by locating graphically the point of intersection of

$$y_1 = 2x - 1,$$

$$y_2 = \cos x.$$

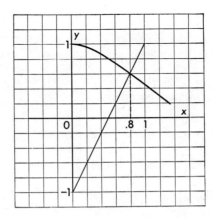

Now
$$f(x) = 2x - \cos x - 1,$$
$$f'(x) = 2 + \sin x.$$
Then

i	x_i	$f(x_i)$	$f'(x_i)$
0	.8	$-.096702$	2.717356
1	.835588	.000443	2.741699
2	.835427	.000067	2.741583
3	.835403		

Example 6.2. Find the root between 2 and 3 of the equation
$$x^4 - x^3 - 2x^2 - 6x - 4 = 0.$$

SOLUTION. We write the function and its derivative in their nested form.
$$f(x) = \{[(x - 1)x - 2]x - 6\}x - 4.$$
$$f'(x) = [(4x - 3)x - 4]x - 6.$$

Since the desired root is between 2 and 3, let us arbitrarily choose $x_0 = 2.5$.

i	x_i	$f(x_i)$	$f'(x_i)$
0	2.5	-8.0625	27.75
1	2.790540	2.591414	46.397506
2	2.734688	.111655	42.431352
3	2.732057	.000259	42.249140
4	2.732051		

Note. In the computation the values of $f'(x_i)$ are computed before those of $f(x_i)$.

Example 6.3. Find the root between 0 and 1 of the equation
$$x^{1.84} - 5.2211x + 2.0123 = 0.$$

SOLUTION. In this case let us take a constant value of $g(x_i) = (y_0 - y_1)/(x_0 - x_1)$, choosing for the two points the values $(0, 2.0123)$ and $(1, -2.2088)$. Thus
$$g(x) = \frac{2.0123 + 2.2088}{0 - 1} = -4.2211.$$

Since the absolute values of y_0 and y_1 are nearly equal, we choose $x_0 = 0.5$.

i	x_i	$\log x_i$	$f(x_i)$	$g(x)$
0	.5	$-.30103$	$-.31892$	-4.2211
1	.424447	$-.37217$	.002860	
2	.425124	$-.371486$	$-.000075$	
3	.425107			

Thus $r = \boxed{.42511}$. Check: $f(r) = -.00002$.

Greater improvement can be achieved only by using more extensive logarithmic tables.

It is noted that Formula 59.2 fails when $g(x_i) = 0$. For the expressions of $g(x_i)$ this will occur at or near the root of $f(x) = 0$ when the slope of the tangent line is nearly horizontal. The procedure then is to solve for the root of the derivative equation $f'(x) = 0$ and to denote it by $x = a$. Then we have three possibilities:

1. If $f(a) = 0$, a is a double root.
2. If $f(a) \neq 0$ and $f(a)$ and $f''(a)$ have like signs, there is no root of $f(x) = 0$ in the neighborhood of $x = a$.
3. If $f(a) \neq 0$ and $f(a)$ and $f''(a)$ have unlike signs, there should be two roots of $f(x) = 0$ in the neighborhood of a, one less than a and one greater than a.

To find the two roots in (3), consider the Taylor series expansion of $f(x)$ about $x = a$; that is,

$$f(x) = f(a) + f'(a)(x - a) + \tfrac{1}{2}f''(a)(x - a)^2 + \cdots.$$

If we neglect all terms higher than the second and remember that $f(x) = f'(a) = 0$, we have

$$f(a) + \tfrac{1}{2}f''(a)(x - a)^2 \doteq 0$$

or

$$x^2 - 2ax + a^2 + 2\frac{f(a)}{f''(a)} \doteq 0,$$

and by solving this quadratic for x we obtain a first approximation to the two roots:

$$x \doteq a \pm \sqrt{-2f(a)/f''(a)}. \tag{59.7}$$

The two values may be improved by successive approximations, using any of the formulas for $g(x_i)$.

Example 6.4. Find the small positive roots of

$$f(x) = .054x^3 + 89.973x^2 - 60x + 10 = 0.$$

SOLUTION. Tabulate the values of the function at small values of x.

x	0	.5	1
$f(x)$	10	2.5	40.027

From these values it appears that there is a possibility of an even number of roots in the neighborhood of $x = .5$. It is therefore desirable to solve first the derivative equation $f'(x) = 0$ for its roots. We have

$$f'(x) = .162x^2 + 179.946x - 60 = 0.$$

Since this is a quadratic equation, we may solve it by using the quadratic formula. Had it been a higher degree equation we could have used the Newton-Raphson method. We find

$$x = \frac{-179.946 \pm \sqrt{(179.946)^2 - 4(.162)(60)}}{2(.162)}$$

$$= \frac{-179.946 \pm 180.054}{.324},$$

$$x(>0) = \frac{.108}{.324} = \frac{1}{3} = .333333.$$

The second derivative is

$$f''(x) = .324x + 179.946,$$

and at $x = \frac{1}{3}$ we have

$$f(\tfrac{1}{3}) = -.001000 \quad \text{and} \quad f''(x) = 180.054.$$

Since these have unlike signs, there should be two roots in the neighborhood of $x = \frac{1}{3}$. Let us obtain the first approximations by Formula 59.7.

$$x = .333333 \pm \sqrt{\frac{.002}{180.054}}$$

$$= .333333 \pm .003317,$$

$$x_1 = .330016 \quad \text{and} \quad x_2 = .336650.$$

We can improve these roots by Newton's method.

		x_1			x_2	
i	x_i	$f(x_i)$	$f'(x_i)$	x_i	$f(x_i)$	$f'(x_i)$
0	.330016	$-.000009$	$-.597297$	.336650	$-.000009$	.597181
1	.330001	$-.00000017$	$-.599998$	.336665	$-.00000056$	.599882
2	.3300007			.3366659		

Thus we have

$$x_1 = \boxed{.330001} \quad \text{and} \quad x_2 = \boxed{.336666}$$

to six decimals.

We can use Newton's formula to obtain useful expressions for finding the roots, reciprocals, etc., of a number. Let us consider, for example, the function $f(x) = N - x^2$: then $f'(x) = -2x$, and we have

$$x_{n+1} = x_n - \frac{N - x_n^2}{-2x_n} = \tfrac{1}{2}[x_n + N x_n^{-1}], \tag{59.8}$$

which yields the solution of $N - x^2 = 0$ or $x = \sqrt{N}$. We exhibit two other expressions for finding the square root of a number; these are obtained from the function $f(x) = x^3 - Nx$.

$$x_{n+1} = \frac{2x_n^3}{3x_n^2 - N} \quad \text{or} \quad x_{n+1} = \frac{x_n(3N - x_n^2)}{2N}. \tag{59.9}$$

Let $f(x) = N - x^{-1}$ then $f'(x) = x^{-2}$ and

$$x_{n+1} = x_n(2 - Nx_n) \tag{59.10}$$

gives a sequence of numbers which converges to the value for N^{-1}.

Let $f(x) = N - x^{-p}$; then $f'(x) = px^{-p-1}$ and

$$x_{n+1} = x_n p^{-1}(p + 1 - Nx_n^p) \tag{59.11}$$

gives values from which we can obtain approximations to the reciprocal of the pth root of a number. Other special formulas can be derived in a similar manner. (See Exercise VIII, Problem 13.)

60.   THE ITERATION METHOD

Another method of solving an equation in one unknown is that of iteration. This method is applicable when the equation $f(x) = 0$ can be solved for the unknown x in terms of a function of x; that is, it is possible to write

$$x = F(x). \tag{60.1}$$

The procedure of iteration is to guess a first approximation of the root, say x_0, to substitute this value into $F(x)$, and obtain a second approximation,

$$x_1 = F(x_0). \tag{60.2}$$

Now repeat the process by substituting x_1 into $F(x)$ to get

$$x_2 = F(x_1).$$

By repeated continuation of the process, we can calculate a sequence of numbers $\{x_i\}$ which may converge to the desired root, r. The method is especially suited to the finding of the roots of an equation in which the function is given in the form of a power series, such as the interpolating polynomials.

Example 6.5. Find the root of the equation

$$3x - \sqrt{1 + \sin x} = 0.$$

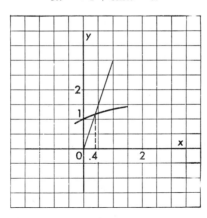

SOLUTION. To get a first approximation, we plot roughly the graph of the two functions,

$$y_1 = 3x$$

and

$$y_2 = \sqrt{1 + \sin x},$$

and determine the abscissa of the point of intersection as $x = .4$. Next we solve $f(x)$ for x,

$$x = \tfrac{1}{3}\sqrt{1 + \sin x},$$

and set up the iteration calculation.

x_0	x_1	x_2	x_3	x_4	x_5	x_6
.4	.3929	.391985	.391865	.391849	.391847	.391847

Thus $\boxed{x = .391847}$ to six decimals accuracy.

The success of the iteration process depends on the convergence of the sequence $\{x_i\}$ to a number r, which is the desired root. It is possible, of course, that the method will not converge. However, the condition for convergence can be established by repeated applications of the theorem of mean value.[1] We assume the development and simply state the condition, which is that

$$|F'(x)| < 1$$

in the neighborhood of the desired root. Furthermore, the smaller the value of $F'(x)$, the more rapid the convergence. A check on the example shows that

$$F'(x) = \tfrac{1}{6}(1 + \sin x)^{-1/2}(\cos x)$$

and, at $x = 0.4$, $F'(.4) = .130$.

61.   SYSTEMS OF LINEAR EQUATIONS

The first discussion of systems of linear equations occurs in an elementary course in algebra, in which the reader is introduced to the method of elimination and the solution of the system by determinants. These are basic methods which should be employed whenever possible. We shall assume that the reader is familiar with the theory of determinants and review briefly the method of solving equations employing them.[2] Let us consider a simple system of three linear equations in three unknowns:

$$a_1x + b_1y + c_1z = d_1,$$

$$a_2x + b_2y + c_2z = d_2, \tag{61.1}$$

$$a_3x + b_3y + c_3z = d_3.$$

[1] See J. B. Scarborough, *Numerical Mathematical Analysis*, second ed. Baltimore: Johns Hopkins University Press, 1950, p. 201.
[2] See, for example, P. S. Dwyer, *Linear Computations*. New York: Wiley, 1951, Chapter 9.

The determinant made up of the coefficients of the unknowns is called the *determinant of the system* and is denoted by D.

$$D = \begin{vmatrix} a_1 & b_1 & c_1 \\ a_2 & b_2 & c_2 \\ a_3 & b_3 & c_3 \end{vmatrix}. \tag{61.2}$$

The values of the unknowns are then found by

$$x = \frac{1}{D} \begin{vmatrix} d_1 & b_1 & c_1 \\ d_2 & b_2 & c_2 \\ d_3 & b_3 & c_3 \end{vmatrix}; \quad y = \frac{1}{D} \begin{vmatrix} a_1 & d_1 & c_1 \\ a_2 & d_2 & c_2 \\ a_3 & d_3 & c_3 \end{vmatrix}; \quad z = \frac{1}{D} \begin{vmatrix} a_1 & b_1 & d_1 \\ a_2 & b_2 & d_2 \\ a_3 & b_3 & d_3 \end{vmatrix}. \tag{61.3}$$

There are three distinct values providing $D \neq 0$. We recall that a determinant is said to be of *rank r* if r is the *order* of the highest order nonvanishing minor. A *matrix* is a rectangular array of mn quantities arranged in m rows and n columns. It is not one quantity, like a determinant, but an array of quantities. The rank of a matrix is the highest rank of the determinants of the highest order that can be formed from the matrix by striking out rows or columns. A matrix may be square, that is, m may be equal to n. Thus we say that D is the matrix of the coefficients. If to this matrix we attach the column of constant terms, we may call the result the *augmented matrix*. We may now state the conditions for solution of (61.1).

1. If the matrix of the coefficients is of rank 3 (in general n), that is, $D \neq 0$, the equations have a unique solution.

2. If the rank of the augmented matrix is greater than the rank of the matrix of coefficients, the equations have no solution.

3. If for n equations in n unknowns the ranks of the augmented matrix and of the matrix of coefficients are both equal to $n - r$, then an infinite number of solutions are expressible in terms of r arbitrary parameters.

The solution of the simple system of two equations in two unknowns is readily adapted to a calculating machine by the following schematic. Consider

$$a_1 x + b_1 y = c_1,$$
$$a_2 x + b_2 y = c_2. \tag{61.4}$$

Arrange the numbers in the following array:

$$\begin{array}{ccc} a_1 & b_1 & c_1 \\ a_2 & b_2 & c_2 \\ \hline D & x & y \end{array}$$

where

$$D = a_1 b_2 - b_1 a_2,$$

$$x = -\frac{1}{D}(b_1 c_2 - c_1 b_2) \qquad \text{[note the } (-) \text{ sign],} \qquad (61.5)$$

$$y = \frac{1}{D}(a_1 c_2 - c_1 a_2),$$

which is accomplished on the machine by cross multiplication, followed by division if required.

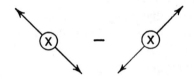

Example 6.6. Solve for x and y in

$$3.1416x + 1.3456y = 7.2184,$$
$$1.3111x - 2.1221y = 3.1234.$$

SOLUTION. The computation is arranged on the calculating sheet as follows. The student should repeat the calculations to check the answers.

$$D = a_1 b_2 - b_1 a_2$$

$$x = -\frac{b_1 c_2 - c_1 b_2}{D}$$

$$y = \frac{a_1 c_2 - c_1 a_2}{D}$$

	a	b	c
	3.1416	1.3456	7.2184
	1.3111	-2.1221	3.1234
	-8.431006	2.3154	$-.0413$

Thus $x = \boxed{2.3154}$ and $y = \boxed{-.0413}$.

For a system of more than two equations the evaluation of the determinants is fairly difficult on a calculating machine, and we rely on a method of elimination which has been developed into a schematic. We now describe this method in detail.

62.   CROUT'S METHOD

One of the best methods of solving a system of linear equation on a desk calculating machine was developed by P. D. Crout in 1941.[3] It is based essentially on elimination, with the work arranged in a schematic. A check is provided so that the work may be examined at regular points, and this is highly recommended. The method is best explained by an example. To keep it simple, consider three equations in three unknowns, $x, y,$ and z.

$$a_1 x + b_1 y + c_1 z = d_1,$$
$$a_2 x + b_2 y + c_2 z = d_2, \qquad (62.1)$$
$$a_3 x + b_3 y + c_3 z = d_3.$$

Form a matrix of the system, plus a check column,

$$\begin{pmatrix} a_1 & b_1 & c_1 & d_1 & e_1 \\ a_2 & b_2 & c_2 & d_2 & e_2 \\ a_3 & b_3 & c_3 & d_3 & e_3 \end{pmatrix}, \qquad (62.2)$$

where

$$e_i = a_i + b_i + c_i + d_i, \qquad (i = 1, 2, 3).$$

A derived matrix

$$\begin{pmatrix} A_1 & B_1 & C_1 & D_1 & E_1 \\ A_2 & B_2 & C_2 & D_2 & E_2 \\ A_3 & B_3 & C_3 & D_3 & E_3 \end{pmatrix} \qquad (62.3)$$

---

[3]Prescott D. Crout, "A Short Method for Evaluating Determinants and Solving Systems of Linear Equations with Real or Complex Coefficients," *Transactions of the American Institute of Electrical Engineers*, **60**, 1235 (1941).

is now computed in the following manner:

STEP 1. *First Column*

$$A_i = a_i, \qquad (i = 1, 2, 3). \tag{62.4}$$

STEP 2. *First Row*

$$B_1 = \frac{b_1}{a_1}; \qquad C_1 = \frac{c_1}{a_1}; \qquad D_1 = \frac{d_1}{a_1}; \qquad E_1 = \frac{e_1}{a_1}. \tag{62.5}$$

STEP 3. *Remaining Second Column*

$$B_2 = b_2 - B_1 A_2,$$
$$B_3 = b_3 - B_1 A_3. \tag{62.6}$$

STEP 4. *Remaining Second Row*

$$C_2 = \frac{c_2 - C_1 A_2}{B_2},$$

$$D_2 = \frac{d_2 - D_1 A_2}{B_2}, \tag{62.7}$$

$$E_2 = \frac{e_2 - E_1 A_2}{B_2}.$$

STEP 5. *Remaining Third Column*

$$C_3 = c_3 - C_2 B_3 - C_1 A_3. \tag{62.8}$$

STEP 6. *Remaining Third Row*

$$D_3 = \frac{d_3 - D_2 B_3 - D_1 A_3}{C_3},$$

$$E_3 = \frac{e_3 - E_2 B_3 - E_1 A_3}{C_3}. \tag{62.9}$$

The solutions are then given by

$$z = D_3,$$
$$y = D_2 - C_2 z, \tag{62.10}$$
$$x = D_1 - C_1 z - B_1 y.$$

The fifth column (E_i) serves as a continuous check on the calculations in that the E_i are equal to *one* plus the sum of the elements in the same row *to the right of the principal diagonal*; thus

$$E_1 = 1 + B_1 + C_1 + D_1,$$
$$E_2 = 1 + C_2 + D_2, \tag{62.11}$$
$$E_3 = 1 + D_3.$$

The check should be made after completing each row.

The calculations adapt themselves readily to desk machine operations, and only the elements of the derived matrix need be recorded; that is, no intermediate quantities have to be written down. The arrangement is illustrated in the following example.

Example 6.7. Solve for x, y, and z in the following system of equations:

$$x + y + z = 1,$$
$$3x + y - 3z = 5,$$
$$x - 2y - 5z = 10.$$

SOLUTION.

	x	y	z	k	CHECK
GIVEN	1	1	1	1	4
MATRIX	3	1	-3	5	6
	1	-2	-5	10	4
DERIVED	1	1	1	1	4
MATRIX	3	-2	3	-1	3
	1	-3	3	2	3
SOLUTIONS	6	-7	2		

A check can also be made on the computations of the solutions by using the last column. Thus

$$z' = E_3,$$
$$y' = E_2 - C_2 z', \tag{62.12}$$
$$x' = E_1 - C_1 z' - B_1 y'$$

and

$$z' = 1 + z,$$

$$y' = 1 + y, \tag{62.13}$$

$$x' = 1 + x.$$

This is illustrated in the following example.

Example 6.8.

x	y	z	w	k	CHECK
2.462	1.349	−2.390	−3.400	0.903	−1.076
−1.000	2.000	3.000	2.000	1.340	7.340
0.983	0.220	−1.600	−0.930	3.000	1.673
1.310	−3.000	2.100	1.200	2.560	4.170
2.462	0.5479	−0.9708	−1.3810	0.3668	−0.4370
−1.000	2.5479	0.7964	0.2429	0.6699	2.7092
0.983	−0.3186	−0.3920	−1.2881	−7.2779	−7.5659
1.310	−3.7178	6.3326	12.0692	4.1973	5.1973
3.721	1.141	−1.871	4.197		SOLUTIONS
4.721	2.141	−.871	5.197		CHECK

A. Symmetrical Coefficients

If the elements of the given matrix are symmetrical about the principal diagonal, the work of computing the auxiliary matrix is cut almost in half. This can be seen by noting that the elements of the auxiliary matrix below the principal diagonal will yield, if divided by its diagonal element, the symmetrically opposite element above this diagonal. Let us follow this through. If the system given by (62.1) were symmetrical, we would have

$$b_1 = a_2, \qquad c_1 = a_3, \qquad c_2 = b_3,$$

so that the given matrix would be

$$\begin{pmatrix} a_1 & a_2 & a_3 & d_1 \\ a_2 & b_2 & b_3 & d_2 \\ a_3 & b_3 & c_3 & d_3 \end{pmatrix} \tag{62.14}$$

and in the derived matrix we would have

$$B_1 = \frac{b_1}{a_1} = \frac{A_2}{A_1},$$

$$C_1 = \frac{c_1}{a_1} = \frac{A_3}{A_1}, \tag{62.15}$$

$$C_2 = \frac{c_2 - C_1 A_2}{B_2} = \frac{b_3 - B_1 A_3}{B_2} = \frac{B_3}{B_2}.$$

During the computation the symmetrically corresponding elements of the derived matrix could therefore be computed as one operation with an additional division.

Various stencils have been devised to guide the computer. One stencil which the author has found convenient to prepare is a rectangular guide card divided by a diagonal so that half is used for calculating the columns and half for the rows by simply rotating the card through 180° each time a change is made.

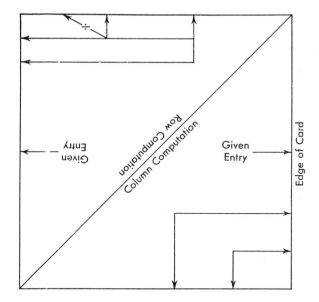

B. The General Case

Crout's method is easily generalized. Let (a_{ij}) be the elements of the given matrix and (A_{ij}), the elements of the derived matrix; then

$$A_{ii} = a_{ii} - \sum_{k=1}^{i-1} A_{ik} A_{ki},$$

$$A_{ij} = a_{ij} - \sum_{k=1}^{j-1} A_{ik} A_{kj}, \qquad (\text{if } i > j), \tag{62.16}$$

$$A_{ij} = \left(a_{ij} - \sum_{k=1}^{i-1} A_{ik} A_{kj}\right) \frac{1}{A_{ii}}, \qquad (\text{if } i < j),$$

and, if we have n variables, x_i, the solution matrix, can be written as a row matrix,

$$x_i = A_{i,n+1} - \sum_{k=i+1}^{n} A_{ik} x_{ik}, \qquad (i = 1, \ldots, n), \tag{62.17}$$

where it is understood that any sum whose lower limit exceeds its upper limit as assumed to be zero.

C. Accuracy Improvements in the Solutions

The values obtained for the unknowns are usually not exact, and their substitution in the original equations may not make the equations balance exactly. Improvements on the solutions may be obtained by calculating the differences and, by treating them as the column of constants, solving for corrections in the first solutions of the unknowns. Since all of the derived matrices except the column of constants remain the same, it is necessary only to annex an additional column to obtain these corrections. For example, suppose that the solutions to Example 6.8 had been

$$x = 3.72,$$

$$y = 1.13,$$

$$z = -1.88, \tag{62.18}$$

$$w = 4.20.$$

If these solutions were then substituted into the original equations, we would have these values for k:

Substituted	Given	Differences
0.896	0.903	.007
1.300	1.340	.040
3.007	3.000	−.007
2.575	2.560	−.015

By employing the difference column as the column of constants in the given matrix, we obtain the corresponding column in the derived matrix

$$.002843$$
$$.016815$$
$$.011318$$
$$-.002296.$$

By solving in the usual manner, we obtain

$$\Delta w = -.0023; \qquad \Delta z = .0084; \qquad \Delta y = .01068; \qquad \Delta x = .0020.$$

Thus

$$x = 3.722; \qquad y = 1.141; \qquad z = -1.872; \qquad w = 4.198,$$

which compares favorably with the solutions obtained earlier. This correction procedure may be repeated as many times as desired.

D. Evaluation of Determinants

Crout's method may be used to find the value of a determinant. Refer to the system of three equations in three unknowns and consider the product of the elements of the main diagonal of the derived matrix, $A_1 B_2 C_3$. We have

$$A_1 = a_1,$$

$$B_2 = b_2 - B_1 A_2 = b_2 - \frac{b_1}{a_1} a_2 = \frac{1}{a_1}(a_1 b_2 - b_1 a_2),$$

$$C_3 = c_3 - C_2 B_3 - C_1 A_3$$

$$= c_3 - \left(\frac{c_2 - C_1 A_2}{B_2}\right)(b_3 - B_1 A_3) - \frac{c_1}{a_1}(a_3)$$

$$= c_3 - \left(\frac{a_1 c_2 - c_1 a_2}{a_1 b_2 - b_1 a_2}\right)\left(\frac{a_1 b_3 - b_1 a_3}{a_1}\right) - \frac{c_1 a_3}{a_1}$$

$$= \frac{1}{a_1}\left[a_1 c_3 - c_1 a_3 - \frac{(a_1 c_2 - c_1 a_2)(a_1 b_3 - b_1 a_3)}{a_1 b_2 - b_1 a_2}\right].$$

The product after some simplification becomes

$$A_1 B_2 C_3 = \frac{1}{a_1}[(a_1 c_3 - c_1 a_3)(a_1 b_2 - b_1 a_2)$$

$$- (a_1 c_2 - c_1 a_2)(a_1 b_3 - b_1 a_3)] \quad (62.19)$$

$$= a_1 b_2 c_3 + a_2 b_3 c_1 + a_3 b_1 c_2 - a_3 b_2 c_1$$

$$- a_2 b_1 c_3 - a_1 b_3 c_2,$$

which is the value of the determinant of the coefficients. This can easily be proved for the general case so that we may state: *the value of a determinant is equal to the product of the elements of the main diagonal of the derived matrix.*

Example 6.9. Find the value of the determinant

$$D = \begin{vmatrix} 1 & 3 & 2 \\ -1 & 4 & 5 \\ 2 & 1 & 6 \end{vmatrix}.$$

SOLUTION. The derived matrix is

$$\begin{pmatrix} 1 & 3 & 2 \\ -1 & 7 & 1 \\ 2 & -5 & 7 \end{pmatrix}.$$

The value of the determinant is

$$D = (1)\,(7)\,(7) = \boxed{49}.$$

It is advantageous to obtain the value of the determinant when solving a system of linear equations. It may be conveniently entered in the computational scheme at the end of the diagonal line through the elements of the main diagonal of the derived matrix.

E.   Cofactors and Matrix Inversion

It is frequently desirable to evaluate the cofactors of the elements of a determinant, and this may be done by following Crout's method. At the same time we can obtain the transpose of the inverse matrix of the given set of equations. Consider again the set of equations in three unknowns (62.1) and recall that the cofactor of any element a_{ij}, of a determinant is the minor of that element multiplied by $(-1)^{i+j}$. In the determinant in (62.1) the cofactors of a_1, b_1, and c_1 are

$$\begin{vmatrix} b_2 & c_2 \\ b_3 & c_3 \end{vmatrix}, \quad (-)\begin{vmatrix} a_2 & c_2 \\ a_3 & c_3 \end{vmatrix}, \quad \text{and} \quad \begin{vmatrix} a_2 & b_2 \\ a_3 & b_3 \end{vmatrix},$$

respectively. Now consider the system

$$a_1 x_1 + b_1 y_1 + c_1 z_1 = 1,$$
$$a_2 x_1 + b_2 y_1 + c_2 z_1 = 0, \qquad\qquad (62.20)$$
$$a_3 x_1 + b_3 y_1 + c_3 z_1 = 0.$$

The solution for x is given by

$$x_1 = \frac{1}{D}\begin{vmatrix} b_2 & c_2 \\ b_3 & c_3 \end{vmatrix} = \frac{1}{D}(\text{cofactor of } a_1).$$

Thus

$$\text{cofactor of } a_1 = Dx_1.$$

Similarly,

$$\text{cofactor of } b_1 = Dy_1,$$

$$\text{cofactor of } c_1 = Dz_1.$$

If we replaced the constants of the system by 0, 1, 0, we would obtain a new set of equations in x, y, z for which the left-hand side is identical to that of (62.1), and if we let the solution of this system be x_2, y_2, z_2 we would have

$$\text{cofactor of } a_2 = Dx_2,$$

$$\text{cofactor of } b_2 = Dy_2,$$

$$\text{cofactor of } c_2 = Dz_2.$$

The final step is to form the system with constant terms 0, 0, 1 and to arrive at solutions x_3, y_3, z_3, from which

$$\text{cofactor of } a_3 = Dx_3,$$

$$\text{cofactor of } b_3 = Dy_3,$$

$$\text{cofactor of } c_3 = Dz_3.$$

The entire process may be combined into one operation. First augment the matrix of the coefficients by the unit matrix (I)

$$\begin{pmatrix} a_1 & b_1 & c_1 & 1 & 0 & 0 \\ a_2 & b_2 & c_2 & 0 & 1 & 0 \\ a_3 & b_3 & c_3 & 0 & 0 & 1 \end{pmatrix}. \tag{62.21}$$

Calculate the derived matrix

$$\begin{pmatrix} A_1 & B_1 & C_1 & D_1 & 0 & 0 \\ A_2 & B_2 & C_2 & D_2 & E_2 & 0 \\ A_3 & B_3 & C_3 & D_3 & E_3 & F_3 \end{pmatrix}. \tag{62.22}$$

Now solve for $x_i, y_i, z_i (i = 1, 2, 3)$ by using the constants $D_i, E_i, F_i (i = 1, 2, 3)$ in turn. We obtain

$$\begin{pmatrix} x_1 & y_1 & z_1 \\ x_2 & y_2 & z_2 \\ x_3 & y_3 & z_3 \end{pmatrix}. \tag{62.23}$$

The elements of this matrix are the cofactors of the elements of the determinant of the system divided by this determinant, D. Thus, to find the cofactors, simply multiply each element of (62.23) by D. The matrix (62.23) is the *transpose* of the *inverse* matrix of the original system; consequently, the inverse matrix is given by

$$\begin{pmatrix} x_1 & x_2 & x_3 \\ y_1 & y_2 & y_3 \\ z_1 & z_2 & z_3 \end{pmatrix}.$$

Example 6.10. Solve the following system of equations. Evaluate the determinant of the system and obtain the value of the cofactors of each element of the determinant of the coefficients.

SOLUTION.

x	y	z	k	CHECK		(I)	
1.36	2.54	−1.62	1.97	4.25	1	0	0
−1.82	3.65	1.81	2.42	6.06	0	1	0
2.38	−1.42	3.24	1.11	5.31	0	0	1
1.36	1.868	−1.191	1.449	3.125	.735	0	0
−1.82	7.050	−.051	.717	1.666	.190	.142	0
2.38	−5.866	5.775	.323	1.324	−.110	.144	.173

$$D = 55.37$$

.464	.733	.323	SOLUTION	
1.463	1.734	1.324	CHECK	

TRANSPOSE OF INVERSE			COFACTORS		
.260	.184	−.110	14.40	10.19	−6.09
−.107	.149	.144	−5.92	8.25	7.97
.189	.009	.173	10.46	.498	9.58

F. Systems with Complex Coefficients

If the coefficients of the system are complex numbers, the solutions will be complex numbers. The method of solution is the same, except that some scheme must be devised for recording the real and imaginary part at each step. Since the product of two complex numbers

$$(a + bi)(c + di) = (ac - bd) + (ad + bc)i \qquad (62.24)$$

is the sum of products of real numbers, it is conceivable that a scheme for desk machines is feasible. In Crout's method the elements of the derived matrix which lie on or below the principal diagonal can be obtained by two machine operations, one for the real part and one for the imaginary part. The elements that lie to the right of the principal diagonal give more trouble because they require a division after the sum of products has been obtained. The division by a complex number may be carried out by a multiplication.

$$\frac{1}{A} = \frac{a}{a^2 + b^2} - \frac{b}{a^2 + b^2} i, \qquad (62.25)$$

where

$$A = a + bi.$$

The method may therefore be carried out by writing the complex number in two-element form in the matrix and augmenting the derived matrix. Let us consider the system

$$\begin{matrix} x & y & z & k \\ \begin{pmatrix} a_{11} + b_{11}i & a_{12} + b_{12}i & a_{13} + b_{13}i & a_{14} + b_{14}i \\ a_{21} + b_{21}i & a_{22} + b_{22}i & a_{23} + b_{23}i & a_{24} + b_{24}i \\ a_{31} + b_{31}i & a_{32} + b_{32}i & a_{33} + b_{33}i & a_{34} + b_{34}i \end{pmatrix} \end{matrix}. \qquad (62.26)$$

When numbers are involved, this system is conveniently written on two lines for each element instead of two columns. (See example.)

The derived matrix is

$$\begin{pmatrix} A_{11} + B_{11}i & A_{12} + B_{12}i & A_{13} + B_{13}i & A_{14} + B_{14}i \\ A_{21} + B_{21}i & A_{22} + B_{22}i & A_{23} + B_{23}i & A_{24} + B_{24}i \\ A_{31} + B_{31}i & A_{32} + B_{32}i & A_{33} + B_{33}i & A_{34} + B_{34}i \end{pmatrix}, \qquad (62.27)$$

where the elements are obtained in the regular manner. However, to accomplish this step it is necessary to record additional data. Following Crout, we supplement the derived matrix both on the left and right. In the left supplementary matrix we form the sum of the squares of the real numbers and the reciprocals of each element of the principal diagonal. Thus

$$\begin{Vmatrix} A_{ii}^2 + B_{ii}^2 & \dfrac{1}{A_{ii} + B_{ii}i} \\[2ex] A_{11}^2 + B_{11}^2 & \dfrac{A_{11}}{LS_{11}} - \dfrac{B_{11}}{LS_{11}}i \\[2ex] A_{22}^2 + B_{22}^2 & \dfrac{A_{22}}{LS_{21}} - \dfrac{B_{22}}{LS_{21}}i \\[2ex] A_{33}^2 + B_{33}^2 & \dfrac{A_{33}}{LS_{31}} - \dfrac{B_{33}}{LS_{31}}i \end{Vmatrix} \tag{62.28}$$

where LS_{ij} are the elements of the left supplementary matrix.

In the right supplementary matrix are recorded the sums of the products which form the numerators of the elements to the right of the principal diagonal before each is divided by the corresponding diagonal elements. Thus in the example

$$\begin{vmatrix} RS_{23} & RS_{24} \\ & RS_{34} \end{vmatrix} \tag{62.29}$$

we have

$$
\begin{aligned}
RS_{23} &= (a_{23} + b_{23}i) - (A_{21} + B_{21}i)(A_{13} + B_{13}i) \\
&= (a_{23} - A_{21}A_{13} + B_{21}B_{13}) + (b_{23} - B_{21}A_{13} - A_{21}B_{13})i, \\
RS_{24} &= (a_{24} + b_{24}i) - (A_{21} + B_{21}i)(A_{14} + B_{14}i) \\
&= (a_{24} - A_{21}A_{14} + B_{21}B_{14}) + (b_{24} - B_{21}A_{14} - A_{21}B_{14})i, \\
RS_{34} &= (a_{34} + b_{34}i) - (A_{31} + B_{31}i)(A_{14} + B_{14}i) \\
&\qquad\qquad\qquad + (A_{32} + B_{32}i)(A_{24} + B_{34}i) \\
&= a_{34} - A_{31}A_{14} + B_{31}B_{14} - A_{32}A_{24} + B_{32}B_{34} \\
&\qquad + (b_{34} - B_{31}A_{14} - A_{31}B_{14} - B_{32}A_{24} - A_{32}B_{34})i.
\end{aligned}
\tag{62.30}
$$

Example 6.11*

		x_1	x_2	x_3	x_4	k	CHECK				
		8.342	−9.012	3.345	−4.518	65.65	63.807				
		7.130	1.132	−1.248	−3.362	−1.810	1.842				
		9.123	4.567	−2.222	8.041	−87.30	−67.791				
		1.071	5.432	7.444	−2.111	6.500	18.336				
		3.789	−2.421	7.342	3.467	−34.25	−22.073				
		−1.242	7.321	−2.181	−7.182	−35.45	−38.734				
		−4.142	8.042	3.732	−2.111	−42.63	−37.109				
		−3.181	−2.131	−7.801	−2.932	14.50	−1.545				
$A^2 + B^2$	$\frac{1}{A + Bi}$	DERIVED MATRIX						RS			
120.43	.069268	8.342	−.55722	.15781	−.5120	4.4403	4.5288				
	−.059204	7.130	.61196	−.28448	.03460	−4.0121	−3.6500				
106.41	.096851	9.123	10.306	−.34279	1.2269	−12.6339	−10.7497	−3.9664	12.749	−132.106	−113.016
	−.004190	1.071	.44587	.97257	−.23533	4.2675	5.0047	9.8703	−1.8783	38.347	46.7846
121.90	.089603	3.789	−1.0697	10.9227	.32911	−3.10756	−1.77845		5.6621	−41.2120	−24.6270
	−.013213	−1.242	4.3102	1.6107	−1.28346	4.51272	3.22921		−13.4889	44.2863	32.4075
115.84	.050184	−4.142	3.78735	5.2576	5.81342	7.1094	−6.1094			−10.12549	−4.3122
	−.078192	−3.181	−1.3688	−12.6300	9.05788	−3.4450	−3.4450			−84.42388	−75.3656
		−.5507	−5.2309	3.6537	−7.1094						
		−.4159	2.0754	−3.4781	−3.4450	SOLUTION					

*The second number in each group is the imaginary part. Thus $x_1 = -.5507 + .4159i$

63.   INHERENT ERRORS IN SYSTEMS OF LINEAR EQUATIONS

The computational methods for solving systems of linear equations can be checked for their accuracy, and errors in computation can be evaluated and corrected. Systems involving approximate numbers may have errors due to the nature of the equations, and these inherent errors may be serious. However, it is possible to find expressions that will permit us to study these errors. Following the procedure of Section 4 (Chapter 1), we obtain expressions for the errors in the variables due to errors in the coefficients and constant terms. Consider the simple system of two equations in two unknowns:

$$a_1 x + b_1 y = c_1$$
$$a_2 x + b_2 y = c_2. \tag{63.1}$$

Let the known errors in a_i, b_i, c_i be $\Delta a_i, \Delta b_i, \Delta c_i (i = 1, 2)$. Then by taking the differentials of the equations of the given system we can write to a *first-order* approximation

$$a_1 \Delta x + b_1 \Delta y = \Delta c_1 - x \Delta a_1 - y \Delta b_1,$$
$$a_2 \Delta x + b_2 \Delta y = \Delta c_2 - x \Delta a_2 - y \Delta b_2, \tag{63.2}$$

which gives us a system of linear equations for the inherent errors in the solution, Δx and Δy. Since the right-hand side of this system is known if we know the errors of the coefficients, we may solve for Δx and Δy.

In practice, however, the actual errors of a_i, b_i, and c_i are not known precisely. What we do know is that they do not exceed a known magnitude. Thus we proceed not to find the actual inherent error but the bound for the largest values of the errors; that is, the right-hand members of (63.2) do not exceed a known constant. This constant is the sum of the absolute values of these terms; thus

$$k_1 = |\Delta c_1| + |x \Delta a_1| + |y \Delta b_1|,$$
$$k_2 = |\Delta c_2| + |x \Delta a_2| + |y \Delta b_2|, \tag{63.3}$$

and we solve for the upper bounds of Δx and Δy by any known method in terms of k_i. If the numbers in the original system are all given to the same degree of accuracy, then the errors on each of them are equal and $k_1 = k_2$.

For example, if a_i, b_i, c_i are given to two decimal places, then

$$|\Delta a_i| \le .005, \qquad |\Delta b_i| \le .005, \qquad |\Delta c_i| \le .005.$$

Let the upper bound of these errors be denoted by ϵ. The upper bound of the right-hand side of (63.2) is given by

$$k_1 = k_2 = (1 + |x| + |y|)\epsilon. \tag{63.4}$$

The solution for Δx and Δy in (63.2) can now be easily accomplished. We note first that the determinant of the system is exactly the same as that of the original equations, so that in applying Crout's method we need only attach a column of constant terms. If all the k_i are equal, we shall replace them by 1 and multiply the results by k. The solutions obtained before multiplying by k is in a sense a measure of sensitivity. Furthermore, since we are seeking the upper bound and the errors may be either positive or negative, we shall always assume the worst case and *always add* regardless of sign. Let us illustrate with an example.

Example 6.12. Find the inherent errors in Example 6.10.

SOLUTION. Augment the given matrix by a column whose elements are all unity. Calculate the corresponding elements in the derived matrix, always adding regardless of sign. Now using these elements calculate the one-row solution matrix, again always adding. Thus

			DERIVED MATRIX
			.735
			.332
			.813
2.400	.373	.813	SOLUTION MATRIX

Now $\epsilon = .005$ and

$$k = (1 + |x| + |y| + |z|) = 2.520(.005) = .0126.$$

By multiplying the solutions by k we obtain

$$\Delta x = .030, \quad \Delta y = .005, \quad \Delta z = .010.$$

This example illustrates the effect of inherent errors. The errors computed are, of course, the upper bounds, and the actual errors should be less. Nevertheless, if the errors all combine to approach the upper bound, the solutions are not so accurate as the given data.

Whether it is realistic to check the solutions by an upper bound on the errors is often questioned. As a compromise, it seems reasonable to compute k, using the sum of the absolute values, but in the computation of the sensitivity factors to *take into account the algebraic signs* and solve in the usual manner. For the foregoing example we have

x	y	z	DERIVED MATRIX
			.7353
			.3317
			.2071
.3425	.3423	.2071	SENSITIVITY
.0043	.0043	.0026	Δ

Between the two extremes discussed there is another method for estimating the inherent errors. This method uses the inverse matrix to obtain the solutions to a system of linear equations. We recall from algebra that a system of linear equations can be written in matrix notation,

$$AX = C,$$

where A is the matrix of the coefficients, X is the matrix of the unknowns, and C is the matrix of the constant terms. The solution is given in the form

$$X = A^{-1}C,$$

where A^{-1} is the inverse of A. By letting the right-hand sides of the system in (63.2) be denoted by δ_1 and δ_2, we can then write the solutions in the form

$$\Delta x = \alpha_1 \delta_1 + \beta_1 \delta_2,$$
$$\Delta y = \alpha_2 \delta_1 + \beta_2 \delta_2,$$

where α_i and $\beta_i (i = 1, 2)$ are the elements of A^{-1}. We can now estimate the bounds by

$$|\Delta x| \leq |\alpha_1|k_1 + |\beta_1|k_2,$$
$$|\Delta y| \leq |\alpha_2|k_1 + |\beta_2|k_2,$$

where the errors have been ignored in calculating α_i and β_i but the bounds are determined by taking the sum of the absolute values and replacing δ_i by k_i. The elements of the inverse matrix can be computed from the transpose of the inverse in the manner described in Section 62E. In Example 6.10 the inverse matrix is

$$A^{-1} = \begin{pmatrix} .260 & -.107 & .189 \\ .184 & .149 & .009 \\ -.110 & .144 & .173 \end{pmatrix}$$

and

$$|\Delta x| \leq |\alpha_1|k_1 + |\beta_1|k_2 + |\gamma_1|k_3 = (.260 + .107 + .189)(.0126) \doteq .0070,$$

$$|\Delta y| \leq (.184 + .149 + .009)(.0126) \doteq .0043,$$

$$|\Delta z| \leq (.110 + .144 + .173)(.0126) \doteq .0054.$$

In general, no technique will improve on the inherent errors, but some measures of safety may be taken. The greatest source of inherent errors arises from the loss of leading significant figures by subtraction. Thus in Example 6.10 we see that C_2 (in the derived matrix) is $-.051$, which has fewer significant figures than the given data.[4] This must be guarded against by carrying the calculations to more figures than the data. In other words, *do not round off until the very end.*

The most troublesome thing in solving systems of linear equations occurs when the determinant of the system D is near zero, not exactly zero, mind you, but close to it to the degree of accuracy of the approximate numbers being used. The solutions are then very sensitive, and some absurd results may occur. Usable answers may still be attainable, however. In using Crout's method, there will be an indication of this situation, as one of the elements along the main diagonal of the derived matrix, A_{ii}, will become small. It would be best if this did not occur at an early stage in the computation, but if it does it can sometimes be corrected by reordering the equations. In fact, in applying Crout's method, particular attention should be paid to the elements of the main diagonal of the derived matrix A_{ii}. They should be allowed to become neither extremely large nor small. If it happens, rearrange the equations. Should D be near zero, the ideal situation would be to have the smallest element of the A_{ii} occur at A_{nn}, that is, the last one. This would prevent the numbers from getting "out of hand." We illustrate with an example.

[4] For this reason Example 6.10 is actually done incorrectly, the mistake being intentional.

Example 6.13.

x	y	z	k	CHECK
.91143	.90274	.89318	.62433	3.33168
.36518	.36161	.34622	.24561	1.31862
.24375	.22100	.65521	.35000	1.46996
.91143	.990466	.979977	.685000	3.655443
.36158	−.000088	132.363646	51.571590	184.939485
.24375	−.020426	3.720000	.396292	1.396320

$$-.000250$$

| 1.171288 | −.883064 | .396292 | SOLUTIONS |
| 2.170723 | .117479 | 1.396320 | CHECK |

We note that the value of $D = -.000250$ is small and that the sensitivities are large. Equally important, we see that $A_{22} = -.000088$ is nearly zero, and as a result other numbers become large and the computational checks fall off. Let us reorder the equations and at the same time compute a set of reasonable inherent errors. Note that the reordering changes the algebraic sign of D but not its absolute value. This is consistent with the theory of determinants.

y	z	x	k	CHECK	I.E.
.22100	.65521	.24375	.35000	1.46996	1
.36161	.34622	.36518	.24561	1.31862	1
.90274	.89318	.91143	.62433	3.33168	1
.221000	2.964751	1.102941	1.583710	6.651403	4.524887
.361610	−.725864	.046364	.450601	1.496966	.876533
.902740	−1.783219	−.001562	1.170359	2.169865	974.229315

$$.000250$$

| −.882170 | .396338 | 1.170359 | SOLUTIONS |
| .118304 | 1.396362 | 2.169865 | CHECK |

$$k = .000017$$

| −894.382 | −44.293 | 974.229 | SENSITIVITY |
| .0152 | .00075 | .0166 | Δ |

64.   OTHER METHODS FOR SYSTEMS OF LINEAR EQUATIONS

Extensive use of large-scale calculating machines has greatly increased the number of methods of solving systems of linear equations. Many
of the new methods are special adaptations of classical methods to particular
calculating machines, depending primarily on the machines' storage capacity
and the effect of round-off errors. An entire book might be written on these
methods. In fact some of the recent books on numerical analysis are largely
devoted to this particular subject. It is not our intention to specialize to such
an extent.

The literature on this subject is extensive, and if the reader wishes to in-
vestigate other methods we recommend the following sources of information:
L. J. Paige and Olga Taussky, eds., "Simultaneous Linear Equations and the
Determination of Eigenvalues," *National Bureau of Standards Applied
Mathematics Series,* **29,** 1953; Olga Taussky, ed., "Contributions to the
Solution of Systems of Linear Equations and the Determination of Eigen-
values," *National Bureau of Standards Applied Mathematical Series,* **39,**
1954; and John Todd, ed., *Survey of Numerical Analysis,* McGraw-Hill, 1962,
Chapter 6 and the bibliography at the end of Chapter 6.

65.   EXERCISE **VIII**

1. Find the smallest positive root of $x^4 - x^3 - 1 = 0$.
2. Find the positive roots of $49x^4 + 84x^3 + 22x^2 - 12x + 1 = 0$.
3. Find a real root of $2x - \cos x - 3 = 0$.
4. Solve for x: $e^x - x^2 = 3$.
5. Solve for x: $\ln x = \sin x$.
6. Solve for x: $3x^2 - 4^x = 5$.
7. Find a root of $x \log_{10} x = -0.15$.
8. Find the smallest positive root of

$$1 - x + \frac{x^2}{2} - \frac{x^3}{3} + \frac{x^4}{4} - \frac{x^5}{5} = 0.$$

9. Investigate the existence of a small positive real root of

$$x^4 - 1.47x^3 + .056x^2 - .944x + 1.528 = 0.$$

10. Find the positive roots of

$$x^3 + 9.531x^2 - 4.6355x + .5449 = 0.$$

11. Find the real root of $x^3 - 17 = 0$ by Newton's method.
12. Find the real root of $x^5 - 17 = 0$ by Newton's method.

13. Apply Newton's formula to the function $f(x) = N - x^p$ and derive an expression for finding the pth root of a number. Apply the resulting formula to Problems 11 and 12.

14. Find $\sqrt{13}$ by Formulas 59.8 and 59.9.

15. Find the reciprocal of 118 by Formula 59.10.

16. Solve the following system of linear equations:

$$.534x - .329y = .720$$
$$.128x + .832y = .314.$$

17. Solve the system $AX = C$ if

$$A = \begin{pmatrix} .139 & .469 & .235 \\ .218 & .327 & .445 \\ .175 & .542 & .655 \end{pmatrix}, \quad C = \begin{pmatrix} .422 \\ .738 \\ .292 \end{pmatrix}$$

(a) by Crout's method;

(b) by computing the inverse A^{-1} and $X = A^{-1}C$.

18. Solve the following system of linear equations:

$$1.932x + 3.864y + 2.898z + 7.728w = 1.462,$$
$$.349x + .700y + 2.439z + 2.000w = 3.832,$$
$$1.682x + 2.264y + 1.463z + .468w = 4.291,$$
$$1.244x + 1.866y + 2.488z + 3.732w = 2.943.$$

19. Solve the following system of linear equations:

$$(2.3 + .5i)x + (1.9 - .2i)y + (.75 + .32i)z = 1.2 + .3i,$$
$$(1.9 - .2i)x + (1.45 + .25i)y + (1.12 - .18i)z = 2.3 + .4i,$$
$$(.75 + .32i)x + (1.12 - .18i)y + (2.38 - .62i)z = 1.25 - .2i.$$

20. Use Crout's method and matrix inversion to solve the following systems (do not use decimals):

(a)
$$x + y + 6z + 3w - v + 4u = 1,$$
$$5x + 3y - 2z + 5w - v + 2u = -3,$$
$$3x + 2y + 4z + 8w + 5v + u = 3,$$
$$x - y - 6z + 3w + 3v - 4u = 3,$$
$$6x + 3y + 2z + 7w + 6v - u = 4,$$
$$9x - 2y - 2z + 6w + 9v = -4.$$

(b)
$$x - y + 2z - u + v = 1,$$
$$x - 4y + 4z - u + v = 10,$$
$$3x - 4y + 6z - 3u + 2v = 7,$$
$$2x + 2y - 4z + u + v = -3,$$
$$2x - y + z - u + v = 2.$$

66.   SYSTEMS OF NONLINEAR EQUATIONS

The solutions of systems of simultaneous nonlinear equations is accomplished either by successive approximations or by the method of iteration. In either case the first approximations are usually obtained from a rough graph. We shall consider the method of successive approximations first; the best-known such method is the Newton-Raphson method.

A.   *The Newton-Raphson Method*

Let us consider the simple case of two equations in two unknowns,

$$f(x, y) = 0,$$
$$g(x, y) = 0,$$
(66.1)

and let (x_0, y_0) be the initial approximate values. The method seeks to obtain a correction, Δx and Δy, on x_0 and y_0, so that the corrected values will be

$$x = x_0 + \Delta x,$$
$$y = y_0 + \Delta y,$$
(66.2)

for which

$$f(x_0 + \Delta x, y_0 + \Delta y) = 0,$$
$$g(x_0 + \Delta x, y_0 + \Delta y) = 0.$$
(66.3)

We may expand (66.3) by Taylor's theorem for a function of two variables (see Formula 3.20, Chapter 1) to obtain

$$f(x + \Delta x, y + \Delta y) = f(x_0, y_0) + f_x(x_0, y_0)\,\Delta x$$
$$+ f_y(x_0, y_0)\,\Delta y + \cdots$$
$$= 0,$$

$$g(x + \Delta x, y + \Delta y) = g(x_0, y_0) + g_x(x_0, y_0)\,\Delta x$$
$$+ g_y(x_0, y_0)\,\Delta y + \cdots$$
$$= 0,$$
(66.4)

where f_x, f_y, g_x, g_y are the usual notations for the partial derivatives. If we ignore all terms of order higher than the first, we are left with a system of two linear equations in the two unknowns Δx and Δy,

$$f_x(x_0, y_0)\,\Delta x + f_y(x_0, y_0)\,\Delta y = -f(x_0, y_0),$$
$$(66.5)$$
$$g_x(x_0, y_0)\,\Delta x + g_y(x_0, y_0)\,\Delta y = -g(x_0, y_0),$$

from which we solve to obtain the corrections. The process may now be repeated by using

$$x_1 = x_0 + \Delta x,$$
$$(66.6)$$
$$y_1 = y_0 + \Delta y,$$

and evaluating the functions and their partial derivatives at (x_1, y_1). The repetition is carried to the desired degree of accuracy.

The computational form is fairly simple.

$f(x, y) = \underline{\quad}$	$f_x(x, y) = \underline{\quad}$	$f_y(x, y) = \underline{\quad}$
$g(x, y) = \underline{\quad}$	$g_x(x, y) = \underline{\quad}$	$g_y(x, y) = \underline{\quad}$

f	f_x	f_y
g	g_x	g_y
D	$(-)\Delta x$	Δy
	x	y

The entries are obtained by cross multiplication, as in Section 61.

Example 6.14. Find the root in the neighborhood of $(3.8, -1.8)$ to satisfy the system

$$x^2 + y - 11 = 0$$

$$y^2 + x - 7 = 0.$$

SOLUTION.

$$f(x, y) = x^2 + y - 11 \qquad f_x = 2x \qquad f_y = 1$$
$$g(x, y) = y^2 + x - 7 \qquad g_x = 1 \qquad g_y = 2y$$

$$x = 3.8 \qquad y = -1.8$$

1.64	7.6	1
.04	1	−3.6
−28.36	−.2096	−.0471
SOLUTION	3.5904	−1.8471
.043872	7.180800	1
.002178	1	−3.694200
−27.527311	−.005966	−.001025
SOLUTION	3.584434	−1.848125
.000042	7.168868	1
0	1	−3.696250
−27.497928	−.000006	−.000002
SOLUTION	3.584428	−1.848127

The extension of this method to more than two equations is straightforward. As the number of equations increases, it becomes more cumbersome to solve the resulting system of linear equations for the corrections on the variables. Some time can be saved by noting that the values of the partial derivatives do not change much. Thus we can leave the determinant of the coefficients unchanged and simply solve for changing constant terms. This is especially easily when done by Crout's method. Let us illustrate with an example of three equations in three unknowns:

$$f(x, y, z) = 0; \qquad g(x, y, z) = 0; \qquad h(x, y, z) = 0.$$

The correction equations are

$$f_x \Delta x + f_y \Delta y + f_z \Delta z = -f,$$
$$g_x \Delta x + g_y \Delta y + g_z \Delta z = -g, \qquad (66.7)$$
$$h_x \Delta x + h_y \Delta y + h_z \Delta z = -h,$$

where the partial derivatives and the functions are evaluated at the approximate point (x_i, y_i, z_i).

Example 6.15. Find a solution to the system

$$x^2 + y^2 + z^2 - 1 = 0 \quad = f(x, y, z),$$
$$2x^2 + y^2 - 4z \quad\quad = 0 \quad = g(x, y, z),$$
$$3x^2 - 4y + z^2 \quad\quad = 0 \quad = h(x, y, z).$$

SOLUTION. The partial derivatives are

$$f_x = 2x \quad\quad f_y = 2y \quad\quad f_z = 2z$$
$$g_x = 4x \quad\quad g_y = 2y \quad\quad g_z = -4$$
$$h_x = 6x \quad\quad h_y = -4 \quad\quad h_z = 2z.$$

Assume $x_0 = y_0 = z_0$.

Δx	Δy	Δz	k
.5	.5	.5	
1	1	1	.25
2	1	−4	1.25
3	−4	1	1
1	1	1	.25
2	−1	6	−.75
3	−7	40	−.125
.375	0	−.125	Δ
.875	.5	.375	$u + \Delta$

Δx	Δy	Δz	k_2	k_3	k_4	k_5
1.75	1	.75	−.156250	−.007744	−.000770	−.000078
3.50	1	−4.00	−.281250	−.015425	−.001538	−.000156
5.25	−4	.75	−.437500	−.023170	−.002311	−.000249
1.75	.571429	.428572	−.089286	−.004425	−.000440	−.000045
3.50	−1	5.5	−.031251	−.000062	−.000002	−.0000015
5.25	−7	37.0	−.005067	−.000010	0	−.0000006
−.084896	−.00382	−.005067	Δ			
.790104	.496618	.369933	$u + \Delta$			
−.004417	−.000007	−.000010	Δ			
.785687	.496611	.369923	$u + \Delta$			
−.000439	−.000002	0	Δ			
.785248	.496609	.369923	$u + \Delta$			
−.000046	.0000018	−.0000006	Δ			
.785202	.496611	.369922	$u + \Delta$			
x	y	z				

In this example the initial values are merely guessed. Some writers prefer always to guess $x_0 = y_0 = z_0 = 0$. However, this author has found it more advantageous to give some value other than zero. After the second correction has been made it is assumed that the determinant of the coefficients will not change much, and even though slightly incorrect it is used for the calculations of the subsequent corrections. These corrections are easily found by Crout's method by simply computing a new column of constant terms for each "go around" and then solving for $\Delta x, \Delta y$, and Δz. Should the convergence be slow or the solutions "jump around," a new determinant of the coefficients should be calculated.

B.   The Exceptional Cases

The foregoing method fails if the determinant D vanishes at or near a solution to the original system. However, this gives additional information about the problem, as the vanishing of D indicates

(a) multiple solutions [$f(x, y) = 0$ and $g(x, y) = 0$ are tangent to each other],

(b) two or more solutions close together, or

(c) no solution in this neighborhood.

Let us again consider the simple system of two equations in two unknowns, so that for this special case we have

$$D(x_i, y_i) = f_x(x_i, y_i) g_y(x_i, y_i) - f_y(x_i, y_i) g_x(x_i, y_i) = 0. \qquad (66.8)$$

Now the locus of points satisfying $D(x, y) = 0$ is the curve on which the loci of $f(x, y) = k_1$ and $g(x, y) = k_2$ have either common tangents or singular points. The procedure is to solve either of the two systems,

$$\begin{matrix} D(x, y) = 0 \\ f(x, y) = 0 \end{matrix} \quad \text{or} \quad \begin{matrix} D(x, y) = 0 \\ g(x, y) = 0, \end{matrix} \qquad (66.9)$$

which can be done provided one of the determinants

$$\begin{vmatrix} D_x & D_y \\ f_x & f_y \end{vmatrix} \quad \text{or} \quad \begin{vmatrix} D_x & D_y \\ g_x & g_y \end{vmatrix}$$

does not vanish in the neighborhood of the point we are considering. Suppose that we solve the first of these two systems and find that the solution is $x = a$ and $y = b$. We now calculate $g(a, b)$, and if the answer is zero the curves are tangent at (a, b); this point is said to be a double solution. If $g(a, b) \neq 0$, there is either no solution or two solutions close together in the neighborhood of (a, b). Usually the case can be decided by graphing the two functions $f(x, y) = 0$ and $g(x, y) = 0$ and determining from the graph whether the two functions intersect. Let us assume that they do. Then we may expand the two functions in Taylor series about the point (a, b) and take into account second-order terms. We obtain

$$f(a, b) + f_x \, \Delta x + f_y \, \Delta x + \tfrac{1}{2} f_{xx} \, \Delta x^2 + f_{xy} \, \Delta x \, \Delta y + \tfrac{1}{2} f_{yy} \, \Delta y^2 = 0,$$

$$g(a, b) + g_x \, \Delta x + g_y \, \Delta y + \tfrac{1}{2} g_{xx} \, \Delta x^2 + g_{xy} \, \Delta x \, \Delta y + \tfrac{1}{2} g_{yy} \, \Delta y^2 = 0,$$
(66.10)

where

$$\Delta x = x - a, \qquad \Delta y = y - b$$

and all the partial derivatives are evaluated at (a, b). We have then a system of simultaneous quadratic equations which we shall simplify somewhat. First, we have $f(a, b) = 0$, and since

$$D = f_x g_y - f_y g_x = 0 \tag{66.11}$$

we have

$$f_x g_y = f_y g_x \quad \text{or} \quad \frac{g_y}{f_y} = \frac{g_x}{f_x} = k, \tag{66.12}$$

so that

$$g_x = k f_x \quad \text{and} \quad g_y = k f_y. \tag{66.13}$$

Thus, if we multiply the first equation of (66.10) by k and subtract from the second, the linear terms are eliminated and we obtain

$$g + \tfrac{1}{2}(g_{xx} - k f_{xx}) \, \Delta x^2 + (g_{xy} - k f_{xy}) \, \Delta x \, \Delta y + \tfrac{1}{2}(g_{yy} - k f_{yy}) \, \Delta y^2$$

$$= g + A \, \Delta x^2 + B \, \Delta x \, \Delta y + C \, \Delta y^2 = 0. \tag{66.14}$$

We now divide the first equation in (66.10) by f_x or f_y, whichever is the larger (let us suppose it is f_y) to obtain

$$\frac{f_x}{f_y} \Delta x + \Delta y + \frac{1}{2 f_y} [f_{xx} \, \Delta x^2 + 2 f_{xy} \, \Delta x \, \Delta y + f_{yy} \, \Delta y^2] = 0.$$

Divide this equation once more, this time by Δx, and solve for $\Delta y / \Delta x = m$ to obtain

$$\frac{\Delta y}{\Delta x} = m = -\frac{1}{f_y} \left[f_x + \frac{\Delta x}{2} (f_{xx} + 2 f_{xy} m + f_{yy} m^2) \right]. \tag{66.15}$$

Consider (66.14) and write it as

$$g + \Delta x^2 \left[A + B\frac{\Delta y}{\Delta x} + C\left(\frac{\Delta y}{\Delta x}\right)^2 \right] = 0;$$

solve for Δx:

$$\Delta x = \pm \left(\frac{-g}{A + Bm + Cm^2}\right)^{1/2}. \qquad (66.16)$$

The system in (66.15) and (66.16) may now be solved by the method of iteration. Let $m_0 = -f_x/f_y$. Using this value of m, solve for Δx by (66.16), and using
m_0 and the new Δx obtain a new m by (66.15). Eventually we will have values
for Δx and m from which we can get approximations to the two solutions
(x_1, y_1) and (x_2, y_2) by

$$\Delta y = m\,\Delta x,$$

$$x = a \pm \Delta x,$$

$$y = b \pm \Delta y.$$

For these values of x and y D will not be zero; they may be improved by the
usual method of successive approximations.

Example 6.16. Investigate the following system for possible solution in the first
quadrant.

$$x^2 + 12y^2 - 1 = 0.$$

$$49x^2 + 49y^2 + 84x + 2324y - 681 = 0.$$

SOLUTION. Since the first equation is an ellipse lying inside the rectangle
$(\pm 1, \pm\frac{1}{2})$, we assume small values for x_0, y_0, say $(.1, .1)$.

$$f_x = 2x, \qquad\qquad f_y = 24y,$$

$$g_x = 98x + 84. \qquad g_y = 98y + 2324.$$

The first step of the solution is

	$x = .1$	$y = .1$
$-.87$	$.2$	2.4
-439.22	93.8	2333.8
241.64	4.040	

Although $D = 241.64$ is not zero for these values of x and y, it is much too small, for the correction on x, $\Delta x = 4.04$, places it outside the x interval for the ellipse. Let us therefore consider the system

$$f(x,y) = x^2 - 12y^2 - 1 = 0,$$
$$D(x,y) = 28(166x - 77xy - 72y) = 0$$

with $D_x = 166 - 77y$ and $D_y = -(77x + 72)$ after dividing out the coefficient 28.

	$x = .1$	$y = .1$	
−.87	.2	−2.4	
8.63	158.3	−79.7	
−395.860	.123	.352	
	.223	.452	
1.501377	.446	10.848	
−3.287292	131.196	−89.171	
−1462.984	−.067135	−.135641	
	.155865	.316359	
.225290	.311730	7.592616	
−.701051	141.640357	−84.001605	
−1101.607	−.012347	−.029165	
.010357	.143518	.287194	(x, y)
−.027766	−.000598	−.001339	$(\Delta x, \Delta y)$
.000982	.142920	.285855	(x, y)
−.002598	−.000056	−.000126	$(\Delta x, \Delta y)$
.000103	.142864	.285729	(x, y)
−.000204	−.000006	−.000013	$(\Delta x, \Delta y)$
	.142858	.285716	(x, y)

After the third step the values of the partial derivatives and the determinant are held constant and only new values of $f(x,y)$ and $D(x,y)$ are computed. These values are put in the extreme left-hand column, and corrections and new values for x and y follow. The value of $g(x,y)$ is now calculated for the last values of x and y to give

$$g(.142858, .285716) = .004114,$$

which is a small number but not quite equal to zero in our degree of accuracy.

The values of x and y are now found more accurately, and, by continuing the process, we obtain

$$x = .142857142, \qquad y = .285714285$$

and

$$g(x, y) = -.0000017.$$

Thus it is assumed that $g(x, y) = 0$ and the solution is a double root.

C.   The Method of Iteration

The second method of solving systems of simultaneous equations is the method of iteration. It may be applied in each case in which it is possible to solve explicitly for each of the variables in terms of functions of the variables. Suppose we have three equations in three unknowns:

$$f(x, y, z) = 0,$$
$$g(x, y, z) = 0, \qquad (66.17)$$
$$h(x, y, z) = 0.$$

If these equations can be solved to give

$$x = F_1(x, y, z),$$
$$y = F_2(x, y, z), \qquad (66.18)$$
$$z = F_3(x, y, z),$$

and the initial approximate values are x_0, y_0, z_0, then we proceed in the following manner:

first
approximation
$$\begin{cases} x_1 = F_1(x_0, y_0, z_0), \\ y_1 = F_2(x_1, y_0, z_0), \\ z_1 = F_3(x_1, y_1, z_0); \end{cases}$$

second
approximation
$$\begin{cases} x_2 = F_1(x_1, y_1, z_1), \\ y_2 = F_2(x_2, y_1, z_1), \\ z_2 = F_3(x_2, y_2, z_1); \\ \text{etc.} \end{cases}$$

The iteration is continued until the values for x, y, and z converge to the desired degree of accuracy. Note that *each new value of a variable is used as soon as it is found*. Thus x_1 is used in finding y_1, and both x_1 and y_1 are used in finding z_1, etc.

Example 6.17. Find the smallest positive root of

$$\sin x - y - .25 = 0.$$

$$\cos y - x + .25 = 0.$$

SOLUTION. Solve for y in the first and x in the second equation.

$$y = \sin x - .25.$$

$$x = \cos y + .25.$$

Let $x_0 = 1.00$, then

i	0	1	2	3	4	5	6	7
x	1.00	1.08	1.0568	1.0634	1.0615	1.0621	1.0617	1.0620
y	.59	.6320	.6208	.6240	.6231	.6234	.6233	.6233

Therefore

$$\boxed{x = 1.0620, \quad y = .6233}.$$

The most troublesome thing about the method of iteration is that the process may converge very slowly or not at all. It is necessary therefore to have a criterion for convergence, and in systems of equations this is given by

$$\left|\frac{\partial F_1}{\partial x}\right| + \left|\frac{\partial F_2}{\partial x}\right| + \left|\frac{\partial F_3}{\partial x}\right| < 1$$

$$\left|\frac{\partial F_1}{\partial y}\right| + \left|\frac{\partial F_2}{\partial y}\right| + \left|\frac{\partial F_3}{\partial y}\right| < 1$$

$$\left|\frac{\partial F_1}{\partial z}\right| + \left|\frac{\partial F_2}{\partial z}\right| + \left|\frac{\partial F_3}{\partial z}\right| < 1$$

in the neighborhood of (x_0, y_0, z_0). In fact, in order for the method to be practical this criterion must be satisfied; that is, the sums of the absolute value of the partials must be considerably less than 1.

Example 6.18. Consider Example 6.16 again and investigate the possibility of using the method of iteration.

SOLUTION. Solve for x and y:

$$x = \pm\sqrt{1 - 12y^2} \qquad\qquad = F_1(y),$$

$$y = \frac{1}{2324}(681 - 84x - 49y^2 - 49x^2) = F_2(x, y).$$

Now

$$\frac{\partial F_1}{\partial x} = 0, \quad \frac{\partial F_2}{\partial x} = \frac{1}{2324}(-84 - 98x),$$

$$\frac{\partial F_1}{\partial y} = \frac{1}{2}(1 - 12y^2)^{-1/2}(-24y),$$

$$\frac{\partial F_2}{\partial y} = \frac{1}{2324}(-98y),$$

and at (.14, .28)

$$|F_{1x}| + |F_{2x}| = .042,$$

$$|F_{1y}| + |F_{2y}| = 13.81 + .012 = 13.822.$$

Thus the method of iteration would not converge.

It is sometimes possible to speed the convergence by rearranging the functional expressions $F_i(x, y, z)$. However, slowly converging processes are frustrating to the computer, and the criterion should be checked whenever possible.

67.   COMPLEX ROOTS OF ALGEBRAIC EQUATIONS

The finding of complex roots of an algebraic equation is more difficult than that of finding the real roots. Consequently it is advisable to find all the real roots first and to reduce the degree of the equation by dividing out the real roots. In so doing, as many significant numbers as possible should be carried, since round-off errors are significant in this procedure. If it is possible to reduce the equation to a quadratic, the complex roots can then be found by the quadratic formula. When there is more than one pair of conjugate complex roots, we employ a numerical procedure that divides out a quadratic factor from the original equation. Many writers have discussed this method in recent years. It is usually credited to S. N. Lin, with a notable improvement by B. Friedman and Y. L. Luke. (See the bibliography.) We now develop the simple process.

Since the complex roots occur in conjugate pairs, $a + bi$ and $a - bi$, there exists a real quadratic factor.

$$(x - a - bi)(x - a + bi) = x^2 + px + q, \tag{67.1}$$

of the original function $f(x)$. The solution thus depends on the values of p and q, and if these can be determined we have

$$\begin{aligned} a &= -\tfrac{1}{2}p, \\ b &= \sqrt{q - a^2}. \end{aligned} \tag{67.2}$$

To obtain a procedure for the determination of p and q, suppose we divide the original function

$$f(x) = a_0 x^n + a_1 x^{n-1} + a_2 x^{n-2} + \cdots + a_{n-2} x^2 + a_{n-1} x + a_n \tag{67.3}$$

by the quadratic

$$x^2 + px + q$$

to arrive at the quotient

$$Q(x) = b_0 x^{n-2} + b_1 x^{n-3} + \cdots + b_{n-2} + b_{n-1} x^{-1} + b_n x^{-2} + R_3, \tag{67.4}$$

where

$$\begin{aligned} b_0 &= a_0, \\ b_1 &= a_1 - b_0 p, \\ b_2 &= a_2 - b_0 q - b_1 p, \\ &\vdots \\ b_i &= a_i - b_{i-2} q - b_{i-1} p, \qquad (i = 2, \ldots, n). \end{aligned} \tag{67.5}$$

Now, if $b_{n-1} = b_n = 0$, there would be no remainder and the quadratic term would be a factor of the original function. Thus it is desired that

$$\begin{aligned} b_{n-1} &= a_{n-1} - b_{n-3} q - b_{n-2} p = 0 = F(p, q), \\ b_n &= a_n - b_{n-2} q - b_{n-1} p = 0 = G(p, q). \end{aligned} \tag{67.6}$$

If we remember that the b_i are functions of p and q, it is easily seen that this is a system of two *nonlinear* equations in the two unknowns p and q. The exact expression for $F(p,q)$ and $G(p,q)$ can be obtained by continuous substitution of the $b_i (i = 0, \ldots, n - 2)$; this yields an equation $G(p,q) = 0$ of degree n and $F(p,q) = 0$ of degree $n - 1$. The system may be solved by either of the two methods discussed in Section 66.

The division of the original function by the quadratic factor could have stopped as soon as the linear term was reached, and this remainder could have been set equal to zero. The result would have been the following system of equations:

$$a_{n-1} - b_{n-3}q - b_{n-2}p = 0 = r_1(p,q),$$
$$a_n - b_{n-2}q = 0 = r_2(p,q). \tag{67.7}$$

This system is especially adaptable to the method of iteration for solution, since

$$q = \frac{a_n}{b_{n-2}},$$
$$p = \frac{a_{n-1} - b_{n-3}q}{b_{n-2}} \tag{67.8}$$

give the explicit solutions for p and q. However, this is often slowly converging, and usually the method of successive approximations is faster. On the other hand, the method of successive approximations requires the partial derivatives of $F(p,q)$ and $G(p,q)$ which are somewhat laborious to find. Various computational schemes have been devised to reduce the amount of labor. One for the general case divides the function $Q(x)$ by the quadratic $x^2 + px + q$ to obtain a second quotient

$$Q_2(x) = c_0 x^{n-4} + c_1 x^{n-5} + \cdots + c_{n-3}x^{-1} + c_{n-2}x^{-2} + c_{n-1}x^{-3}, \tag{67.9}$$

where

$$c_0 = b_0 = a_0,$$
$$c_1 = b_1 - c_0 p,$$
$$c_2 = b_2 - c_0 q - c_1 p, \tag{67.10}$$
$$\vdots$$
$$c_i = b_i - c_{i-2}q - c_{i-1}p, \qquad (i = 2, \ldots, n - 2),$$
$$c_{n-1} = b_{n-1} - c_{n-3}q - c_{n-2}p;$$

it can be shown that

$$F_p = -c_{n-2} = G_q,$$
$$F_q = -c_{n-3}, \qquad (67.11)$$
$$G_p = -c_{n-1}.$$

The computational scheme may be arranged in the following manner: b_i and c_i are computed from Formulas 67.5 and 67.10 with $p = p_i$ and $q = q_i$, p_i and q_i being the last approximate values in the sequence of successive approximations.

a_0	b_0	c_0
a_1	b_1	c_1
a_2	b_2	c_2
$\vdots$	$\vdots$	$\vdots$
a_{n-4}	b_{n-4}	c_{n-4}
a_{n-3}	b_{n-3}	c_{n-3}
a_{n-2}	b_{n-2}	c_{n-2}
a_{n-1}	b_{n-1}	c_{n-1}
a_n	b_n	
b_{n-1}	c_{n-2}	c_{n-3}
b_n	c_{n-1}	c_{n-2}
D	Δp	$(-)\Delta q$
	p_{i+1}	q_{i+1}

Note that the true values of c_i are entered in the determinant of the system. The fact that they are the negative of the partial derivatives is accounted for in the solution for Δp and Δq, as shown by the $(-)$ on Δq.

After a few steps, there is little change in the c_i, and it may suffice to take the last values of c_i and D, thus saving some computation. The initial approximations of p and q may be guessed, the simplest being $p = q = 0$. Also a good initial value is

$$q_0 = \frac{a_n}{a_{n-2}} \quad \text{and} \quad p_0 = \frac{a_{n-1}}{a_{n-2}}.$$

Example 6.19. Find the roots of

$$7x^4 + 38x^3 + 61x^2 - 30x + 12 = 0.$$

FIRST SOLUTION.

METHOD OF SUCCESSIVE APPROXIMATIONS

$$b_0 = a_0 = c_0$$
$$b_1 = a_1 - b_0 p$$
$$b_2 = a_2 - b_0 q - b_1 p$$
$$b_3 = a_3 - b_1 q - b_2 p$$
$$b_4 = a_4 - b_2 q - b_3 p$$

$$c_1 = b_1 - c_0 p$$
$$c_2 = b_2 - c_0 q - c_1 p$$
$$c_3 = b_3 - c_1 q - c_2 p$$

		c_1	
		c_2	
		c_2	
		c_3	
b_3		Δp	$(-)\Delta q$
b_4	D		

i	a_i	b_i	c_i	b_i	c_i	b_i	c_i
p,q		0	7 .152122	-.4703	-.0346	-.457646	.146514
0	0	0	7	7	7	7	7
1	38	38	38	41.2921	44.5842	41.203522	44.407044
2	61	61	61	80.6619	101.8720	78.831029	98.128137
3	-30	-30	-30	9.3640	58.8170	.039812	38.441508
4	12	12		19.1948		.468370	
	-30	-30	38	101.8720	44.5842	98.128137	44.407044
	12	12	61	58.8170	101.8720	38.441508	98.128137
D,Δ	4861	-.4703	-.0346	.012654	.181114	-.002132	.005608
				9.3640 19.1948	.039812 .468370		
				7755.5955	7922.0575	7922.0575	

p,q	-.459778	.152122		-.4597756	.1521175		
	7			7			
	41.218446			41.2184292			
	78.886481			78.8864055			
	.000036			.0000000		98.128137	44.407044
	-.000353			-.0000028		38.441508	98.128137
Δ	.0000024	-.0000045		0 0	7922.0575		

After the third step, c_i and D are held constant, the values being entered at the extreme right of the calculating sheet. New values of b_i and corrections are then calculated. After five complete steps we have, to seven decimal places,

$$p = -.4597756 \quad \text{and} \quad q = .1521175.$$

From these we get

$$a = -\tfrac{1}{2}p = .2298878,$$
$$b = \sqrt{q - a^2} = .3150700,$$

and

$$x = .2298878 \pm .3150700i \,.$$

The quotient $Q(x)$ yields a second quadratic,

$$Q(x) = b_0 x^2 + b_1 x + b_2$$
$$= 7x^2 + 41.2184292x + 78.8864055,$$

which is solved by the quadratic formula to give

$$x = -2.9441735 \pm 1.6128635i \,.$$

It should be noted that the computed values for $b_0, b_1,$ and b_2 are used in the quotient which is solved by the quadratic formula and that the solutions obtained from this equation cannot be any more accurate than the degree of accuracy to which $b_0, b_1,$ and b_2 have been obtained. In fact, rounding-off errors often make the second pair of roots less accurate. The usual practice is to obtain the first pair of roots more accurately than necessary.

SECOND SOLUTION.

METHOD OF ITERATION

$$b_0 = a_0$$
$$b_1 = a_1 - b_0 p$$
$$b_2 = a_2 - b_0 q - b_1 p$$

$$q = \frac{a_4}{b_2}$$
$$p = \frac{a_3 - b_1 q}{b_2}$$

a_0	a_1	a_2	a_3	$\dot{a}_4$
7	38	61	-30	12

i	q	p	b_0	b_1	b_2
0	.0	0	7	38	61
1	.1967	−.6143	7	42.3001	85.6081
2	.140173	−.419695	7	40.937865	77.200206
3	.155439	−.471026	7	41.297182	79.363973
4	.151202	−.456683	7	41.196781	78.755456
5	.152370	−.460630	7	41.224410	78.922610
6	.152047	−.459539	7	41.216773	78.876386
7	.152136	−.459840	7	41.218880	78.889138
8	.152112	−.459757	7	41.218299	78.885617
9	.152118	−.459780	7	41.218460	78.886598
10	.152117	−.459774			

With the solution for p and q the values for x are found by the first method. Note that in finding p_i we use q_i and not q_{i-1}.

The large amount of writing in the first solution can be greatly reduced by the use of stencils. However, since we are illustrating a method, all details must necessarily be exhibited.

A combination of the two methods is frequently advantageous, especially in troublesome problems. The combination consists of first applying the method of iteration for three or four steps and then shifting to the method of successive approximations. If this is done, in many cases only one calculation of c_i and D is necessary.

Many calculators prefer to divide through by a_0, thus always making the leading coefficients equal to one. If this is done, care must be taken to determine a sufficient number of places to carry.

If there are two pairs of conjugate complex roots close together, the value of D in the method of successive approximations is near zero and the method of iteration converges slowly, if at all. The method of successive approximations may still be used by resorting to the approach employed in the exceptional case discussed in Section 66B. It is then necessary to obtain the values of the partial derivatives of $D(p,q) = 0$. We have

$$D(p,q) = c_{n-2}^2(p,q) - c_{n-1}(p,q)\,c_{n-3}(p,q) \tag{67.12}$$

and

$$D_p(p,q) = 2c_{n-2}\frac{\partial c_{n-2}}{\partial p} - c_{n-1}\frac{\partial c_{n-3}}{\partial p} - c_{n-3}\frac{\partial c_{n-1}}{\partial p}$$

$$D_q(p,q) = 2c_{n-2}\frac{\partial c_{n-2}}{\partial q} - c_{n-1}\frac{\partial c_{n-3}}{\partial q} - c_{n-3}\frac{\partial c_{n-1}}{\partial q}. \tag{67.13}$$

Now

$$\frac{\partial c_i}{\partial p} = -2d_{i-1} \quad \text{and} \quad \frac{\partial c_i}{\partial q} = -2d_{i-2}, \tag{67.14}$$

where

$$\begin{aligned} d_0 &= c_0, \\ d_1 &= c_1 - d_0 p, \\ d_i &= c_i - d_{i-2}q - d_{i-1}p, \end{aligned} \tag{67.15}$$

so that

$$\begin{aligned} D_p(p, q) &= 2(d_{n-2}c_{n-3} + d_{n-4}c_{n-1} - 2d_{n-3}c_{n-2}) \\ D_q(p, q) &= 2(d_{n-3}c_{n-3} + d_{n-5}c_{n-1} - 2d_{n-4}c_{n-2}). \end{aligned} \tag{67.16}$$

This procedure becomes quite laborious and its solution still depends on the determinant for the system;

$$\begin{aligned} F(p, q) &= 0, \\ D(p, q) &= 0. \end{aligned} \tag{67.17}$$

A method of separating the roots is discussed in the next section.

Example 6.20. Find the roots of

$$x^4 + x^3 + 4.2505x^2 + 2x + 4 = 0.$$

SOLUTION. First obtain an approximate root by the method of iteration

a_i	1	1	4.2505	2	4
i	q	p	b_0	b_1	b_2
0	.94	.47	1	.53	3.0614
1	1.31	.43	1	.57	2.6954
2	1.48	.43	1	.57	2.5254
3	1.58	.44			

Now, with the values $p = .45$ and $q = 1.60$, change to the method of successive approximations.

p, q		.45	1.6		.475	1.797		.487214	1.895661
i	a_i	b_i	c_i		b_i	c_i		b_i	c_i
0	1	1	1		1	1		1	1
1	1	.55	.10		.525	.050		.512786	.025572
2	4.2505	2.403	.758		2.204125	.383375		2.105002	.196882
3	2								
4	4								

.03865	.758	.10	.009616	.383375	.050	.002345	.196882	.025572
.137808	−.46245	.758	.034620	−.262337	.383375	.008487	−.142055	.196882
D, Δ .620809	.024993	.197052	.160093	.012214	.098661	.042395	.005770	.047271

We note that D is getting smaller, which indicates that the roots are close together. In this fourth-degree equation this can also be seen by the fact that $p \sim b_1$ and $q \sim b_2$. However, continuing three more times yields

$$p = .495985 \quad \text{and} \quad q = 1.968143,$$

and the last value of $D = .004106$. These values satisfy $F(p,q) = 0$ and $G(p,q) = 0$ to six decimal places. The solutions are

$$\boxed{x = -.247992 \pm 1.380812i}$$

and

$$\boxed{x = -.252008 \pm 1.403162i}\ \cdot$$

68.   GRAEFFE'S ROOT-SQUARING METHOD

It was shown in the last section that if the roots of an algebraic equation are close together there is considerable trouble in finding them to a high degree of accuracy. Some of this trouble may be alleviated by transforming the original equation into one whose roots are powers of those of the original equation and thus are widely separated. The most easily applied procedure is to transform the original equation into one whose roots are the squares of the original and then repeat this process. This method is known as *Graeffe's root-squaring process.*

Consider the equation

$$f(x) = a_0 x^n + a_1 x^{n-1} + a_2 x^{n-2} + \cdots + a_{n-1}x + a_n = 0 \qquad (68.1)$$

with the n roots $x_1, x_2, \ldots, x_n$. By the factor theorem it can be written in the form

$$f(x) = a_0(x - x_1)(x - x_2) \cdots (x - x_n) = 0. \qquad (68.2)$$

If we multiply the equation by

$$(-1)^n f(-x) = a_0(x + x_1)(x + x_2)\cdots(x + x_n), \tag{68.3}$$

we obtain

$$F(x^2) = (-1)^n f(-x)f(x)$$
$$= a_0(x^2 - x_1^2)(x^2 - x_2^2)\cdots(x^2 - x_n^2). \tag{68.4}$$

Letting $y = x^2$ and setting the function equal to zero,

$$F(y) = a_0(y - x_1^2)(y - x_2^2)\cdots(y - x_n^2) = 0, \tag{68.5}$$

we see that the roots of this equation are the square of the roots of the original. The multiplication of the two functions (68.1) and (68.3) can be accomplished easily by a schematic. We note that by arranging the coefficients of the two functions in the following manner

a_0	a_1	a_2	a_3	a_4	a_5	$\cdots$
a_0	$-a_1$	a_2	$-a_3$	a_4	$-a_5$	$\cdots$

a_0^2	$-a_1^2$	a_2^2	$-a_3^2$	a_4^2	$-a_5^2$	$\cdots$
	$2a_0a_2$	$-2a_1a_3$	$2a_2a_4$	$-2a_3a_5$	$2a_4a_6$	$\cdots$
		$2a_0a_4$	$-2a_1a_5$	$2a_2a_6$	$-2a_3a_7$	$\cdots$
			$2a_0a_6$	$-2a_1a_7$	$2a_2a_8$	$\cdots$
				$2a_0a_8$	$-2a_1a_9$	$\cdots$
					$2a_0a_{10}$	$\cdots$

b_0	b_1	b_2	b_3	b_4	b_5	$\cdots$

we obtain the coefficients of the new function

$$F(x^2) = b_0(x^n)^2 + b_1(x^{n-1})^2 + b_2(x^{n-2})^2 + \cdots + b_{n-1}x^2 + b_n \tag{68.6}$$

with

$$b_0 = a_0^2,$$
$$b_1 = -a_1^2 + 2a_0a_2,$$
$$b_2 = a_2^2 - 2a_1a_3 + 2a_0a_4, \tag{68.7}$$
$$\vdots$$
$$b_5 = -a_5^2 + 2a_4a_6 - 2a_3a_7 + 2a_2a_8 - 2a_1a_9 + 2a_0a_{10}$$
$$\vdots$$

These coefficients have the following characteristics:

1. The terms alternate in sign in both directions.

2. The first term is the square of the corresponding original coefficient.

3. To this is added, algebraically, twice the product of the coefficients equally removed from the one under consideration until either the first or last one is reached.

Consider, for example, b_3:

1. The first term is $-a_3^2$.

2. The second term is $2a_2a_4$, a_2 and a_4 being adjacent to a_3.

3. The third term is $-2a_1a_5$, a_1 and a_5 each being two terms removed from a_3.

4. The fourth is $2a_0a_6$, a_0 and a_6 each being three terms removed from a_3; this is also the last term since it employs a_0.

The general procedure is to continue the process until the original equation has been broken up into n simple equations, from which the roots can easily be found. The stopping point is established when the *double products in the second row have no effect on the coefficients of the next transformed equation*. Suppose we have carried the process k times. Then our last equation is

$$b_0(x^k)^n + b_1(x^k)^{n-1} + b_2(x^k)^{n-2} + \cdots + b_{n-1}(x^k) + b_n = 0,$$

from which we write

$$x_1^k = \frac{-b_1}{b_0} \quad \text{and} \quad x_1 = \left(\frac{-b_1}{b_0}\right)^{1/k}$$

$$x_2^k = \frac{-b_2}{b_1} \quad \text{and} \quad x_2 = \left(\frac{-b_2}{b_1}\right)^{1/k} \qquad (68.8)$$

$$x_i^k = \frac{-b_i}{b_{i-1}} \quad \text{and} \quad x_i = \left(\frac{-b_i}{b_{i-1}}\right)^{1/k}, \qquad (i = 1, \ldots, n).$$

If the equation has complex roots, *it cannot be broken into the linear factors* (68.8); this will become evident when the double products do not all disappear and when, as the process continues, the signs of some of the coefficients fluctuate. This development must then be modified. However, since Graeffe's method does not adapt itself readily to calculating machines, we shall not give it more detailed treatment, for the other methods discussed in this chapter will solve the algebraic equations.[5] If trouble develops because the roots are close together, we recommend that Graeffe's method be applied once or twice in order to separate the roots somewhat before one of the other methods is used.

Example 6.21. Find the roots of

$$2x^4 - 6.001x^3 + 3.999x^2 - 8.002x + 16 = 0.$$

SOLUTION. A tabulation yields

x	0	1	2	3
$f(x)$	16	7.996	$-.016$	27.28

which indicates two roots in the neighborhood of $x = 2$. Instead of using the exceptional case of the Newton-Raphson method, let us apply Graeffe's method twice to obtain

$$f(x) = 16z^4 - 529.02432z^3 + 4865.02432z^2 - 12304.38912z + 65536,$$

$$f'(x) = 64z^3 - 1587.07296z^2 + 9730.04864z - 12304.38912,$$

where

$$z = x^4.$$

Then

i	z	$f(z)$	$f'(z)$
0	16	$-4195. +$	-770.28864
1	11	$48980. +$	-12125.68224
2	15	$143. +$	-7445.07552
3	15.019281	$1.01 +$	-7342.016163
4	15.019418		
0	17	$-407. +$	8874.35232
1	17.045870	11.89323	9394.27144
2	17.044604	$-.01047$	9379.82802
3	17.044605		

[5]For additional discussion of Graeffe's method, see J. B. Scarborough, *Numerical Mathematical Analysis*. Baltimore: The Johns Hopkins Press, 1950, pp. 213–234.

Therefore

$$x_1 = z_1^{1/4} = \boxed{1.968626}$$

and

$$x_2 = z_2^{1/4} = \boxed{2.031874}.$$

When these two roots are divided out of the original equation by synthetic division, we are left with

$$2x^2 + 2x + 4 = 0,$$

which we solve by the quadratic formula to get

$$x = \boxed{-.5 \pm 1.322876i}.$$

69.   EXERCISE IX

1. Solve the following systems of nonlinear equations:

(a) $\begin{cases} x^3 - 3x^2y + y^2 = 7, \\ x^2 - 4x + y^2 - 4y + 4 = 0; \end{cases}$

(b) $\begin{cases} x^2 - 3\sin y - 4 = 0, \\ y^2 - 3\sin x - 4 = 0; \end{cases}$ for positive x.

(c) $\begin{cases} 121x^2 - 32y^2 = 121, \\ 7x^2 + 7xy + 7y^2 + 70x - 63y = 34; \end{cases}$ for positive x.

(d) $\begin{cases} 17x^2 + 2y^2 - 102x + 28y + 250 = 0, \\ 5x^2 + 7xy + y^2 + 19x - 7y - 54 = 0. \end{cases}$

2. Find all the roots of the following algebraic equations:

(a) $x^6 + x^5 + x^4 + x^3 + x^2 + x + 1 = 0.$
(b) $x^5 - 2x^4 + 3x^2 - 4x + 2 = 0.$
(c) $63x^5 - 134x^4 + 8x^3 + 197x^2 - 268x + 142 = 0.$
(d) $49x^4 + 7x^3 + 32x^2 - 17x + 25 = 0.$
(e) $9x^4 - 24x^3 + 44x^2 - 37x + 22 = 0.$

3. Verify the formulas in (67.11) when $n = 5$.

4. Use mathematical induction to prove the formulas (67.11).

5. Check the criterion (66.19) for the systems in Problem 1.

7

Differential and Difference Equations

70. INTRODUCTION

The numerical solution of differential and difference equations is a subject that would constitute an entire book in itself.[1] In this introductory book on numerical methods we limit ourselves to a discussion of the fundamental methods that will solve almost any equations or systems thereof. Ordinary differential equations are considered first; difference equations and their application to partial differential equations follow. In the first case the problem is to find the values of a function that will satisfy the differential equation which has numerical coefficients and given initial conditions. These values are found by starting with the initial values and then constructing the function by short steps for (usually) equal intervals of the independent variable. Thus the function is generated over a certain range. The numerical solution of differential equations is troublesome in three ways: (1) getting the solution started; (2) choosing the interval length large enough to reduce the amount of labor but not large enough to make the solution inaccurate; and (3) checking the solution for errors. Appropriate remarks are made as each method is discussed.

[1]See W. E. Milne, *Numerical Solution of Differential Equations.* New York: Wiley, 1953.

71.   EULER'S METHOD

The simplest method for the numerical solution of a differential equation is due to Euler. It should, however, be employed with caution, since it can be very inaccurate. Consider a first-order differential equation:

$$\frac{dy}{dx} = f(x, y), \tag{71.1}$$

the solution of which may be

$$y = F(x). \tag{71.2}$$

Let us now assume that the function in (71.2) has a smooth curve, so that for a short distance we may approximate it by a straight line increment; that is,

$$\Delta y_i \doteq \left(\frac{dy}{dx}\right)_i \Delta x \tag{71.3}$$

and

$$y_{i+1} \doteq y_i + \Delta y_i = y_i + \left(\frac{dy}{dx}\right)_i \Delta x, \tag{71.4}$$

where

$$\left(\frac{dy}{dx}\right)_i = f(x_i, y_i).$$

Formulas 71.3 and 71.4 permit us to generate the function $y = F(x)$ in a step-by-step procedure. The assumptions made, however, necessitate the taking of small increments on x, and the error can grow as we proceed. The advantage lies in the simplicity of the computational procedure.

Example 7.1. Solve the differential equation

$$\frac{dy}{dx} = x + y$$

if $y_0 = 1$ at $x_0 = 0$.

SOLUTION. The computation is arranged in the following schematic. Each value of y is computed by Formula 71.4 and the value of $y' = f(x, y)$ from the given equation. The value of Δx is chosen to be 0.1.

x	y	y'
0	1.0000	1.0000
.1	1.1000	1.2000
.2	1.2200	1.4200
.3	1.3620	1.6620
.4	1.5282	1.9282
.5	1.7210	2.2210
.6	1.9431	2.5431
.7	2.1974	2.8974
.8	2.4871	3.2871
.9	2.8158	3.7158
1.0	3.1874	4.1874

A continuation of the method with the same increment value of x yields

x	1.5	2.0	2.5
y	5.8543	10.4548	18.1689

The exact solution to this simple equation is

$$y = 2e^x - x - 1,$$

and the values may be found at given values for x.

x	0	.5	1.0	1.5	2.0	2.5
y (EULER)	1.000	1.7210	3.1874	5.8543	10.4548	18.1689
y (EXACT)	1.000	1.7974	3.4366	6.4634	11.7781	20.8650

We note that the values found by Euler's method are getting farther and farther away from the true values. This is characteristic of Euler's method, and for this reason it should not be employed for a large range of the independent variable.

To overcome the errors of Euler's method, it may be modified to give somewhat better results. The modification consists of finding the *average* value of the derivative over the interval for x by a series of successive approximations. The procedure is as follows:

(a) compute $y'_{00} = f(x_0, y_0)$ and $y_{10} = y_0 + y'_{00}\Delta x$;
(b) compute $y'_{10} = f(x_1, y_{10})$ and $\frac{1}{2}(y'_{00} + y'_{10})$;
(c) compute $y_{11} = y_0 + \frac{1}{2}(y'_{00} + y'_{10})\Delta x$ and $y'_{11} = f(x_1, y_{11})$;
(d) compute $\frac{1}{2}(y'_{00} + y'_{11})$ and $y_{12} = y_0 + \frac{1}{2}(y'_{00} + y'_{11})\Delta x$, etc.

The calculations are continued until agreement is reached to the desired degree of accuracy. The procedure is then repeated for the next interval. Applying it to the example, we arrange the calculations as follows:

x	y_{i0}	y_{i0}'	y_{i1}	y_{i1}'	y_{i2}	y_{i2}'	y_{i3}
0	1.0000	1.0000					
.1	1.1000	1.2000	1.1100	1.2100	1.1105	1.2105	1.1105
.2	1.2316	1.4316	1.2426	1.4426	1.2432	1.4432	1.2432
.3	1.3875	1.6875	1.3997	1.6997	1.4003	1.7003	1.4004
.4	1.5704	1.9704	1.5839	1.9839	1.5846	1.9846	1.5846
.5	1.7831	2.2831	1.7980	2.2980	1.7987	2.2987	1.7988

It is apparent that accurate results with Euler's method are obtained only after considerable labor. It is therefore recommended for "quick and dirty" answers. It is also sometimes used to start a solution.

72.   MILNE'S METHOD

We now consider a method devised by W. E. Milne.[2] Fundamentally, it employs two quadrature formulas, one for predicting and the second for checking the prediction. There are many ways of deriving the prediction formula, but we limit our derivation to a simple algebraic development from the formulas given in Chapter 5.

Let us write our equation (51.23) for the derivative at x_1, x_2, x_3, and x_4, for five points (see Table IX, p. 366, for A_{ki}'):

$$y_1' \doteq \frac{1}{12h}(-3y_0 - 10y_1 + 18y_2 - 6y_3 + y_4),$$

$$y_2' \doteq \frac{1}{12h}(y_0 - 8y_1 + 8y_3 - y_4),$$

$$y_3' \doteq \frac{1}{12h}(-y_0 + 6y_1 - 18y_2 + 10y_3 + 3y_4),$$ (72.1)

$$y_4' \doteq \frac{1}{12h}(3y_0 - 16y_1 + 36y_2 - 48y_3 + 25y_4),$$

[2]"Numerical Integration of Ordinary Differential Equations," *American Mathematical Monthly*, **33**, 455–460 (1926).

and solve this system for y_4 in terms of y_0, y_1', y_2', and y_3'. This is easily accomplished by adding the first and third to obtain

$$y_1 - y_3 \doteq y_4 - 3h(y_1' + y_3') - y_0 \tag{72.2}$$

and substituting this value into the second equation,

$$12hy_2' \doteq y_0 - 8[y_4 - 3h(y_1' + y_3') - y_0] - y_4, \tag{72.3}$$

from which we get

$$y_4 \doteq y_0 + \frac{4h}{3}(2y_1' - y_2' + 2y_3'). \tag{72.4}$$

Since we can choose the points x_i to suit ourselves, we may write the general formula

$$y_{i+1} \doteq y_{i-3} + \frac{4h}{3}(2y_{i-2}' - y_{i-1}' + 2y_i'), \tag{72.5}$$

where $h = \Delta x$. This formula yields a value of y in terms of the value of y four steps back and the values of the derivative of y at the preceding three steps. With this predictor, or extrapolation formula, there is used a corrector formula which may be obtained from the last three equations of (72.1) simply by multiplying y_3' by 4 and adding:

$$y_2' \doteq \frac{1}{12h}(y_0 - 8y_1 + 8y_3 - y_4)$$

$$4y_3' \doteq \frac{1}{12h}(-4y_0 + 24y_1 - 72y_2 + 40y_3 + 12y_4)$$

$$y_4' \doteq \frac{1}{12h}(3y_0 - 16y_1 + 36y_2 - 48y_3 + 25y_4)$$

$$y_2' + 4y_3' + y_4' \doteq \frac{1}{12h}(-36y_2 + 36y_4)$$

or

$$y_4 \doteq y_2 + \frac{h}{3}(y_2' + 4y_3' + y_4'). \tag{72.6}$$

Formulas 72.5 and 72.6 will keep the solution going once it has been started, but the method is dependent on the knowledge of four values. These initial four values may be obtained by using Taylor's series expansion or the modified Euler method. Still a third and quite favorable method results from formulas obtained from Taylor's series. Let us rewrite Formula 3.19 in two forms:

$$f(x_0 + h) = y_1 = y_0 + y_0'h + \frac{1}{2}y_0''h^2 + \frac{1}{3!}y_0'''h^3 + \frac{1}{4!}y_0^{iv}h^4 + \cdots,$$

$$f(x_0 - h) = y_{-1} = y_0 - y_0'h + \frac{1}{2}y_0''h^2 - \frac{1}{3!}y_0'''h^3 + \frac{1}{4!}y_0^{iv}h^4 + \cdots. \tag{72.7}$$

The function $y' = f(x)$ may also be represented in the neighborhood of $x = x_0$ by Taylor's series:

$$y_1' = y_0' + y_0''h + \frac{1}{2}y_0'''h^2 + \frac{1}{3!}y_0^{iv}h^3 + \frac{1}{4!}y_0^{v}h^4 + \cdots,$$

$$y_{-1}' = y_0' - y_0''h + \frac{1}{2}y_0'''h^2 - \frac{1}{3!}y_0^{iv}h^3 + \frac{1}{4!}y_0^{v}h^4 + \cdots.$$

By adding and subtracting the last two equations, we may solve for y_0''' and y_0^{iv} to get

$$h^2 y_0''' = y_1' + y_{-1}' - 2y_0' - \frac{1}{12}y_0^{v}h^4 - \cdots,$$

$$\frac{1}{3}h^3 y_0^{iv} = y_1' - y_{-1}' - 2y_0''h - \cdots,$$

and on substituting into (72.7) we have

$$y_1 = y_0 + y_0'h + \frac{1}{2}y_0''h^2 + \frac{1}{6}h(y_1' + y_{-1}' - 2y_0')$$

$$+ \frac{1}{8}h(y_1' - y_{-1}' - 2y_0''h) + \text{higher order terms} \tag{72.8}$$

$$= y_0 + \frac{h}{24}(y_{-1}' + 16y_0' + 7y_1') + \frac{1}{4}y_0''h^2 + \text{h.o.t.}$$

Similarly

$$y_{-1} = y_0 - \frac{h}{24}(7y_{-1}' + 16y_0' + y_1') + \frac{1}{4}y_0''h^2 + \text{h.o.t.} \tag{72.9}$$

We may repeat the entire procedure for y_2 to get

$$y_2 = y_0 + \frac{2h}{3}(5y_1' - y_0' - y_{-1}') - 2h^2 y_0'' + \text{h.o.t.} \tag{72.10}$$

We now have a sufficient number of formulas to get the solution started. The procedure is as follows:

1. We are given $y' = f(x, y), x_0, y_0$.
2. Differentiate y' to obtain $y'' = f'(x, y)$ and choose $h = \Delta x$.
3. Calculate $y_0', y_0'', 2h^2 y_0''$, and $\frac{1}{4}h^2 y_0''$. These remain constant.
4. Use Euler's formulas for trial values:

$$y_1' = y_0' + hy_0'',$$
$$y_{-1}' = y_0' - hy_0''.$$

5. Compute trial values of y_1 and y_{-1} by Formulas 72.8 and 72.9.
6. Compute new values of y_1' and y_{-1}' from given differential equation.
7. Recompute y_1 and y_{-1} by Formulas 72.8 and 72.9.
8. Continue Steps 6 and 7 until values converge to the desired degree of accuracy.
9. Compute y_2 by Formula 72.10.
10. Compute y_2' from given differential equation.
11. Check y_2 by Formula 72.6, that is,

$$y_2 = y_0 + \frac{h}{3}(y_0' + 4y_1' + y_2').$$

12. Recompute y_2' and y_2.
13. Continue until y_2 converges to the desired degree of accuracy.

Let us illustrate the entire Milne method by an example.

Example 7.2. Solve the differential equation

$$y' = \frac{2x - 1}{x^2} y + 1$$

with $x_0 = 1, y_0 = 2$.

       SOLUTION. By differentiation we find

$$y'' = \frac{1}{x^2}(-y' + 2y + 2x).$$

Choose $\Delta x = .1$, let $A(x) = (2x - 1)/x^2$, and arrange the work as follows:

1. Getting the solution started.

x	y	y'	$A(x)$	
1.0	2.0000	3.0000		$y_0'' = \quad 3.0000$
				$2h^2 y_0'' = \quad .0600$
0.9	1.7150	2.70000	.987654	$\frac{1}{4} h^2 y_0'' = \quad .0075$
1.1	2.3150	3.3000	.991736	$16 y_0' = 48.0000$
0.9	1.715197	2.693827		$y_0 + \frac{1}{4} y_0'' h^2 = \quad 2.0075$
1.1	2.314854	3.295867		
0.9	1.715192	2.694021		
1.1	2.314850	3.295724		
0.9	1.715192	2.694016		
1.1	2.314850	3.295720		
1.2	2.658972	3.585111	.972222	
1.2	2.658933	3.585073		
1.2	2.658932	3.585072		

2. Continuing the solution.

	CORRECTED		PREDICTED			
x	y	y'	y	y'	$A(x)$	D
0.9	1.715192	2.694016				
1.0	2.000000	3.000000				
1.1	2.314850	3.295720				
1.2	2.658932	3.585072				
1.3	3.031728	3.870276	3.031782	3.870327	.946746	−54
1.4	3.432894	4.152657	3.432923	4.152683	.918367	−29
1.5	3.862194	4.433062	3.862208	4.433074	.888889	−14
1.6	4.319459	4.712035	4.319468	4.712043	.859375	−9
1.7	4.804566	4.989952	4.804571	4.989956	.830450	−5
1.8	5.317423	5.267067	5.317426	5.267070	.802469	−3
1.9	5.857959	5.543568	5.857961	5.543569	.775623	−2
2.0	6.426121	5.819591	6.426122	5.819592	.750000	−1

The choice of Δx should always be such that only one correction is necessary at each step. A check can be established. If the remainder term is carried in the derivation of the predictor and corrector formulas, it can be shown that their respective errors are approximated by

$$+ \tfrac{28}{90}h^5 y^v \quad \text{and} \quad - \tfrac{1}{90}h^5 y^v.$$

Thus the error of the predictor is approximately 28 times the error in the corrector and in the opposite direction. We compute the difference, $D = y_c - y_p$, between the two values, and if $D/29$ is not significant we assume that y_c is correct. In the example it is significant at $x = 1.3$; a more correct value would be $y = 3.031726$. However, it is seen that the values of D get better, and thus there is no need to make Δx smaller.

The differential equation of this example may be solved by analytical methods; the solution is

$$y = x^2(1 + e^{(1/x)-1}).$$

At $x = 2$ we have $y = 6.42612$ from a five-place table of the exponential function.

The predictor formula (72.5) employs four of the preceding points. It is, of course, possible to develop formulas that employ more points by considering derivative formulas that employ more points. The utilization of more points, however, increases the amount of labor to start the solution and to keep it going.

73.   THE RUNGE-KUTTA METHOD

The second method that we shall consider in detail is known as the Runge-Kutta method and is essentially a refinement of what may be called averaging methods. Consider again a first-order differential equation.

$$\frac{dy}{dx} = y' = f(x, y), \tag{73.1}$$

with initial values x_0 and y_0. The increment for advancing the dependent variable is now given by

$$\Delta y = \tfrac{1}{6}(k_1 + 2k_2 + 2k_3 + k_4), \tag{73.2}$$

where

$$k_1 = hf(x_0, y_0),$$
$$k_2 = hf(x_0 + \tfrac{1}{2}h, y_0 + \tfrac{1}{2}k_1),$$
$$k_3 = hf(x_0 + \tfrac{1}{2}h, y_0 + \tfrac{1}{2}k_2),$$
$$k_4 = hf(x_0 + h, y_0 + k_3).$$

(73.3)

The values at (x_1, y_1) are then given by

$$x_1 = x_0 + h \quad \text{and} \quad y_1 = y_0 + \Delta y.$$

(73.4)

The increment on y for the second interval is computed by the same formulas, with (x_0, y_0) replaced by (x_1, y_1). Thus all intervals are computed in the same manner by using for the initial values those at the beginning of each interval. The method needs no special formulas to get the solution started, and it adapts itself very nicely to a computational form. In order to exhibit this computational form, let us employ a double subscript notation in which the first subscript denotes the interval in which we are working and the second the entries in that interval. Thus we have

$$x_{11} = x_0, y_{11} = y_0 \quad \text{and} \quad y'_{11} = f(x_0, y_0) = f(x_{11}, y_{11}).$$

Now we see that

$$k_1 = hf(x_0, y_0) = hy'_{11}$$

and

$$y_0 + \frac{1}{2}k_1 = y_0 + \frac{1}{2}hy'_{11} = y_0 + \frac{\Delta x}{2}y'_{11}.$$

Thus we have

$$x_{12} = x_{11} + \frac{\Delta x}{2}, \qquad y_{12} = y_{11} + \frac{\Delta x}{2}y'_{11}, \qquad y'_{12} = f(x_{12}, y_{12}).$$

Continuing, we see that

$$k_2 = hf(x_0 + \tfrac{1}{2}h, y_0 + \tfrac{1}{2}k_1) = \Delta x y'_{12},$$
$$k_3 = hf(x_0 + \tfrac{1}{2}h, y_0 + \tfrac{1}{2}k_2) = \Delta x y'_{13},$$
$$k_4 = hf(x_0 + h, y_0 + k_3) = \Delta x y'_{14},$$

so that

$$\Delta y_1 = \frac{\Delta x}{6}(y'_{11} + 2y'_{12} + 2y'_{13} + y'_{14}).$$

(73.5)

The computational form for a first-order differential equation follows.

x	y	$\dfrac{dy}{dx} = y'$	Auxiliary Computations
$x_{11} = x_0$	$y_{11} = y_0$	$y'_{11} = f(x_{11}, y_{11})$	Whatever is necessary to compute $f(x, y)$
$x_{12} = x_{11} + \dfrac{\Delta x}{2}$	$y_{12} = y_{11} + y'_{11}\dfrac{\Delta x}{2}$	$y'_{12} = f(x_{12}, y_{12})$	
$x_{13} = x_{11} + \dfrac{\Delta x}{2}$	$y_{13} = y_{11} + y'_{12}\dfrac{\Delta x}{2}$	$y'_{13} = f(x_{13}, y_{13})$	
$x_{14} = x_{11} + \Delta x$	$y_{14} = y_{11} + y'_{13}\Delta x$	$y'_{14} = f(x_{14}, y_{14})$	

$$\Delta y_1 = \frac{\Delta x}{6}(y'_{11} + 2y'_{12} + 2y'_{13} + y'_{14})$$

$x_{21} = x_{11} + \Delta x$	$y_{21} = y_{11} + \Delta y_1$	$y'_{21} = f(x_{21}, y_{21})$	
$x_{22} = x_{21} + \dfrac{\Delta x}{2}$	$y_{22} = y_{21} + y'_{21}\dfrac{\Delta x}{2}$	$y'_{22} = f(x_{22}, y_{22})$	
$x_{23} = x_{21} + \dfrac{\Delta x}{2}$	$y_{23} = y_{21} + y'_{22}\dfrac{\Delta x}{2}$	$y'_{23} = f(x_{23}, y_{23})$	
$x_{24} = x_{21} + \Delta x$	$y_{24} = y_{21} + y'_{23}\Delta x$	$y'_{24} = f(x_{24}, y_{24})$	

$$\Delta y_2 = \frac{\Delta x}{6}(y'_{21} + 2y'_{22} + 2y'_{23} + y'_{24})$$

$x_{31} = x_{21} + \Delta x$	$y_{31} = y_{21} + \Delta y_2$	$y'_{31} = f(x_{31}, y_{31})$	

The required values for x, y, and $f(x, y)$ are given in the first line of each box.

Note that at each step within an interval the values at the beginning of the interval are used.

Example 7.3. Let us again solve the differential equation

$$y' = \frac{2x - 1}{x^2} y + 1$$

with $x_0 = 1, y_0 = 2$.

SOLUTION. Let $A(x) = (2x - 1)/x^2$. Choose $\Delta x = .2$. Then

$$y' = A(x)y + 1 \quad \text{and} \quad \frac{\Delta x}{6} = .033333,$$

and the calculations are arranged as follows:

x	y	y′	A(x)
1.0	2.000000	3.000000	1.000000
.1	2.300000	3.280993	.991736
.1	2.328099	3.308860	
.2	2.661772	3.587833	.972222
		.658913	
1.2	2.658913	3.585054	
.3	3.017418	3.856728	.946746
.3	3.044586	3.882450	
.4	3.435403	4.154961	.918367
		.773938	
1.4	3.432851	4.152617	
.5	3.848113	4.420545	.888889
.5	3.874906	4.444361	
.6	4.321723	4.713981	.859375
		.886538	
1.6	4.319389	4.711975	
.7	4.790586	4.978342	.830450
.7	4.817223	5.000463	
.8	5.319482	5.268719	.802469
		.997933	
1.8	5.317322	5.266986	
.9	5.844021	5.532757	.775623
.9	5.870598	5.553371	
2.0	6.427996	5.820997	.750000
		1.108664	
2.0	6.425986		

The error at $x=2.00$ is .00013 or .002%.

74.　　ACCURACY AND CHOICE OF METHOD

The accuracy of a step-by-step solution of a differential equation is often difficult to determine. The Milne method offers a check by the computation of the quantities, D. The Runge-Kutta method has no such check, and the error cannot be determined, although it is near the order of h^5. Improvement on the accuracy of any method can be achieved by taking smaller intervals. However, a decrease of interval size adds to the mount of labor and increases the possible round-off-error. The choice of method is also difficult. The advantages of the Runge-Kutta method are that no special procedures are needed to start the solution, the interval length can be changed at any time, and its computational routine has fewer formulas and is easily mastered The advantages of the Milne method are that it may be more accurate for some problems, it offers a check at each step, and the computational procedure requires fewer evaluations of the derivative.

As a check on the calculations, it is advantageous to plot the resulting functions and periodically check by recomputing portions with out-of-phase intervals. We may also remark again that the most common mistake in the use of the Runge-Kutta method is that the student fails to employ the initial value of y at each interval, that is, in computing y_{i3}, the incorrect y_{i2} is used instead of the correct y_{i1}, and similarly for y_{i4}.

It is believed that the methods discussed in this chapter will solve most ordinary differential equations with numerical coefficients and sufficient initial conditions. Special equations often require special treatment, but the addition of more methods would further complicate the choice on simple problems.

The reader should also consider the possibility of combining the two methods. Thus the Runge-Kutta method could start the solution, which after four or more points could be continued by the Milne method. Also the corrector formula (72.6) could be used as a periodic check on the solution obtained by the Runge-Kutta method.

75.　　HIGH ORDER DIFFERENTIAL EQUATIONS

The solution of higher order differential equations in which we can solve for the highest order derivative may be obtained by repeated application of the methods already discussed. We first apply the method to obtain the next lower order derivative and then apply it again to obtain the next lower order derivative, and so on until we arrive at the function. We shall show the details of the Milne and the Runge-Kutta methods.

Consider first the second-order differential equation

$$\frac{d^2x}{dt^2} = f(x, \dot{x}, t), \tag{75.1}$$

in which t is the independent variable with initial conditions, $t_0, x_0, \dot{x}_0$, and use the popular notation of a dot denoting differentiation with respect to t, that is,

$$\frac{dx}{dt} = \dot{x}; \qquad \frac{d^2x}{dt^2} = \ddot{x}; \quad \text{etc.} \tag{75.2}$$

A.   The Milne Method

1. To start the solution, differentiate $\ddot{x} = f(x, \dot{x}, t)$ to obtain $\dddot{x} = f(x, \dot{x}, t)$ and calculate the constants

$a_1 = \dddot{x}_0$	$a_2 = 2h^2 a_1$	$a_3 = .25h^2 a_1$	$a_4 = \dot{x}_0 + a_3$
$b_1 = \ddot{x}_0$	$b_2 = 2h^2 b_1$	$b_3 = .25h^2 b_1$	$b_4 = x_0 + b_3$

Record also $16\ddot{x}_0$ and $16\dot{x}_0$.

2. Obtain trial values of $\ddot{x}_i$ from

$$\ddot{x}_{-1} = \ddot{x}_0 - ha_1,$$

$$\ddot{x}_1 = \ddot{x}_0 + ha_1.$$

3. Compute trial values of $\dot{x}_i(i = -1, 1)$ by

$$\dot{x}_{-1} = a_4 - \frac{h}{24}(7\ddot{x}_{-1} + 16\ddot{x}_0 + \ddot{x}_1),$$

$$\tag{75.3}$$

$$\dot{x}_1 = a_4 + \frac{h}{24}(\ddot{x}_{-1} + 16\ddot{x}_0 + 7\ddot{x}_1).$$

4. Compute trial values of $x_i(i = -1, 1)$ by

$$x_{-1} = b_4 - \frac{h}{24}(7\dot{x}_{-1} + 16\dot{x}_0 + \dot{x}_1),$$

$$\tag{75.4}$$

$$x_1 = b_4 + \frac{h}{24}(\dot{x}_{-1} + 16\dot{x}_0 + 7\dot{x}_1).$$

5. Compute new values of $\ddot{x}_1$ and $\ddot{x}_{-1}$ from given equation.
6. Repeat Steps 3 to 5 until there is no change.
7. Compute $\dot{x}_2$ and x_2 by

$$\dot{x}_2 = \dot{x}_0 + \frac{2h}{3}(5\ddot{x}_1 - \ddot{x}_0 - \ddot{x}_{-1}) - a_2,$$

$$x_2 = x_0 + \frac{2h}{3}(5\dot{x}_1 - \dot{x}_0 - \dot{x}_{-1}) - b_2. \tag{75.5}$$

8. Compute $\ddot{x}_2$ from given equation.
9. Check $\dot{x}_2$ and x_2 by

$$\dot{x}_2 = \dot{x}_0 + \tfrac{1}{3}h(\ddot{x}_0 + 4\ddot{x}_1 + \ddot{x}_2),$$

$$x_2 = x_0 + \tfrac{1}{3}h(\dot{x}_0 + 4\dot{x}_1 + \dot{x}_2). \tag{75.6}$$

10. Repeat Steps 8 and 9 until convergence.
11. Compute $\dot{x}_3$ by

$$\dot{x}_3 = \dot{x}_{-1} + \frac{4h}{3}(2\ddot{x}_0 - \ddot{x}_1 + 2\ddot{x}_2). \tag{75.7}$$

12. Compute x_3 by

$$x_3 = x_1 + \frac{h}{3}(\dot{x}_1 + 4\dot{x}_2 + \dot{x}_3). \tag{75.8}$$

13. Compute $\ddot{x}_3$ from given equation.
14. Recompute $\dot{x}_3$ by

$$\dot{x}_3 = \dot{x}_1 + \frac{h}{3}(\ddot{x}_1 + 4\ddot{x}_2 + \ddot{x}_3). \tag{75.9}$$

15. Repeat Steps 12 to 14 until there is no change.
16. Continue the process by Steps 11 to 15.

Example 7.4. Find the values of the function satisfying

$$\ddot{x} = \dot{x} + 6x$$

with $x = 2, \dot{x} = 1$ at $t = 0$ in the interval $0 \le t \le .5$.

SOLUTION. Choose $\Delta t = .1$. Differentiate to get

$$\dddot{x} = \ddot{x} + 6\dot{x}.$$

The calculations are then arranged as follows:

t	x	$\dot{x}$	$\ddot{x}$	
0	2.0000	1.0000	13.0000	$a_1 = \quad 19.0000$
				$a_2 = \qquad .3800$
$-.1$	1.9618	$-.2050$	11.1	$a_3 = \qquad .0475$
$.1$	2.1682	2.3950	14.9	$b_2 = \qquad .2600$
				$b_3 = \qquad .0325$
$-.1$	1.962222	$-.220687$	11.5658	$16\ddot{x}_0 = 208.0000$
$.1$	2.168587	2.411647	15.4042	$16\dot{x}_0 = \quad 16.0000$
				$a_4 = \qquad 1.0475$
$-.1$	1.962211	$-.220382$	11.552645	$b_4 = \qquad 2.0325$
$.1$	2.168603	2.412145	15.423169	
$-.1$	1.962211	$-.220391$	11.552884	
$.1$	2.168603	2.412163	15.423763	
$-.1$	1.962211	$-.220391$	11.552875	
$.1$	2.168603	2.412164	15.423781	
$.2$	2.492080	4.124402	19.076882	
$.2$	2.492480	4.125734	19.080614	
$.2$	2.492484	4.125858	19.080762	
$.2$	2.492484	4.125863	19.080767	

CORRECTED				APPROXIMATIONS			
t	x	$\dot{x}$	$\ddot{x}$	t	x	$\dot{x}$	$\ddot{x}$
$-.1$	1.962211	$-.220391$	11.552875	$.3$	3.008389	6.277976	24.328310
0	2.000000	1.000000	13.000000	$.3$	3.008501	6.281336	24.332342
$.1$	2.168603	2.412164	15.423781				
$.2$	2.492484	4.125863	19.080767	$.4$	3.769461	9.057574	31.674400
$.3$	3.008506	6.281470	24.332506	$.4$	3.769610	9.062036	31.679696
$.4$	3.769616	9.062213	31.679909				
$.5$	4.849856	12.710176	41.809312	$.5$	4.849650	12.704010	41.801910
				$.5$	4.849848	12.709938	41.809026

The calculations for continuing the solution are stopped after three approximations. If these are not sufficiently accurate, the interval length should be shortened.

Second-Order Differential Equation.

$$\frac{d^2x}{dt^2} = f(x, \dot{x}, t)$$

Initial conditions: $x_0, \dot{x}_0, t_0$

t	x	$\dot{x}$	$\ddot{x}$	AUXILIARY COMPUTATIONS
$t_{11} = t_0$	$x_{11} = x_0$	$\dot{x}_{11} = \dot{x}_0$	$\ddot{x}_{11} = f(x_0, \dot{x}_0, t)$	Whatever is necessary to compute $f(x, \dot{x}, t)$
$t_{12} = t_{11} + \dfrac{\Delta t}{2}$	$x_{12} = x_{11} + \dot{x}_{11}\dfrac{\Delta t}{2}$	$\dot{x}_{12} = \dot{x}_{11} + \ddot{x}_{11}\dfrac{\Delta t}{2}$	$\ddot{x}_{12} = f(x_{12}, \dot{x}_{12}, t_{12})$	
$t_{13} = t_{11} + \dfrac{\Delta t}{2}$	$x_{13} = x_{11} + \dot{x}_{12}\dfrac{\Delta t}{2}$	$\dot{x}_{13} = \dot{x}_{11} + \ddot{x}_{12}\dfrac{\Delta t}{2}$	$\ddot{x}_{13} = f(x_{13}, \dot{x}_{13}, t_{13})$	
$t_{14} = t_{11} + \Delta t$	$x_{14} = x_{11} + \dot{x}_{13}\Delta t$	$\dot{x}_{14} = \dot{x}_{11} + \ddot{x}_{13}\Delta t$	$\ddot{x}_{14} = f(x_{14}, \dot{x}_{14}, t_{14})$	
	$\Delta x_1 = \dfrac{\Delta t}{6}(\dot{x}_{11} + 2\dot{x}_{12} + 2\dot{x}_{13} + \dot{x}_{14})$	$\Delta \dot{x}_1 = \dfrac{\Delta t}{6}(\ddot{x}_{11} + 2\ddot{x}_{12} + 2\ddot{x}_{13} + \ddot{x}_{14})$		
$t_{21} = t_{11} + \Delta t$	$x_{21} = x_{11} + \Delta x_1$	$\dot{x}_{21} = \dot{x}_{11} + \Delta \dot{x}_1$	$\ddot{x}_{21} = f(x_{21}, \dot{x}_{21}, t_{21})$	
$t_{22} = t_{21} + \dfrac{\Delta t}{2}$	$x_{22} = x_{21} + \dot{x}_{21}\dfrac{\Delta t}{2}$	$\dot{x}_{22} = \dot{x}_{21} + \ddot{x}_{21}\dfrac{\Delta t}{2}$	$\ddot{x}_{22} = f(x_{22}, \dot{x}_{22}, t_{22})$	
$t_{23} = t_{21} + \dfrac{\Delta t}{2}$	$x_{23} = x_{21} + \dot{x}_{22}\dfrac{\Delta t}{2}$	$\dot{x}_{23} = \dot{x}_{21} + \ddot{x}_{22}\dfrac{\Delta t}{2}$	$\ddot{x}_{23} = f(x_{23}, \dot{x}_{23}, t_{23})$	
$t_{24} = t_{21} + \Delta t$	$x_{24} = x_{21} + \dot{x}_{23}\Delta t$	$\dot{x}_{24} = \dot{x}_{21} + \ddot{x}_{23}\Delta t$	$\ddot{x}_{24} = f(x_{24}, \dot{x}_{24}, t_{24})$	
	$\Delta x_2 = \dfrac{\Delta t}{6}(\dot{x}_{21} + 2\dot{x}_{22} + 2\dot{x}_{23} + \dot{x}_{24})$	$\Delta \dot{x}_2 = \dfrac{\Delta t}{6}(\ddot{x}_{21} + 2\ddot{x}_{22} + 2\ddot{x}_{23} + \ddot{x}_{24})$		
$t_{31} = t_{21} + \Delta t$	$x_{31} = x_{21} + \Delta x_2$	$\dot{x}_{31} = \dot{x}_{21} + \Delta \dot{x}_2$	$\ddot{x}_{31} = f(x_{31}, \dot{x}_{31}, t_{31})$	

B.   The Runge-Kutta Method

In applying the Runge-Kutta method to higher order equations, simply repeat the process for each derivative until the function is obtained. The schematic is readily adapted to machine calculations which are again worked from the right to the left. See p. 244.

Example 7.5. Solve Example 7.4 by the Runge-Kutta method.

SOLUTION.

t	x	$\dot{x}$	$\ddot{x}$
0	2.000000	1.000000	13.000000
.05	2.050000	1.650000	13.950000
.05	2.082500	1.697500	14.192500
.10	2.169750	2.419250	15.437750
		.168571	1.412046
.10	2.168571	2.412046	15.423472
.15	2.289173	3.183220	16.918258
.15	2.327732	3.257959	17.224351
.20	2.494367	4.134481	19.100683
		.323815	1.713490
.20	2.492386	4.125536	19.079852
.25	2.698663	5.079529	21.271507
.25	2.746362	5.189111	21.667283
.30	3.011297	6.292264	24.360046
		.515918	2.155291
.30	3.008304	6.280827	24.330651
.35	3.322345	7.497360	27.431430
.35	3.383172	7.652399	27.951431
.40	3.773544	9.075970	31.717234
		.760939	2.780227
.40	3.769243	9.061054	31.676512
.45	4.222296	10.644880	35.978656
.45	4.301487	10.859987	36.668909
.50	4.855242	12.727945	41.859397
		1.079979	3.647184

t	x	$\dot{x}$	$\ddot{x}$
.50	4.849222	12.708238	41.803570

The particular differential equation used in these examples may be solved by analytical means to yield the solution

$$x = e^{3t} + e^{-2t}.$$

At $t = 0.5$ we have $x = 4.849568$. Thus the errors committed by our step-by-step methods are

MILNE METHOD	$-.000288$	.006%
RUNGE-KUTTA METHOD	.000346	.007%

Improvements on the numerical solutions may be obtained by taking smaller interval length. This, however, adds considerably to the amount of labor involved.

76.   SYSTEMS OF EQUATIONS

Systems of differential equations may be solved by either of our two methods. The procedure is to apply the method of our choice to each of the equations of our system. As before, it must be possible to express the highest order derivative as a function of the variables and lower order derivatives. We illustrate by an example.

Example 7.6. Find the values of the functions that satisfy the system of differential equations

$$2\ddot{y} - \dot{x} - 4y - 4t = 0$$

$$4\dot{x} + 2\dot{y} - 3x = 0,$$

with $x = \frac{7}{3}, y = 4, \dot{y} = -3.5$ at $t = 0$.

SOLUTION. Transform the given equations into the following system

$$\ddot{y} = .5\dot{x} + 2y + 2t$$

$$\dot{x} = .75x - .5\dot{y}$$

and choose $\Delta t = .1$.

The Runge-Kutta Method.

t	x	$\dot{x}$	y	$\dot{y}$	$\ddot{y}$
0	2.3333	3.5000	4.0000	−3.5000	9.7500
.05	2.5083	3.3875	3.8250	−3.0125	9.4438
.05	2.5027	3.3909	3.8486	−3.0278	9.4926
.10	2.6724	3.2796	3.6972	−2.5507	9.2342
		.3389		−.3022	.9476
.10	2.6722	3.2804	3.6978	−2.5524	9.2358
.15	2.8362	3.1724	3.5702	−2.0906	9.0266
.15	2.8308	3.1736	3.5933	−2.1011	9.0734
.20	2.9896	3.0648	3.4877	−1.6451	8.9078
		.3173		−.2097	.9057
.20	2.9895	3.0655	3.4881	−1.6467	8.9090
.25	3.1428	2.9577	3.4058	−1.2012	8.7904
.25	3.1374	2.9566	3.4280	−1.2072	8.8343
.30	3.2852	2.8456	3.3674	−.7633	8.7576
		.2957		−.1204	.8819
.30	3.2852	2.8463	3.3677	−.7648	8.7586
.35	3.4275	2.7341	3.3295	−.3269	8.7260
.35	3.4219	2.7307	3.3514	−.3285	8.7682
.40	3.5583	2.6127	3.3348	.1120	8.7760
		.2731		−.0327	.8754
.40	3.5583	2.6134	3.3350	.1106	8.7767
.45	3.6890	2.4920	3.3405	.5494	8.8270
.45	3.6829	2.4862	3.3625	.5520	8.8681
.50	3.8069	2.3565	3.3902	.9974	8.9586
		.2488		.0552	.8854
.50	3.8071	2.3573	3.3902	.9960	8.9590

The Milne Method. To get the solution started, we need

$$\ddot{y} = .5\ddot{x} + 2\dot{y} + 2$$

$$\ddot{x} = .75\dot{x} - .5\ddot{y}.$$

t	x	$\dot{x}$	y	$\dot{y}$	$\ddot{y}$	CONSTANTS		
							FOR (x)	FOR (y)
0	2.3333	3.5000	4.0000	−3.5000	9.7500	a_1		−6.1250
						a_2		−.1225
−.1	1.9718	3.7250	4.3998	−4.5056	10.3625	a_3		−.0153
.1	2.6718	3.2750	3.6978	−2.5556	9.1375	b_1	−2.25	
						b_2	−.0450	.1950
−.1	1.9716	3.7316	4.3999	−4.5090	10.4654	b_3	−.0056	.0244
.1	2.6720	3.2816	3.6978	−2.5523	9.2364	$16\ddot{u}_0$		156.0000
						$16\dot{u}_0$	56.0000	−56.0000
−.1	1.9715	3.7332	4.3999	−4.5091	10.4664	a_4		−3.5153
.1	2.6720	3.2802	3.6978	−2.5523	9.2357	b_4	2.3274	4.0244
.2	2.9921	3.0674	3.4882	−1.6467	8.9101			
.2	2.9896	3.0655	3.4881	−1.6466	8.9090			
.2	2.9895	3.0654	3.4881	−1.6466	8.9089			
−.1	1.9715	3.7332	4.3999	−4.5091	10.4664			
0	2.3333	3.5000	4.0000	−3.5000	9.7500			
.1	2.6720	3.2802	3.6978	−2.5523	9.2357			
.2	2.9895	3.0654	3.4881	−1.6466	8.9089			
.3	3.2849	2.8461	3.3677	−.7648	8.7585	PREDICTED		
.3	3.2849	2.8460	3.3677	−.7646	8.7584	CORRECTED		
.4	3.5583	2.6134	3.3350	.1106	8.7767	PREDICTED		
.4	3.5583	2.6134	3.3350	.1107	8.7767	CORRECTED		
.5	3.8069	2.3571	3.3902	.9961	8.9590	PREDICTED		
.5	3.8068	2.3570	3.3902	.9962	8.9589	CORRECTED		

The true solutions are $x(.5) = 3.8071$ and $y(.5) = 3.3902$.

The fewer formulas used by the Runge-Kutta method add to its advantages in the solution of systems of differential equations. Since one of its disadvantages is that there is no test of its accuracy, we may use the corrector formulas of Milne's method as a periodic check.

77.   DIFFERENCE EQUATIONS

A general definition of a differential equation describes it as involving one or more derivatives of the dependent variable. In a similar manner we may say that a difference equation is one that involves one or more of the differences of the dependent variable. To be a little more precise, let us recall the definition of a derivative of a simple function $f(x)$ which states that it is the limiting value of the quotient

$$\frac{f(x + h) - f(x)}{h}. \tag{77.1}$$

The expression in (77.1), known as a *difference quotient*, is a good approximation to the derivative, especially if h is very small. Thus, if we were to replace all the derivatives in a differential equation by the corresponding difference quotients, we would have a *difference equation*. The subject of difference equations is quite extensive. We limit ourselves, however, to those that permit us to obtain numerical solutions of partial differential equations.

We are concerned, therefore, with partial difference quotients of the second and higher orders. Let us begin with a function $u(x, y)$ of two variables, and let us divide the xy-plane into a network by two families of parallel lines

$$\begin{aligned} x &= mh, \quad (m = 0, 1, 2, \ldots), \\ y &= nh, \quad (n = 0, 1, 2, \ldots), \end{aligned} \tag{77.2}$$

as is done in the construction of ordinary graph paper. The points of intersection of these lines are called lattice points. For each of the variables of the function $u(x, y)$ we have a forward and backward difference quotient. Thus, with respect to x,

$$\begin{aligned} u_x &= \frac{u(x + h, y) - u(x, y)}{h} \\ u_{\bar{x}} &= \frac{u(x, y) - u(x - h, y)}{h} \end{aligned} \tag{77.3}$$

and with respect to y

$$u_y = \frac{u(x, y + h) - u(x, y)}{h}$$

$$u_{\bar{y}} = \frac{u(x, y) - u(x, y - h)}{h}$$

(77.4)

in which the forward difference quotients are denoted by u_x and u_y, the backward difference quotients by $u_{\bar{x}}$ and $u_{\bar{y}}$.

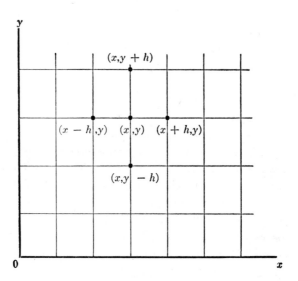

Figure 7.1

We now define a second difference quotient of $u(x, y)$ with respect to x as the difference quotient of the first difference quotients, that is,

$$u_{\bar{x}x} = \frac{u_x - u_{\bar{x}}}{h} = \frac{u(x + h, y) - 2u(x, y) + u(x - h, y)}{h^2}$$

(77.5)

and similarly

$$u_{\bar{y}y} = \frac{u_y - u_{\bar{y}}}{h} = \frac{u(x, y + h) - 2u(x, y) + u(x, y - h)}{h^2}.$$

(77.6)

It is our purpose to employ these definitions of difference quotients to replace partial derivatives in a partial differential equation and to solve the resulting difference equation. In so doing it should be remembered that the functions occurring in the difference equations are defined at the lattice points only. To get a better description of the function, it then becomes necessary to increase the number of lattice points.

78.   PARTIAL DIFFERENTIAL EQUATIONS

In our discussion of the numerical solution of partial differential equations we limit ourselves to those equations that can be replaced by the equivalent difference equation and consider the methods of solving the resulting difference equations. Furthermore, we have selected only a few methods, which, however, are sufficient to solve many problems.[3]

The general procedure is to replace the partial derivatives by the equivalent difference quotients and then to obtain the solution at the lattice points. Let us consider some well-known partial differential equations.

I. LAPLACE'S EQUATION IN TWO DIMENSIONS

$$\frac{\partial^2 V}{\partial x^2} + \frac{\partial^2 V}{\partial y^2} = 0. \tag{78.1}$$

Transforming to a difference equation by

$$u_{\bar{x}x} \sim \frac{\partial^2 V}{\partial x^2} \quad \text{and} \quad u_{\bar{y}y} \sim \frac{\partial^2 V}{\partial y^2}, \tag{78.2}$$

we have

$$h^{-2}[u(x + h, y) - 2u(x, y) + u(x - h, y)]$$
$$+ h^{-2}[u(x, y + h) - 2u(x, y) + u(x, y - h)] = 0,$$

and by solving this equation for $u(x, y)$ we obtain

$$u(x, y) = \tfrac{1}{4}[u(x + h, y) + u(x, y + h) + u(x - h, y) + u(x, y - h)]. \tag{78.3}$$

We see that in this equation the value of $u(x, y)$ at any interior lattice point is the arithmetic mean of the values of $u(x, y)$ at the four lattice points surrounding it.

---

[3]For a more detailed discussion of partial differential equations, see W. E. Milne, *Numerical Solutions of Differential Equations*. New York: Wiley, 1953, Part II; or see F. D. Murnaghan, *Introduction to Applied Mathematics*. New York: Wiley, 1948, Chapters 5–7.

II. POISSON'S EQUATION IN TWO DIMENSIONS

$$\frac{\partial^2 V}{\partial x^2} + \frac{\partial^2 V}{\partial y^2} = -4\pi\rho(x, y). \tag{78.4}$$

Again by using the transformation (78.2) and solving for $u(x, y)$ we obtain

$$u(x, y) = \tfrac{1}{4}[u(x + h, y) + u(x, y + h) + u(x - h, y)$$
$$+ u(x, y - h)] + \pi h^2 \rho(x, y). \tag{78.5}$$

In this case the value of $u(x, y)$ at an interior lattice point depends on the values of $u(x, y)$ at the four adjacent points, the value of h, and the value of the function $\rho(x, y)$.

III. THE PARABOLIC EQUATION

$$\frac{\partial u}{\partial t} = c^2 \frac{\partial^2 u}{\partial x^2}. \tag{78.6}$$

In dividing the xt-plane into a network, let us choose different increments on x and t,

$$\Delta t = k \quad \text{and} \quad \Delta x = h.$$

The transformation to a difference equation yields

$$k^{-1}[u(x, t + k) - u(x, t)]$$
$$= c^2 h^{-2}[u(x + h, t) - 2u(x, t) + u(x - h, t)]. \tag{78.7}$$

Let $c^2 k h^{-2} = r$. Then we have

$$u(x, t + k) = r[u(x + h, t) + u(x - h, t)] + (1 - 2r)u(x, t), \tag{78.8}$$

from which we can calculate the values of $u(x, t + k)$ from the values at $u(x, t), u(x + h, t)$, and $u(x - h, t)$ once we have chosen k and h so that r is known.

IV. TWO-DIMENSIONAL HEAT-FLOW EQUATION

$$\frac{\partial T}{\partial t} = \alpha^2 \left(\frac{\partial^2 T}{\partial x^2} + \frac{\partial^2 T}{\partial y^2} \right). \tag{78.9}$$

Let $\Delta t = k, \Delta y = \Delta x = h$; the difference equation is

$$k^{-1}[T(x, y, t + k) - T(x, y, t)] = \alpha^2 h^{-2}[T(x + h, y, t)$$
$$- 2T(x, y, t) + T(x - h, y, t) + T(x, y + h, t) \tag{78.10}$$
$$- 2T(x, y, t) + T(x, y - h, t)].$$

If we choose $4k = h^2\alpha^{-2}$, we obtain

$$T(x, y, t + k) = \tfrac{1}{4}[T(x + h, y, t) + T(x, y + h, t)$$
$$+ T(x - h, y, t) + T(x, y - h, t)], \tag{78.11}$$

an equation that gives the temperature at any interior lattice point at a time $t + k$ in terms of the temperatures at four adjacent points at time t.

It should now be clear how each partial differential equation is changed to an equivalent difference equation. This difference equation is rearranged to give an expression for a particular value of the function in terms of the values of the function at adjacent points and other constants or known functional values. Frequently the resulting expression also depends on the choice of the increments on the independent variables. Since these expressions give the values of the function at interior lattice points, its values on the boundaries must be known. We shall now turn to the problem of finding the values at the interior points, having given the necessary boundary conditions.

79.   THE METHOD OF ITERATION

To illustrate this method, let us first consider a simple equation in two variables, such as Laplace's equation. In the last section we obtained the

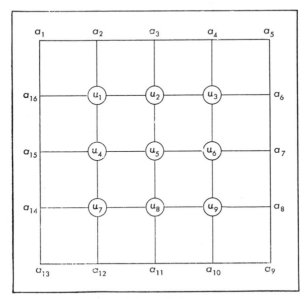

Figure 7. 2

equivalent difference equation

$$u(x, y) = \tfrac{1}{4}[u(x + h, y) + u(x, y + h) + u(x - h, y) + u(x, y - h)] \quad (79.1)$$

for a network of small squares of side h. Let the known boundary values of the function $u(x, y)$ be denoted by a_i. We first cover the area with a coarse network of squares as shown in Fig. 7.2. The first approximations to the interior points are now computed in the following order:

$u_5 = \tfrac{1}{4}(a_7 + a_3 + a_{15} + a_{11})$	$u_2 = \tfrac{1}{4}(u_3 + a_3 + u_1 + u_5)$
$u_1 = \tfrac{1}{4}(u_5 + a_3 + a_1 + a_{15})$	$u_4 = \tfrac{1}{4}(u_5 + u_1 + a_{15} + u_7)$
$u_3 = \tfrac{1}{4}(a_7 + a_5 + a_3 + u_5)$	$u_6 = \tfrac{1}{4}(a_7 + u_3 + u_5 + u_9)$
$u_7 = \tfrac{1}{4}(u_5 + a_{15} + a_{13} + a_{11})$	$u_8 = \tfrac{1}{4}(u_9 + u_5 + u_7 + a_{11})$
$u_9 = \tfrac{1}{4}(a_7 + u_5 + a_{11} + a_9)$	

$$(79.2)$$

We note that the values of $u_i (i = 5, 2, 4, 6, 8)$ are calculated according to the schematic which is the general scheme in (79.1).

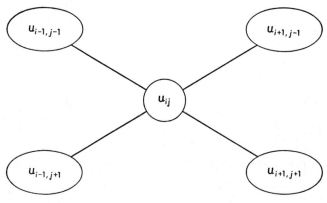

Figure 7.3

The values of u_i $(i = 1, 3, 7, 9)$ are calculated according to the schematic in Fig. 7.3, which is used to get only the first approximation.

The second approximations are now computed in order by the schematic in Fig. 7.4.

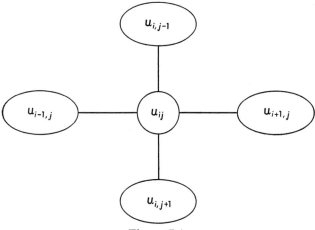

Figure 7.4

$$2u_1 = \tfrac{1}{4}(u_2 + a_2 + a_{16} + u_4) \qquad 2u_6 = \tfrac{1}{4}(a_7 + 2u_3 + 2u_5 + u_9)$$

$$2u_2 = \tfrac{1}{4}(u_3 + a_3 + 2u_1 + u_5) \qquad 2u_7 = \tfrac{1}{4}(u_8 + 2u_4 + a_{14} + a_{12})$$

$$2u_3 = \tfrac{1}{4}(a_6 + a_4 + 2u_2 + u_6) \qquad 2u_8 = \tfrac{1}{4}(u_9 + 2u_5 + 2u_7 + a_{11}) \qquad (79.3)$$

$$2u_4 = \tfrac{1}{4}(u_5 + 2u_1 + a_{15} + u_7) \qquad 2u_9 = \tfrac{1}{4}(a_8 + 2u_6 + 2u_8 + a_{10})$$

$$2u_5 = \tfrac{1}{4}(u_6 + 2u_2 + 2u_4 + u_8)$$

It is to be noted that the new values of u_i are used as soon as they are available. The successive approximations are calculated by the formulas in (79.3) with the new values just found.

Example 7.7. Find the function satisfying Laplace's two-dimensional equation with the boundary conditions

$$(u = 0, x = 0); \qquad (u = \tfrac{1}{2}x^2, y = 0); \qquad (u = 8 + 2y, x = 4);$$
$$(u = x^2, y = 4).$$

SOLUTION. For the first coarse network take $x = y = 0, 1, 2, 3, 4$. The boundary values are calculated at these points and placed on the square array. The calculations are then carried out in the manner outlined and are continued until there

y \ x	0	1.0	2.0	3.0	4
0	0	.5	2.0	4.5	8
1	0	1.625	3.6875	6.625	10
		1.5625	3.6719	6.5586	
		1.5547	3.6982	6.5722	
		1.5640	3.7088	6.5698	
		. . .	. . .	. . .	
		1.5670	3.7054	6.5670	
2	0	2.0625	4.50	8.0625	12
		2.0469	4.6797	8.0908	
		2.0576	4.6992	8.0704	
		2.0658	4.6931	8.0656	
		. . .	. . .	. . .	
		2.0626	4.6876	8.0626	
3	0	2.125	4.9375	9.125	14
		1.9961	4.9502	9.0102	
		2.0002	4.9274	8.9994	
		1.9983	4.9227	8.9971	
		. . .	. . .	. . .	
		1.9956	4.9197	8.9956	
4	0	1.0	4.0	9.0	16

is no change; the numbers are obtained after 10 calculations. The network is now changed to a finer mesh by halving the interval on both x and y. This necessitates calculating the boundary values from the given conditions and then proceeding with the calculations according to Formula 79.1 and the schematics of Figs. 7.3 and 7.4. The values from the coarse network are used as the first approximations. After an entry at each interior point has been established, only the schematic of Fig. 7.4 is used. The calculations are arranged as follows:

x → y ↓	0	.5	1.0	1.5	2.0	2.5	3.0	3.5	4.0
0		.125	.500	1.125	2.000	3.125	4.500	6.125	8
.5	0	.5168	1.1317	1.9431	2.9604	4.1931	5.6317	7.2668	9
		.5011	1.1310	1.9421	2.9602	4.1930	5.6317	7.2511	
		4.992	1.1299	1.9432	2.9629	4.1944	5.6316	7.2510	
		. . . . . .	. . . . . .	. . . . . .	. . . . . .	. . . . . .	. . . . . .	. . . . . .	
		.5060	1.1414	1.9581	2.9782	4.2081	5.6414	7.2560	
1.0	0	.7478	1.5670	2.5553	3.7054	5.0553	6.5670	8.2478	10
		.7439	1.5782	2.5578	3.7155	5.0578	6.5807	8.2473	
		.7460	1.5805	2.5615	3.7184	5.0626	6.5827	8.2480	
		. . . . . .	. . . . . .	. . . . . .	. . . . . .	. . . . . .	. . . . . .	. . . . . .	
		.7577	1.6017	2.5879	3.7468	5.0879	6.6017	8.2577	
1.5	0	.9074	1.8856	3.0056	4.2886	5.7556	7.3856	9.1574	11
		.9064	1.8882	3.0069	4.2914	5.7570	7.3894	9.1582	
		.9075	1.8924	3.0104	4.2967	5.7614	7.3946	9.1606	
		. . . . . .	. . . . . .	. . . . . .	. . . . . .	. . . . . .	. . . . . .	. . . . . .	
		.9233	1.9198	3.0452	4.3333	5.7952	7.4198	9.1733	
2.0	0	.9962	2.0626	3.2930	4.6876	6.2933	8.0626	9.9962	12
		.9959	2.0748	3.2964	4.7009	6.2967	8.0762	9.9998	
		.9992	2.0783	3.3019	4.7054	6.3028	8.0808	10.0020	
		. . . . . .	. . . . . .	. . . . . .	. . . . . .	. . . . . .	. . . . . .	. . . . . .	
		1.0159	2.1090	3.3400	4.7462	6.3400	8.1090	10.0159	
2.5	0	1.0146	2.1223	3.4164	4.9225	6.6664	8.6223	10.7646	13
		1.0145	2.1253	3.4180	4.9262	6.6682	8.6262	10.7664	
		1.0161	2.1327	3.4236	4.9333	6.6736	8.6352	10.7709	
		. . . . . .	. . . . . .	. . . . . .	. . . . . .	. . . . . .	. . . . . .	. . . . . .	
		1.0313	2.1604	3.4598	4.9717	6.7098	8.6604	10.7813	
3.0	0	.9398	1.9956	3.3276	4.9197	6.8276	8.9956	11.4398	14
		.9398	2.0184	3.3337	4.9361	6.8322	9.0198	11.4463	
		.9380	2.0208	3.3401	4.9417	6.8415	9.0260	11.4420	
		. . . . . .	. . . . . .	. . . . . .	. . . . . .	. . . . . .	. . . . . .	. . . . . .	
		.9488	2.0416	3.3672	4.9711	6.8672	9.0416	11.4488	
3.5	0	.7489	1.6808	2.9788	4.6568	6.7288	9.1808	11.9989	15
		.7176	1.6787	2.9798	4.6612	6.7310	9.1874	11.9709	
		.7167	1.6793	2.9826	4.6638	6.7357	9.1832	11.9688	
		. . . . . .	. . . . . .	. . . . . .	. . . . . .	. . . . . .	. . . . . .	. . . . . .	
		.7222	1.6900	2.9964	4.6785	6.7464	9.1900	11.9722	
4.0	0	.25	1.00	2.25	4.00	6.25	9.00	12.25	16

The last set of entries were obtained after 30 iterations.

If the boundary values are obtained from empirical data, the values at the desired points when the mesh is halved are approximated by graphical means or by fitting the known points. The values at the interior points cannot be any more accurate than the approximated boundary values.

80.   THE METHOD OF RELAXATION

This is a second method for solving the problem discussed in the last section. In the iteration method we employed the four adjacent points and sought to obtain the values to satisfy (79.1), that is,

$$u_{ij} = \tfrac{1}{4}(u_{i+1,j} + u_{i,j-1} + u_{i-1,j} + u_{i,j+1}). \tag{80.1}$$

This condition, of course, is not satisfied until the very last set of entries. Thus at any prior set of entries there is a *residual*, R_{ij}, at each point.

$$R_{ij} = u_{i+1,j} + u_{i,j-1} + u_{i-1,j} + u_{i,j+1} - 4u_{ij} \tag{80.2}$$

has a definite nonzero value. The method of relaxation seeks to make all of these residuals zero by continuously altering the values of the function at the interior points. Therefore it is desirable to develop a process for doing these alterations or, as it has been termed, relaxations.

Let us again make up a lattice network and this time use the double subscript notation

$$
\begin{array}{ccccccc}
u_{11} & u_{12} & u_{13} & u_{14} & \cdots & u_{1n} \\
u_{21} & u_{22} & u_{23} & u_{24} & \cdots & u_{2n} \\
u_{31} & u_{32} & u_{33} & u_{34} & \cdots & u_{3n} \\
u_{41} & u_{42} & u_{43} & u_{44} & \cdots & u_{4n} \\
\vdots & & & & & \\
u_{n1} & u_{n2} & u_{n3} & u_{n4} & \cdots & u_{nn}
\end{array}
$$

Consider as an illustration the point P_{33}. The residual at this point is

$$R_{33} = u_{34} + u_{23} + u_{32} + u_{43} - 4u_{33}. \tag{80.3}$$

If we alter the value of the function at this point by an amount Δu_{33}, the residual will also be altered, and we have

$$R_{33} + \Delta R_{33} = u_{34} + u_{23} + u_{32} + u_{43} - 4(u_{33} + \Delta u_{33}). \tag{80.4}$$

By a simple subtraction we see that

$$\Delta R_{33} = -4\Delta u_{33} \tag{80.5}$$

or that the resulting change in the residual is a negative four times the change in the function at that point. If we now wish to make the residual zero, that is, make $\Delta R_{33} = -R_{33}$, then we simply change the value of the function by an amount

$$\Delta u_{33} = \tfrac{1}{4} R_{33}, \tag{80.6}$$

and $R_{33} = 0$.

However, a change in u_{33} will affect the residuals at the four adjacent points. Thus

$$R_{23} = u_{24} + u_{13} + u_{22} + u_{33} - 4u_{23}, \tag{80.7}$$

and a change in u_{33} gives

$$R_{23} + \Delta R_{23} = u_{24} + u_{13} + u_{22} + (u_{33} + \Delta u_{33}) - 4u_{23}, \tag{80.8}$$

from which we see that

$$\Delta R_{23} = \Delta u_{33}.$$

The same is true for R_{34}, R_{32}, and R_{43}. Consequently, if the value of a function is changed (relaxed), the residuals of the four adjacent interior points must be changed by the same amount.

This defines the process for performing the method of relaxation. Having obtained values at all the interior points, we then calculate all the residuals at these points. The method of relaxation begins by "relaxing" the value of the function with the *largest* residual by the amount $\Delta u_{ij} = \tfrac{1}{4} R_{ij}$. *This makes* $R_{ij} = 0$ *and necessitates the changing of* $R_{i+1,j}, R_{i-1,j}, R_{i,j+1}, R_{i,j-1}$ *by the amount* Δu_{ij}. This step is very important, and the failure to carry it out constitutes the most frequent error made by the inexperienced computer. All the corrections resulting from a change in a point must be made before proceeding to another point. After the corrections reducing the largest residual to zero have been made, we proceed to the residual which has now become the largest. The corrections are made until all the R_{ij} are zero or as nearly zero as possible.

Let us illustrate the method by an example.

Example 7.8. Solve the problem in Example 7.7 by the method of relaxation.

SOLUTION. Consider first the coarse network of $x = y = i (i = 0, 1, 2, 3, 4)$. The first values of the interior points are computed in exactly the same manner as in Example 7.7. The residuals R_{ij} are calculated and recorded in the left column of each block. The largest residual, $R_{22} = .7500$, is at the point P_{22}, which has a function value of $u_{22} = 4.5000$. This value is altered by the amount $\frac{1}{4}R_{22} = \frac{1}{4}(.7500) = .1875$, which is recorded in the right column of each block. This reduces R_{22} to zero and changes R_{23} to .1875, R_{12} to .1875, R_{21} to .1875, and R_{32} to .1875. After these changes have been made, the largest residual is $R_{31} = R_{33} = -.500$. Suppose we choose to work on R_{33} and change u_{33} by the amount $\frac{1}{4}R_{33} = -.125$. This changes R_{33} to zero, R_{23} to .0625, and R_{32} to .0625. Note that there are no residuals at the boundary points. Next, we change the functional value u_{31} to make R_{31} zero, etc. The completed calculations are arranged as follows:

x / y		0	1			2			3			4
			R	u	Δu	R	u	Δu	R	u	Δu	
0	0			.5			2			4.5		8
1	0		−.25	1.625		0	3.6875		−.25	6.625		10
			0	1.5625	−.0625	.1875			0	6.5625	−.0625	
						.1250						
						.0625		.0156				
			.0156		.0039	.0001	3.7031		.0156		.0039	
			0	1.5664		.0040			0	6.5664		
						.0079		.0020				
			.0020		.0005	−.0001	3.7051		.0020		.0005	
			0	1.5669		.0004			0	6.5669		
			.0002			.0009		.0002	.0002			
						.0001	3.7053					
2	0		0	2.0625		.75	4.5	.1875	0	8.0625		12
			.1875			0	4.6875		.1875			
			.0625			.0156			.0625			
			0			0			0			
			.0039			.0020			.0039			
			0			0			0			
			.0005			.0002			.0005			
			0			0			0			
3	0		−.5	2.125		0	4.9375		−.5	9.125		14
			0	2.000	−.125	.1875			0	9.000	−.125	
						.0625						
			−.0156		−.0039	−.0625		−.0156	−.0156		−.0039	
			0	1.9961		−.0001	4.9219		0	8.9961		
						−.0040						
						−.0079	4.9199	−.0020	−.0020			
			−.0020		−.0005	.0001			0	8.9956	−.0005	
			0	1.9956		−.0004						
						−.0009		−.0002				
			−.0002			−.0001	4.9197		−.0002			
4	0			1			4			9		16

If the functional values are required at a finer mesh, we could again halve the intervals as we did in Example 7.7. and obtain the values at the finer mesh points by the method of relaxation. We should obtain the same values as were obtained previously. The calculations are left as an exercise for the reader. The schematic for performing the calculations may be slightly improved by noting the order in which the points are relaxed. Thus the corrections listed in the right column could be numbered by a colored pencil.

81.   DIRECT STEP-BY-STEP METHOD

Equations of the parabolic or hyperbolic type may be solved by a direct step-by-step method to show the growth of the function, provided sufficient boundary conditions are given. Let us consider the parabolic equation (78.6). We saw in Section 78 that we could obtain an expression for $u(x, t + k)$ in terms of $u(x, t)$, $u(x + h, t)$ and $u(x - h, t)$, that is,

$$u(x, t + k) = r[u(x + h, t) + u(x - h, t)] + (1 - 2r)u(x, t), \quad (81.1)$$

where $r = c^2 k h^{-2}$.

This expression gives the growth of the function as t increases; it is dependent on the choice of h and k and having sufficient boundary values. Let us consider an example.

Example 7.9. Find the values of the function satisfying

$$\frac{\partial U}{\partial t} = 4 \frac{\partial^2 U}{\partial x^2}$$

with boundary conditions

$$U = 0 \quad \text{at} \quad x = 0 \quad \text{and} \quad x = 8,$$

$$U = 4x - \tfrac{1}{2}x \quad \text{at} \quad t = 0.$$

SOLUTION. Formula 81.1 would simplify to

$$u(x, t + k) = \tfrac{1}{2}[u(x + h, t) + u(x - h, t)] \quad (81.2)$$

if we could choose h and k such that $r = c^2 k h^{-2}$ is $\tfrac{1}{2}$. Let us therefore choose $h = 1$. Then $r = 4k = \tfrac{1}{2}$ would yield $k = \tfrac{1}{8}$ making the increment on $t = \tfrac{1}{8}$. We may now arrange the work according to the following schematic. The entries in the first row, first and last columns, are calculated from the boundary conditions, and the other entries are taken from Formula 81.2.

x t	0	1	2	3	4	5	6	7	8
0	0	3.5000	6.0000	7.5000	8.0000	7.5000	6.0000	3.5000	0
1/8	0	3.0000	5.5000	7.0000	7.5000	7.0000	5.5000	3.0000	0
2/8	0	2.7500	5.0000	6.5000	7.0000	6.5000	5.0000	2.7500	0
3/8	0	2.5000	4.625	6.0000	6.5000	6.0000	4.6250	2.5000	0
4/8	0	2.3125	4.2500	5.5625	6.0000	5.5625	4.2500	2.3125	0
5/8	0	2.1250	3.9375	5.1250	5.5625	5.1250	3.9375	2.1250	0
6/8	0	1.9688	3.6250	4.7500	5.1250	4.7500	3.6250	1.9688	0
7/8	0	1.8125	3.3594	4.3750	4.7500	4.3750	3.3594	1.8125	0
8/8	0	1.6797	3.0938	4.0547	4.3750	4.0547	3.0938	1.6797	0

Formula 81.2 is a simple averaging formula and could yield large errors. In fact under certain conditions this formula will lead to unstable solutions, and it is usually desirable to have $r < \frac{1}{2}$. The formula can be improved if the function $U(x, t)$ has continuous partial derivatives with respect to x of order 6 and with respect to t of order 3. Then it can be shown[4] that

$$U(x, t + k) = \frac{1}{6}[U(x + h, t) + 4U(x, t) + U(x - h, t)]$$
$$+ \text{error function} \tag{81.3}$$

if h and k are chosen so that $r = \frac{1}{6}$. In Example 7.9 this can be accomplished by different combinations of h and k, such as $(2, \frac{1}{6}), (4, \frac{2}{3})$, and $(1, \frac{1}{24})$.

Improvements on the functional values may also be obtained by choosing a finer mesh, that is, smaller values for h and k. Remember, however, that the formula for the calculation of the values of the function depends on h and k through r, and thus the formula will be changed whenever h and k are changed.

82.   REMARKS

We have described three methods for the numerical solution of partial differential equations. All are based on the idea of replacing the partial derivatives by difference quotients and then solving the resulting difference equation. There is indeed much more to the theory than that. In general,

[4]W. E. Milne, *Numerical Solution of Differential Equations*. New York: Wiley 1953, Chapter 8.

however, most of the methods have been developed in order to solve specific problems. The foregoing is intended only as an introduction.[5]

We close this chapter with a remark on stability. The step-by-step procedures discussed may generate solutions that will become unstable for certain equations. For ordinary differential equations we have indicated (Section 74) that the local error is of the order of h^5 and can be minimized by choosing smaller values of h. For partial differential equations greater accuracy can be achieved by choosing a finer mesh. A thorough discussion of stability is beyond the scope of this book and properly belongs in a second course on numerical analysis after the reader has attained additional maturity in mathematics, which is not required in this first course. Furthermore, in spite of all the recent literature on this subject, it is still a fruitful field for additional research. For those who wish to pursue the subject we recommend John Todd, *Survey of Numerical Analysis*. New York: McGraw-Hill, 1962, pp. 336–340, 380–435, and the references cited there.

83.   EXERCISE X

1. Solve the following differential equations by the Milne and Runge-Kutta methods. (Carry solutions reasonably far.)

(a) $y' = \dfrac{y^2 x^2 + y}{x}$ with $y = -3$ at $x = 1$.

(b) $y' = x^2 y^2 - xy$ with $y = 1$ at $x = 0$.

(c) $xy''' - 2y'' - 12x^3 = 0$ with $y'' = y = 0, y' = 1$ at $x = 1$.

(d) $\begin{cases} \dot{x} - 2y = 0, \\ \dot{y} - z = 0, \\ \dot{z} + 2x = 0. \end{cases}$ with $x = 1, y = 2, z = 3$ at $t = 0$.

(e) $\left. \begin{cases} \ddot{x} + 2\dot{y} + 150A(x,y)x = 0 \\ \ddot{y} + 150A(x,y)y = 2(\dot{x} - 1) \end{cases} \right\}$ where $A(x,y) = 1 - (x^2 + y^2)^{-\frac{1}{2}}$

and at $t = 0$

$x = .63813, \dot{x} = -.91781, y = -.82945, \dot{y} = -1.70032$.

2. Continue the Milne method solution of Example 7.4 to $t = 1.0$, using $\Delta t = .1$.

---

[5]If the reader finds a need for additional information, he is advised to consult the references already given. For information on triangular networks, block relaxation, and the Rayleigh-Ritz method consult J. B. Scarborough, *Numerical Mathematical Analysis*, second ed. Baltimore: Johns Hopkins University Press, 1950, Chapter 12; R. V. Southwell, *Relaxation Methods in Theoretical Physics*. London: Oxford University Press, 1946; H. W. Emmons, "The Numerical Solution of Partial Differential Equations," *Quarterly of Applied Mathematics*, (October 1944). **2**, 3, 173–195.

3. Solve Example 7.4 by the Runge-Kutta method with $\Delta t = .2, \Delta t = .4$, and $\Delta t = .8$ and compare the answers at $t = .8$.

4. Solve Example 7.6 by the Runge-Kutta method with $\Delta t = .25$ and compare the answers at $t = .5$.

5. Apply the Runge-Kutta method to Example 7.3 with $x = .1$ and compare the answer at $x = 2.0$ with Example 7.2.

6. Use Formula 51.23 and Table IX to write the derivatives at x_0, x_1, and x_2 for three points (x_i, y_i) $(i = 0, 1, 2)$. Derive two predictor formulas and two corrector formulas for y_2.

7. Use the formulas derived in Problem 6 to continue the solution of Example 7.2 beyond $x = 1.2$ and compare the answers at $x = 2.0$.

8. Solve the differential equation $y'' = -(1 + \sqrt{x})y$ with $y(0) = 1$ and $y'(0) = 0$ by either method. Continue solution until $y(x) < 0$ and approximate the value of x_0 for which $y(x_0) = 0$.

9. Solve the partial differential equation

$$\frac{\partial^2 V}{\partial x^2} + \frac{\partial^2 V}{\partial y^2} = -4\pi xy$$

with the boundary conditions

$$v = 0 \text{ at } x = 0, \qquad v = x - 2y \text{ at } x = 4,$$
$$v = x \text{ at } y = 0, \qquad v = 4 - x - y \text{ at } y = 4.$$

10. Solve Example 7.9 using (81.3) with $h = 1, k = \frac{1}{24}$; solve also with $h = 4, k = \frac{2}{3}$.

8

Empirical Data.
Principle of Least Squares

84.   INTRODUCTION

The fitting of empirical data by formulas or equations may be accomplished in two distinct manners. One is to have the formula satisfied exactly at the observational points; this was the case in the interpolation formulas discussed in the preceding chapters. The other is to have the approximating function come as close as possible to the values at the given points and still retain a predetermined characteristic which will show the general nature of the data but will not necessarily pass exactly through the given points. This second manner can be a most desirable way to study data which have been obtained from experimental observations and thus contain various errors of measurements.

The most frequently employed method to obtain functional representation of the second kind is known as the *method of least squares*. We shall discuss its application to the fitting of empirical data.

85.   THE PRINCIPLE OF LEAST SQUARES

Let us consider a set of m points $(x_j, y_j)(j = 1, \ldots, m)$, which have been obtained by measurements and which should be related by some function, $y = f(x)$. As a first consideration let us designate the function as a polynomial of degree $n < m$,

$$y = a_0 + a_1 x + a_2 x^2 + \cdots + a_n x^n = \sum_{i=0}^{n} a_i x^i. \qquad (85.1)$$

We propose to determine this polynomial, that is, to find the values of the coefficients a_i $(i = 0, \ldots, n)$ such that the polynomial (85.1) is a "good fit" to the data (x_j, y_j). If we substitute the points into the polynomial, we have the m equations

$$R_1 = a_0 + a_1 x_1 + a_2 x_1^2 + \cdots + a_n x_1^n - y_1,$$

$$R_2 = a_0 + a_1 x_2 + a_2 x_2^2 + \cdots + a_n x_2^n - y_2,$$
$$\vdots \hspace{6cm} (85.2)$$
$$R_m = a_0 + a_1 x_m + a_2 x_m^2 + \cdots + a_n x_m^n - y_m,$$

which are not equal to zero because the polynomial does not necessarily pass exactly through the points. The difference between the polynomial value and the observed functional value,

$$\sum_{i=0}^{n} a_i x_j^i - y_j, \qquad (j = 1, \ldots, m),$$

is called the *residual* and is denoted by R_j. Thus we have the m *residual equations* exhibited in (85.2). The principle of least squares states that the best representation of the data is that which makes the *sum of the squares of the residuals a minimum*. We therefore try to make the function

$$f(a_0, a_1, \ldots, a_n) = R_1^2 + R_2^2 + R_3^2 + \cdots + R_m^2 \qquad (85.3)$$

a minimum. The condition which fulfills this requirement is that the partial derivatives be zero.[1] Thus

$$\frac{\partial f}{\partial a_0} = 2\left(R_1 \frac{\partial R_1}{\partial a_0} + R_2 \frac{\partial R_2}{\partial a_0} + \cdots + R_m \frac{\partial R_m}{\partial a_0} \right) = 0,$$

$$\frac{\partial f}{\partial a_1} = 2\left(R_1 \frac{\partial R_1}{\partial a_1} + R_2 \frac{\partial R_2}{\partial a_1} + \cdots + R_m \frac{\partial R_m}{\partial a_1} \right) = 0, \qquad (85.4)$$
$$\vdots$$
$$\frac{\partial f}{\partial a_n} = 2\left(R_1 \frac{\partial R_1}{\partial a_n} + R_2 \frac{\partial R_2}{\partial a_n} + \cdots + R_m \frac{\partial R_m}{\partial a_n} \right) = 0.$$

[1]See P. Franklin, *Methods of Advanced Calculus*, New York: McGraw-Hill, 1944.

Now

$$\frac{\partial R_j}{\partial a_0} = \frac{\partial}{\partial a_0}(a_0 + a_1 x_j + a_2 x_j^2 + \cdots + a_n x_j^n - y_j) = 1,$$

$$\frac{\partial R_j}{\partial a_1} = \frac{\partial}{\partial a_1}(a_0 + a_1 x_j + a_2 x_j^2 + \cdots + a_n x_j^n - y_j) = x_j,$$

$$\frac{\partial R_j}{\partial a_2} = \frac{\partial}{\partial a_2}(a_0 + a_1 x_j + a_2 x_j^2 + \cdots + a_n x_j^n - y_j) = x_j^2,$$ (85.5)

$$\vdots$$

$$\frac{\partial R_j}{\partial a_n} = \frac{\partial}{\partial a_n}(a_0 + a_1 x_j + a_2 x_j^2 + \cdots + a_n x_j^n - y_j) = x_j^n$$

for $(j = 1, \ldots, m)$. The system in (84.5) thus becomes

$$R_1 + R_2 + R_3 + \cdots + R_m = 0,$$

$$x_1 R_1 + x_2 R_2 + x_3 R_3 + \cdots + x_m R_m = 0,$$

$$x_1^2 R_1 + x_2^2 R_2 + x_3^2 R_3 + \cdots + x_m^2 R_m = 0,$$ (85.6)

$$\vdots$$

$$x_1^n R_1 + x_2^n R_2 + x_3^n R_n + \cdots + x_m^n R_m = 0.$$

If we replace R_j by their values from (85.2) and collect the coefficients of the $n + 1$ unknowns a_i $(i = 0, \ldots, n)$, we have

$$m a_0 + \sum x_j a_1 + \sum x_j^2 a_2 + \cdots + \sum x_j^n a_n - \sum y_j = 0,$$

$$\sum x_j a_0 + \sum x_j^2 a_1 + \sum x_j^3 a_2 + \cdots + \sum x_j^{n+1} a_n - \sum x_j y_j = 0,$$

$$\sum x_j^2 a_0 + \sum x_j^3 a_1 + \sum x_j^4 a_2 + \cdots + \sum x_j^{n+2} a_n - \sum x_j^2 y_j = 0,$$ (85.7)

$$\vdots$$

$$\sum x_j^n a_0 + \sum x_j^{n+1} a_1 + \sum x_j^{n+2} a_2 + \cdots + \sum x_j^{2n} a_n - \sum x_j^n y_j = 0,$$

where all summations are 1 to m, that is,

$$\sum x_j^3 = x_1^3 + x_2^3 + x_3^3 + \cdots + x_m^3,$$

$$\sum x_j^2 y_j = x_1^2 y_1 + x_2^2 y_2 + \cdots + x_m^2 y_m.$$

The expressions in (85.7) are known as *normal equations*. All of the summations

are known so that (85.7) is a system of $n + 1$ linear equations in the $n + 1$ unknowns a_i $(i = 0, \ldots, n)$, the solution of which yields the coefficients a_i so
that the polynomial

$$y = a_0 + a_1 x + a_2 x^2 + \cdots + a_n x^n$$

is now determined. The procedure is to calculate all the sums indicated from
the given data, insert these sums into the system (85.7), and solve for a_i $(i = 0,$
$\ldots, n)$. Various short cuts for accomplishing this are discussed later.

The principle of least squares is not limited to polynomials. The desired
function could take any known form as long as the resulting normal equations
can be solved. This, of course, is easiest if the normal equations are linear.

Since the subject of analytical geometry has disappeared as a formal course
from the college curriculum, textbooks on this subject are also disappearing.
The part of analytical geometry being incorporated into books dealing with
the calculus usually does not include the subject of the representation of
empirical data, and students who are fortunate enough to have a textbook
that includes this topic frequently find that it is severed by the instructor. It
is thus possible that students may arrive at this stage of mathematical maturity
without having encountered the principle of least squares. We shall therefore
discuss this principle and its application in some detail and introduce elementary examples along with the advanced applications.

86.   ELEMENTARY APPLICATIONS

Let there be given m ordered pairs (x_j, y_j), which may be the result
of observed experimental data

x	x_1	x_2	x_3	$\cdots$	x_m
y	y_1	y_2	y_3	$\cdots$	y_m

and let it be desired to fit this data with a relation between x and y.

I. STRAIGHT LINE. The simplest relation between x and y is the
linear form

$$y = a + bx.$$

Our problem is to find the undetermined coefficients a and b such that the line is a good fit to the tabulated data. An application of the principle of least squares will result in (85.7), the normal equations, which, for this case, reduce to the two equations

$$ma + \sum x_j b = \sum y_j,$$
$$\sum x_j a + \sum x_j^2 b = \sum x_j y_j; \tag{86.1}$$

the solutions of this system are

$$a = \frac{1}{\Delta}[(\sum y_j)(\sum x_j^2) - (\sum x_j y_j)(\sum x_j)],$$

$$b = \frac{1}{\Delta}[m\sum x_j y_j - (\sum y_j)(\sum x_j)],$$

where

$$\Delta = m\sum x_j^2 - (\sum x_j)^2.$$

With this determination of a and b we have the least squares fit to the data.

Example 8.1. Fit a straight line to the data

x	-3	-1	1	4	5	7	10
y	-2	-1	0	1.5	2	3	4.5

SOLUTION. Calculate the values

$$m = 7, \quad \sum x_j = 23, \quad \sum x_j^2 = 201, \quad \sum y_j = 8, \quad \sum x_j y_j = 89.$$

The normal equations (86.1) are

$$7a + 23b = 8,$$
$$23a + 201b = 89,$$

with solutions

$$a = -\tfrac{1}{2} \quad \text{and} \quad b = \tfrac{1}{2},$$

and the equation of the line is

$$y = -\tfrac{1}{2} + \tfrac{1}{2}x \quad \text{or} \quad 2y + 1 = x.$$

II. PARABOLA. Before considering this case, let us adopt the convenient notation

$$
\begin{aligned}
S_0 &= m, & k_0 &= \sum_{j=1}^{m} y_j, \\
S_1 &= \sum_{i=1}^{m} x_i, & k_1 &= \sum_{j=1}^{m} x_j y_j, \\
S_2 &= \sum_{i=1}^{m} x_i^2, \quad (86.2) \quad \text{and} & k_2 &= \sum_{j=1}^{m} x_j^2 y_j, \\
&\vdots & &\vdots \\
S_k &= \sum_{i=1}^{m} x_i^k, & k_k &= \sum_{j=1}^{m} x_j^k y_j.
\end{aligned}
\tag{86.3}
$$

One form of the parabola is the quadratic function

$$ y = a + bx + cx^2, \tag{86.4} $$

which has the three undetermined coefficients a, b, and c. The normal equations become (in our new notation)

$$
\begin{aligned}
ma + S_1 b + S_2 c &= k_0, \\
S_1 a + S_2 b + S_3 c &= k_1, \\
S_2 a + S_3 b + S_4 c &= k_2,
\end{aligned}
\tag{86.5}
$$

and we can use Crout's method to solve for a, b, and c.

Example 8.2. Fit the given data (x_j, y_j) by a parabola.

SOLUTION. We have $m = 7$ and calculate the following table to get the sums.

GIVEN		CALCULATED				
x	y	x^2	x^3	x^4	xy	$x^2 y$
−2	0	4	−8	16	0	0
−1	4	1	−1	1	−4	4
0	6	0	0	0	0	0
1	6	1	1	1	6	6
2	4	4	8	16	8	16
3	0	9	27	81	0	0
4	−6	16	64	256	−24	−96
7	14	35	91	371	−14	−70
S_1	k_0	S_2	S_3	S_4	k_1	k_2

The normal equations are

$$7a + 7b + 35c = 14$$
$$7a + 35b + 91c = -14$$
$$35a + 91b + 371c = -70$$

with solutions

$$a = 6, \qquad b = 1, \qquad c = -1$$

and

$$y = 6 + x - x^2.$$

The role of x and y can be interchanged to fit the data by an equation of the form

$$x = a + by + cy^2. \tag{86.6}$$

Example 8.3. Fit the given data (x_j, y_j) by a parabola of the form

$$x = a + by + cy^2.$$

SOLUTION. The following table is calculated to give the sums for the $m = 7$ observations. Note the change in the definitions of the sums.

GIVEN		CALCULATED				
x	y	y^2	y^3	y^4	yx	y^2x
1	0	0	0	0	0	0
2	2	4	8	16	4	8
2	-2	4	-8	16	-4	8
5	4	16	64	256	20	80
5	-4	16	-64	256	-20	80
10	6	36	216	1296	60	360
10	-6	36	-216	1296	-60	360
35	0	112	0	3136	0	896
k_0	S_1	S_2	S_3	S_4	k_1	k_2

The resulting normal equations are

$$7a + 0b + 112c = 35$$
$$0a + 112b + 0c = 0$$
$$112a + 0b + 3136c = 896$$

with solutions

$$a = 1, \qquad b = 0, \qquad c = \tfrac{1}{4},$$

and the equation is

$$x = 1 + \tfrac{1}{4}y^2 \quad \text{or} \quad y^2 = 4(x - 1).$$

III. CUBIC. Let us consider the cubic

$$y = a_0 + a_1 x + a_2 x^2 + a_3 x^3. \tag{86.7}$$

It is required to obtain the coefficients a_i $(i = 0, 1, 2, 3)$ by the method of least squares. We shall need the sums (86.2) and (86.3), and a schematic for calculating them can be arranged as follows:

x^0	x	x^2	x^3	x^4	x^5	x^6	y	xy	x^2y	x^3y
1	x_1	x_1^2	x_1^3	x_1^4	x_1^5	x_1^6	y_1	$x_1 y_1$	$x_1^2 y_1$	$x_1^3 y_1$
1	x_2	x_2^2	x_2^3	x_2^4	x_2^5	x_2^6	y_2	$x_2 y_2$	$x_2^2 y_2$	$x_2^3 y_2$
1	x_3	x_3^2	x_3^3	x_3^4	x_3^5	x_3^6	y_3	$x_3 y_3$	$x_3^2 y_3$	$x_3^3 y_3$
.										
.										
.										
1	x_m	x_m^2	x_m^3	x_m^4	x_m^5	x_m^6	y_m	$x_m y_m$	$x_m^2 y_m$	$x_m^3 y_m$
$S_0 = m$	S_1	S_2	S_3	S_4	S_5	S_6	k_0	k_1	k_2	k_3

The normal equations can then be written in this manner:

$$S_0 a_0 + S_1 a_1 + S_2 a_2 + S_3 a_3 = k_0$$
$$S_1 a_0 + S_2 a_1 + S_3 a_2 + S_4 a_3 = k_1$$
$$S_2 a_0 + S_3 a_1 + S_4 a_2 + S_5 a_3 = k_2$$
$$S_3 a_0 + S_4 a_1 + S_5 a_2 + S_6 a_3 = k_3.$$

Let us consider an example.

Example 8.4. Fit a cubic to the data

x	-4	-2	-1	0	1	3	4	6
y	-35.1	15.1	15.9	8.9	$.1$	$.1$	21.1	135

SOLUTION. Let us first obtain the required sums.

x^0	x	x^2	x^3	x^4	x^5	x^6	y	xy	x^2y	x^3y
1	−4	16	−64	256	−1024	4096	−35.1	140.4	−561.6	2246.4
1	−2	4	−8	16	−32	64	15.1	−30.2	60.4	−120.8
1	−1	1	−1	1	−1	1	15.9	−15.9	15.9	−15.9
1	0	0	0	0	0	0	8.9	0	0	0
1	1	1	1	1	1	1	.1	.1	.1	.1
1	3	9	27	81	243	729	.1	.3	.9	2.7
1	4	16	64	256	1024	4096	21.1	84.4	337.6	1350.4
1	6	36	216	1296	7776	46656	135.0	810.0	4860.0	29160.0
8	7	83	235	1907	7987	55643	161.1	989.1	4713.3	32622.9

The normal equations are

$$8a_0 + 7a_1 + 83a_2 + 235a_3 = 161.1$$
$$7a_0 + 83a_1 + 235a_2 + 1907a_3 = 989.1$$
$$83a_0 + 235a_1 + 1907a_2 + 7987a_3 = 4713.3$$
$$235a_0 + 1907a_1 + 7987a_2 + 55643a_3 = 32622.9.$$

Solving by Crout's method, we obtain the values of a_i,

a_0	a_1	a_2	a_3
9.011039	−8.966140	−1.000093	.999074.

The cubic is given by

$$.999x^3 - 1.000x^2 - 8.966x + 9.011 = 0.$$

A check on the given points shows a good fit.

x	−4	−2	−1	0	1	3	4	6
y (GIVEN)	−35.1	15.1	15.9	8.9	.1	.1	21.1	135
y (CALC.)	−35.1	15.0	16.0	9.0	.0	.1	21.1	135
DIFF.	0	.1	−.1	−.1	.1	0	0	0

87.   EVENLY SPACED INTERVALS

As we have seen so often in the past, great simplification occurs if the data are given at equally spaced values of the argument. In such a case we have

$$x_j = x_1 + (j - 1)h, \qquad (j = 1, \ldots, m), \tag{87.1}$$

where h is the interval length between the equidistant x-points. There are four main advantages which may now be realized.

I. THE VALUES OF THE ARGUMENT MAY BE TRANSFORMED TO THE INTEGERS, $0, 1, 2, \ldots, m$.

This fact is accomplished by changing the variable to

$$x_j' = \frac{x_j - x_1}{h}. \tag{87.2}$$

It is now easily seen that

$$x_1' = \frac{x_1 - x_1}{h} = 0,$$

$$x_2' = \frac{x_2 - x_1}{h} = \frac{x_1 + h - x_1}{h} = 1,$$

$$\vdots$$

$$x_j' = \frac{x_j - x_1}{h} = \frac{x_1 + (j - 1)h - x_1}{h} = j - 1.$$

II. THE DATA MAY BE EASILY CENTRALIZED ABOUT THE ARITHMETIC MEAN.[2] Centralizing the data about the arithmetic mean is accomplished by the transformation

$$X_j = x_j - \bar{x} \quad \text{and} \quad Y_j = y_j - \bar{y}, \tag{87.3}$$

where

$$\bar{x} = \frac{1}{m} \sum_{j=1}^{m} x_j \quad \text{and} \quad \bar{y} = \frac{1}{m} \sum_{j=1}^{m} y_j. \tag{87.4}$$

For equally spaced intervals we have

$$\bar{x} = \frac{1}{m} \sum_{j=1}^{m} [x_1 + (j - 1)h] = \frac{1}{m}\left(mx_1 + h \sum_{j=1}^{m-1} j\right)$$

$$= x_1 + \tfrac{1}{2}(m - 1)h, \tag{87.5}$$

[2]We invite attention to Tables XIV and XV and the facts about summations which precede them.

since

$$\sum_{k=1}^{m-1} k = \tfrac{1}{2}(m - 1)m.$$

Thus

$$X_j = x_j - \bar{x} = x_1 + (j - 1)h - x_1 - \tfrac{1}{2}(m - 1)h$$
$$= \tfrac{1}{2}(2_j - m - 1)h. \tag{87.6}$$

We now have some very useful properties.

Property A. *If m is odd, $\bar{x} = x_M$ where x_M is the "middle" value of the set x_j.*

   PROOF. Let $m = 2r - 1$, an odd number; then

$$M = \tfrac{1}{2}(m + 1) = \tfrac{1}{2}(2r - 1 + 1) = r$$

and

$$\bar{x} = x_1 + \tfrac{1}{2}(m - 1)h = x_1 + \tfrac{1}{2}(2r - 1 - 1)h$$
$$= x_1 + (r - 1)h$$
$$= x_r = x_M.$$

Corollary. In this case $X_M = 0$.

   PROOF.

$$X_M = x_M - \bar{x} = x_M - x_M = 0.$$

Property B. *The set X_j consists of two identical sets except for algebraic sign.*

   PROOF. By formula 87.6 we have

$$X_1 \quad = \tfrac{1}{2}(2 - m - 1)h = \tfrac{1}{2}(1 - m)h,$$
$$X_2 \quad = \tfrac{1}{2}(4 - m - 1)h = \tfrac{1}{2}(3 - m)h,$$
$$X_3 \quad = \tfrac{1}{2}(6 - m - 1)h = \tfrac{1}{2}(5 - m)h,$$
$$\vdots$$
$$X_M \quad = \tfrac{1}{2}(2M - m - 1)h,$$
$$\vdots$$
$$X_{m-2} = \tfrac{1}{2}(2m - 4 - m - 1)h = \tfrac{1}{2}(m - 5)h,$$
$$X_{m-1} = \tfrac{1}{2}(2m - 2 - m - 1)h = \tfrac{1}{2}(m - 3)h,$$
$$X_m \quad = \tfrac{1}{2}(2m - m - 1)h = \tfrac{1}{2}(m - 1)h,$$

from which it is easily seen that

$$
\begin{aligned}
X_1 &= -X_m, \\
X_2 &= -X_{m-1}, \\
X_3 &= -X_{m-2}, \\
&\vdots \\
X_{M-1} &= -X_{M+1},
\end{aligned}
\tag{87.7}
$$

and at the midpoint we have $X_M = 0$ if m is odd and X_M is not a member of the set if m is even.

Property C. *The summation of X_j^i over values for j assumes three forms:*
(a) *if i is an odd integer*

$$
\sum_{j=1}^m X_j^i = 0;
\tag{87.8}
$$

(b) *if i is an even integer and $m = 2r - 1$ is an odd integer*

$$
\sum_{j=1}^m X_j^i = 2h^i \sum_{k=1}^{r-1} k^i;
\tag{87.9}
$$

(c) *if i is an even integer and $m = 2r$ is an even integer*

$$
\sum_{j=1}^m X_j^i = \left(\frac{1}{2}\right)^i 2h^i \sum_{k=1}^r (2k-1)^i.
\tag{87.10}
$$

PROOF. The truth of the property may be established directly from Property B. By the equalities (87.7) we see that a summation of X_j would result in a cancellation of all the terms. Since the sign will be retained when the term is raised to an odd power, we see that the cancellation will still hold when summing X_j^i, provided i is odd. Thus (a) of Property C follows directly.

To prove (b), we see that for $m = 2r - 1$, $X_j = (j - r)h$ or the set (X_j) is composed of two sets $[(k - r)h]$ and $[(r - k)h]$ with k running from 1 to r. If these quantities are raised to an even power, they are all positive. Thus

$$
\sum_{j=1}^m X_j^i = \sum_{j=1}^r 2[(j-r)h]^i = 2h^i \sum_{k=1}^{r-1} k^i.
$$

Part (c) follows in the same manner. As with $m = 2r$, we have $X_j = \frac{1}{2}(2j - 2r - 1)h$ which consists of two sets $[\frac{1}{2}(n - 2r)h]$ and $[\frac{1}{2}(2r - n)h]$, with n being the odd integers from 1 to $2r$. Thus with i even we have

$$\sum_{j=1}^{r} X_j^i = \left(\frac{1}{2}\right)^i 2h^i \sum_{k=1}^{r} (2k - 1)^i.$$

III. THE NORMAL EQUATIONS ARE GREATLY SIMPLIFIED. To ease the notation let us define

$$S_i = \begin{cases} \sum_{k=1}^{r-1} k^i, & \text{if } m \text{ is odd} \\[2mm] \left(\frac{1}{2}\right)^i \sum_{k=1}^{r} (2k - 1)^i, & \text{if } m \text{ is even.} \end{cases} \qquad (i = 2, 4, \ldots, 2n) \quad (87.11)$$

Then for equally spaced intervals the normal equations in (85.7) may be transformed to the simple system represented schematically by

b_0	b_1	b_2	b_3	$\cdots$	b_n	c
m	0	$2S_2h^2$	0	$\cdots$	$2S_nh^n$	$\sum Y_j$
0	$2S_2h^2$	0	$2S_4h^4$	$\cdots$	$2S_{n+1}h^{n+1}$	$\sum X_j Y_j$
$2S_2h^2$ $\vdots$	0	$2S_4h^4$	0	$\cdots$	$2S_{n+2}h^{n+2}$	$\sum X_j^2 Y_j$
$2S_nh^n$	$2S_{n+1}h^{n+1}$	$\cdots$	$\cdots$	$\cdots$	$2S_{2n}h^{2n}$	$\sum X_j^n Y_j$

(87.12)

where in the last row and last column of b_n, $S_{n+q} = 0$ if $n + q$ is odd ($q = 0, 1, \ldots, n$).

IV. THE COMPUTATION OF THE CONSTANTS IN THE NORMAL EQUATIONS MAY BE SIMPLIFIED. The centralization of the data about the arithmetic mean permits us to reduce the calculation of the constant terms in the normal equation considerably. First, we have

$$\sum_{j=1}^{m} Y_j = \sum_{j=1}^{m} (y_j - \bar{y}) = \sum_{j=1}^{m} y_j - \sum_{j=1}^{m} \bar{y} \qquad (87.13)$$

$$= m\bar{y} - m\bar{y} = 0.$$

Second, we have by (87.7)

$$\sum_{j=1}^{m} X_j Y_j = X_1 Y_1 + X_2 Y_2 + X_3 Y_3 + \cdots$$
$$+ X_{m-2} Y_{m-2} + X_{m-1} Y_{m-1} + X_m Y_m$$
$$= X_1 Y_1 + X_2 Y_2 + X_3 Y_3$$
$$+ \cdots - X_3 Y_{m-2} - X_2 Y_{m-1} - X_1 Y_m \quad (87.14)$$
$$= X_1 (Y_1 - Y_m) + X_2 (Y_2 - Y_{m-1})$$
$$+ X_3 (Y_3 - Y_{m-2}) + \cdots$$
$$= \sum_{j=1}^{r} X_j D(Y_j),$$

where

$$D(Y_j) = Y_j - Y_{m-j+1} = y_{M+j} - y_{M-j}. \quad (87.15)$$

In general, if i is *odd*, we have

$$\sum_{j=1}^{m} X_j^i Y_j = \sum_{j=1}^{r} X_j^i D(Y_j). \quad (87.16)$$

Third, we have by (87.7), if i is *even*,

$$\sum_{j=1}^{m} X_j^i Y_j = \sum_{j=1}^{r} X_j^i S(Y_j), \quad (87.17)$$

where

$$S(Y_j) = Y_j + Y_{m-j+1} = y_{M+j} + y_{M-j} - 2\bar{y}. \quad (87.18)$$

Let us put all of these advantages from equidistant data together and see how they ease the calculation.

Example 8.5. Fit a cubic to the data

x	1	2	3	4	5	6	7	8	9	10	11
y	108.0	55.9	.1	−54.1	−100.0	−131.9	−143.9	−129.9	−84.1	0	127.9

SOLUTION. Since h is already equal to 1, we begin by centralizing the data. We have $m = 11$ (an odd number); therefore

$$\bar{x} - x_M = 6, \qquad \bar{y} = -32.00, \qquad 2\bar{v} = -64.00.$$

We now arrange the data in columns, using the formulas above. To obtain $S(Y)$ and $D(Y)$, we add a column of identifying numbers, I, which has 0 at (x_M, y_M) and then order the terms in each direction. This identifying column is also carried over to the transformed data. Thus, to find the entry at $I = 2$, we have

$$D_2(Y) = y \text{ (at } I = 2 \text{ below 0)} - y \text{ (at } I = 2 \text{ above 0), etc.}$$

At $I = 0$ we have

$$S(Y) = D(Y) = y_M - \bar{y}.$$

As a check $\sum S(Y) = 0$.

x	y	I	X	I	$S(Y)$	$D(Y)$
1	108.0	5	0	0	-99.9	-99.9
2	55.9	4	1	1	-179.9	-43.9
3	.1	3	2	2	-120.0	-75.8
4	-54.1	2	3	3	-20.0	-84.2
5	-100.0	1	4	4	119.9	-55.9
6	-131.9	0	5	5	299.9	19.9
7	-143.9	1			0	
8	-129.9	2				
9	-84.1	3				
10	0	4				
11	127.9	5				

The normal equations (87.12) are now easily obtained.

b_0	b_1	b_2	b_3	c
11	0	110	0	0
0	110	0	1958	-572.2
110	0	1958	0	8576.0
0	1958	0	41030	-4013.8

These can be solved directly by elimination to yield

$$b_0 = -99.95337,$$
$$b_1 = -22.983804,$$
$$b_2 = 9.995337,$$
$$b_3 = .998990,$$

and we have

$$Y = .998990\,X^3 + 9.995337\,X^2 - 22.983804\,X - 99.95337.$$

The transformation back to (x, y) can easily be accomplished by a Horner's method division, using -6 as the divisor and adding $\bar{y}$ to the constant term.

.998990	9.995337	-22.983804	-99.95337	$\underline{\quad}-6$
	4.001397	-46.992186	181.999746	
	-1.992543	$\boxed{-35.036928}$	-32.00000	
	$\boxed{-7.986483}$		149.999746	
$\boxed{.998990}$				

Thus

$$y = .999x^3 - 7.986x^2 - 35.037x + 150.000.$$

88.   THE NIELSEN-GOLDSTEIN METHOD[3]

It was shown in the last section that for equally spaced values of the argument the normal equations simplify to those given in (87.12). If we further transform these equations by dividing *successive* equations by $2h^i(i = 0, \ldots, n)$ and then replacing b_i by $a_i h^{-i}$, we have a system of equations in a_i which may be represented by

α_0	α_1	α_2	α_3		α_n	c	
$\frac{1}{2}m$	0	S_2	0	$\cdots$	S_n	$\frac{1}{2}\sum Y_j$	
0	S_2	0	S_4	$\cdots$	S_{n+1}	$\frac{1}{2}h^{-1}\sum X_j Y_j$	
S_2	0	S_4	0	$\cdots$	S_{n+2}	$\frac{1}{2}h^{-2}\sum X_j^2 Y_j$	(88.1)
0	S_4	0	S_6	$\cdots$	S_{n+3}	$\frac{1}{2}h^{-3}\sum X_j^3 Y_j$	
$\vdots$							
S_n	S_{n+1}	S_{n+2}	S_{n+3}	$\cdots$	S_{2n}	$\frac{1}{2}h^{-n}\sum X_j^n Y_j$	

where $S_i = 0$ if i is an odd number.

Before proceeding with the solution of this system of equations divide each equation, except the first, by S_2. Letting $S_i' = S_i S_2^{-1}$, we have the following system:

[3]K. L. Nielsen and L. Goldstein, "An Algorithm for Least Squares," *Journal of Mathematics and Physics*, **26**, 120–132 (July, 1941).

α_0	α_1	α_2	α_3		α_n	c
$\tfrac{1}{2}m$	0	S_2	0	$\cdots$	S_n	0
0	1	0	S'_4	$\cdots$	S'_{n+1}	c_2
1	0	S'_4	0	$\cdots$	S'_{n+2}	c_3
0	S'_4	0	S'_6	$\cdots$	S'_{n+3}	c_4
$\vdots$						
S'_n	S'_{n+1}	S'_{n+2}	S'_{n+3}	$\cdots$	S'_{2n}	c_{n+1}

$$(88.2)$$

where again $S'_i = S_i = 0$, if i is an odd number, and

$$c_i = \tfrac{1}{2}S_2^{-1}h^{-i+1}\sum_{j=1}^{m}X_j^{i-1}Y_j, \qquad (i = 2, \cdots, n+1). \qquad (88.3)$$

The sums S_i [see (87.11)] and S'_i are functions of the number of observations only. In fact, they can be calculated by the formulas.[4]

Case 1.

$$\sum_{k=1}^{r}k^i = \frac{1}{i+1}r^{i+1} + \frac{1}{2}r^i + \frac{1}{2}\binom{i}{1}B_1 r^{i-1} - \frac{1}{4}\binom{i}{3}B_2 r^{i-3} + \cdots. \qquad (88.4)$$

Case 2. $m = 2r$.

$$\left(\frac{1}{2}\right)^i \sum_{k=1}^{r}(2k-1)^i = \left(\frac{1}{2}\right)^i \left(\sum_{k=1}^{2r}k^i - 2^i\sum_{k=1}^{r}k^i\right), \qquad (88.5)$$

where $B_s(s = 1, 2, \ldots)$ are the Bernoulli numbers.

Let us now solve the system in (88.2) by Crout's method. We would first have the derived matrix

$$\begin{pmatrix} A_{11} & A_{12} & \cdots & A_{1,n+1} & K_1 \\ A_{21} & A_{22} & \cdots & A_{2,n+1} & K_2 \\ A_{31} & A_{32} & \cdots & A_{3,n+1} & K_3 \\ \vdots & & & & \\ A_{n+1,1} & A_{n+1,2} & \cdots & A_{n+1,n+1} & K_{n+1} \end{pmatrix} \qquad (88.6)$$

[4]E. P. Adams, *Smithsonian Mathematical Formulae and Tables of Elliptic Functions*, Washington, D.C.: Smithsonian Institution, 1947, p. 27.

where

$$A_{ii} = S'_{2i-2} - \sum_{w=1}^{i-2} A_{iw} A_{wi},$$

$$A_{ij} = \frac{S'_{i+j-2} - \sum_{w=1}^{i-2} A_{iw} A_{wj}}{A_{ii}}, \qquad \text{if } (j > i), \tag{88.7}$$

$$A_{ij} = A_{ji} A_{jj}, \qquad \text{if } (j < i),$$

$(i = 2, \ldots, n + 1)$,
and

$$K_i = \frac{c_i - \sum_{j=1}^{i-1} K_j A_{ij}}{A_{ii}}, \qquad (i = 1, \ldots, n + 1), \tag{88.8}$$

with

$$A_{ij} = 0 \text{ if } i + j \text{ is an odd number.}$$

The elements of the solution matrix are given by

$$a_i = K_{i+1} - \sum_{j=i+2}^{n} a_j A_{i+1\ j+1}, \qquad (i = 0, \ldots, n). \tag{88.9}$$

Now, since S_i and S'_i depend only on the number of observations, so do the A_{ij} which consequently can be computed once and for all and tabulated. It is not necessary to tabulate all of the A_{ij}, since there are certain interrelations. In fact, the relations among the A_{ij} form a nice algebraic study. Table XVI, p. 380, exhibits values of A_{ij} sufficient to compute fourth-degree polynomials for $5 \le m \le 100$ observations and sixth-degree polynomials for $6 \le m \le 50$ observations. By use of these tables we may simultaneously compute these polynomials up to the sixth degree (or fourth) which gives the least squares fit to the data. This is accomplished by a simple substitution in a set of formulas.

Let us concentrate on polynomials up to and including the sixth degree. The derived matrix of the normal equations is

$$\begin{Vmatrix} \alpha_0 & \alpha_1 & \alpha_2 & \alpha_3 & \alpha_4 & \alpha_5 & \alpha_6 & c \\ A_{11} & 0 & A_{13} & 0 & A_{15} & 0 & A_{17} & 0 \\ 0 & 1 & 0 & A_{24} & 0 & A_{26} & 0 & K_2 \\ 1 & 0 & A_{33} & 0 & A_{35} & 0 & A_{37} & K_3 \\ 0 & A_{24} & 0 & A_{44} & 0 & A_{46} & 0 & K_4 \\ A_{24} & 0 & A_{53} & 0 & A_{55} & 0 & A_{57} & K_5 \\ 0 & A_{26} & 0 & A_{64} & 0 & A_{66} & 0 & K_6 \\ A_{26} & 0 & A_{73} & 0 & A_{75} & 0 & A_{77} & K_7 \end{Vmatrix}$$

(88.10)

Now it can be shown that

$$\begin{aligned} A_{15} &= A_{13}A_{24}; & A_{53} &= A_{35}A_{33}; & A_{73} &= A_{37}A_{33}; \\ A_{17} &= A_{13}A_{26}; & A_{64} &= A_{46}A_{44}; & A_{75} &= A_{57}A_{55}. \end{aligned}$$

(88.11)

Using these relations, we see that the values of K_i are given by

$$K_1 = 0,$$

$$K_2 = c_2,$$

$$K_3 = \frac{c_3}{A_{33}},$$

$$K_4 = \frac{c_4 - c_2 A_{24}}{A_{44}} = \frac{K_4'}{A_{44}},$$

$$K_5 = \frac{c_5 - c_3 A_{35}}{A_{55}} = \frac{K_5'}{A_{55}},$$

(88.12)

$$K_6 = \frac{c_6 - c_2 A_{26} - A_{46}K_4'}{A_{66}},$$

$$K_7 = \frac{c_7 - c_3 A_{37} - A_{57}K_5'}{A_{77}},$$

where

$$K_4' = c_4 - c_2 A_{24},$$

$$K_5' = c_5 - c_3 A_{35}.$$

(88.13)

The solution for $a_i (i = 0, \ldots, 6)$, depends on the degree, n, of the equation desired. Their formulas can be exhibited in the following table:

TABLE 8.I. FORMULAS FOR α_i

α_i	$n = 6$	$n = 5$	$n = 4$	$n = 3$	$n = 2$	$n = 1$
α_6	K_7					
α_5	K_6	K_6				
α_4	$K_5 - \alpha_6 A_{57}$	K_5	K_5			
α_3	$K_4 - \alpha_5 A_{46}$	$K_4 - \alpha_5 A_{46}$	K_4	K_4		
α_2	$K_3 - \alpha_6 A_{37} - \alpha_4 A_{35}$	$K_3 - \alpha_4 A_{35}$	$K_3 - \alpha_4 A_{35}$	K_3	K_3	
α_1	$K_2 - \alpha_5 A_{26} - \alpha_3 A_{24}$	$K_2 - \alpha_5 A_{26} - \alpha_3 A_{24}$	$K_2 - \alpha_3 A_{24}$	$K_2 - \alpha_3 A_{24}$	K_2	K_2
α_0	$-A_{13}(\alpha_6 A_{26} + \alpha_4 A_{24} + \alpha_2)$	$-A_{13}(\alpha_4 A_{24} + \alpha_2)$	$-A_{13}(\alpha_4 A_{24} + \alpha_2)$	$-\alpha_2 A_{13}$	$-\alpha_2 A_{13}$	0

In Table 8.1 the values of α_i must be obtained from the same column in which they are used. Even so, we can see that many of the values are the same. Thus, using the notation $[\alpha_i]_n$ where n designates the degree of the equation, we have

$$[\alpha_5]_6 = [\alpha_5]_5; \; [\alpha_4]_5 = [\alpha_4]_4; \; [\alpha_3]_4 = [\alpha_3]_3; \; [\alpha_2]_3 = [\alpha_2]_2;$$

$$[\alpha_1]_2 = [\alpha_1]_1;$$

$$[\alpha_3]_6 = [\alpha_3]_5; \; [\alpha_2]_5 = [\alpha_2]_4; \; [\alpha_1]_4 = [\alpha_1]_3; \; [\alpha_0]_3 = [\alpha_0]_2;$$

$$[\alpha_1]_6 = [\alpha_1]_5; \; [\alpha_0]_5 = [\alpha_0]_4.$$

(88.14)

The identities in (88.14) save much computation when we find the polynomials of degree one through six simultaneously.

The calculating procedure may now be summarized into the following steps:

1. Locate the midpoint of the data and order the identifying numbers.
2. Calculate $\bar{x}, \bar{y}, X, S(Y), D(Y)$ and check $\Sigma S(Y) = 0$.
3. Look up S_2 and A_{ij} in Table XVI, p. 380.
4. Calculate

$$p_i = \sum_{j=1}^{M} X_j^{i-1} D_j(Y), \qquad (i = 2, 4, 6),$$

$$p_i = \sum_{j=1}^{M} X_j^{i-1} S_j(Y), \qquad (i = 3, 5, 7).$$

(88.15)

5. Calculate

$$C_i = \frac{p_i h^{-i+1}}{2S_2}.$$

6. Calculate K_i by (88.12).
7. Calculate α_i using the formulas in Table 8.1. A column for each degree of the polynomial desired is needed.
8. The next step is to obtain the $b_i (i = 0, \dots, n)$ from the formulas

$$b_i = [\alpha_i]_n h^{-i}, \qquad (i = 1, \dots, n)$$

and

$$b_0 = [\alpha_0]_n + \bar{y}.$$

9. The mean values are now removed from the computation and α_i are obtained by a repeated synthetic division by $-\bar{x}$.

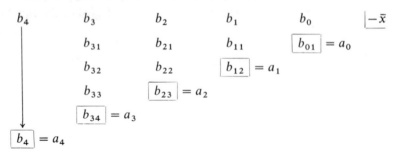

where

$$
\begin{array}{ll}
b_{31} = b_3 \;+ b_4(-\bar{x}) & b_{21} = b_2 \;+ b_{31}(-\bar{x}) \\
b_{32} = b_{31} + b_4(-\bar{x}) & b_{22} = b_{21} + b_{32}(-\bar{x}) \\
b_{33} = b_{32} + b_4(-\bar{x}) & b_{23} = b_{22} + b_{33}(-\bar{x}) \\
b_{34} = b_{33} + b_4(-\bar{x}) & \\
\\
b_{11} = b_1 \;+ b_{21}(-\bar{x}) & b_{01} = b_0 \;+ b_{11}(-\bar{x}) \\
b_{12} = b_{11} + b_{22}(-\bar{x}) &
\end{array}
$$

All of the formulas can be placed on one sheet, which also gives a pattern for a calculation schematic. We exhibit one for polynomials up to and including the fourth degree as shown on pages 287 and 288.

POLYNOMIAL FITTING OF DATA

$$y = \sum_{i=0}^{n} a_i x^i, \quad (n \leq 4)$$

Formulas

x	y	I	X	I	$S(Y)$	$D(Y)$	AUXILIARY	CONSTANTS
x_1	y_1							A_{13} A_{33}
x_2	y_2							
x_3	y_3		$x_i - x$					A_{24} A_{44}
.	.							
.	.							A_{35} A_{55}
.	.				$y_{M+i} + y_{M-i} - 2\bar{y}$	$y_{M+i} - y_{M-i}$		
x_{M-3}	y_{M-3}	3						From Table XVI, p. 282
x_{M-2}	y_{M-2}	2						
x_{M-1}	y_{M-1}	1						m = number of observations
x_M	y_M	0			Check:			$h = x_2 - x_1$
x_{M+1}	y_{M+1}	1			$\sum_{i=1}^{m} S_i(Y) = 0$			$\bar{x} = \dfrac{1}{m}\sum_{i=1}^{m} x_i$
x_{M+2}	y_{M+2}	2						$\bar{y} = \dfrac{1}{m}\sum_{i=1}^{m} y_i$
x_{M+3}	y_{M+3}	3						$S_2 = $ [table]
.	.							$p_2 = \sum_{j=1}^{M} X_j\, D_j(Y)$
.	.							$p_3 = \sum_{j=1}^{M} X_j^2\, S_j(Y)$
x_{m-1}	y_{m-1}							$p_4 = \sum_{j=1}^{M} X_j^3\, D_j(Y)$
x_m	y_m							$p_5 = \sum_{j=1}^{M} X_j^4\, S_j(Y)$

i	h^{-i+1}	C_i	K_i	$[a_{i-1}]_4$	$[a_{i-1}]_3$	$[a_{i-1}]_2$	$[a_{i-1}]_1$
1	1	0	0	$-A_{13}(a_4A_{24}+a_2)$	$-a_2A_{13}-a_3A_{24}$	$-a_2A_{13}$	0
2	h^{-1}	$p_2h^{-1}/2S_2$	C_2	$K_2-a_3A_{24}$	K_2	K_2	K_2
3	h^{-2}	$p_3h^{-2}/2S_2$	C_3/A_{33}	$K_3-a_4A_{35}$	K_3	K_3	
4	h^{-3}	$p_4h^{-3}/2S_2$	$[C_4-K_2A_{24}]/A_{44}$	K_4	K_4		
5	h^{-4}	$p_5h^{-4}/2S_2$	$[C_5-C_3A_{35}]/A_{55}$	K_5			

b_4	b_3	b_2	b_1	b_0	$-\bar{x}$	
$[a_4]_4h^{-4}$	$[a_3]_4h^{-3}$	$[a_2]_4h^{-2}$	$[a_1]_4h^{-1}$	$[a_0]_4+\bar{y}$		

Computation scheme:

$[a_3]_4h^{-3}$:
$b_{31}=b_3-\bar{x}b_4$
$b_{32}=b_{31}-\bar{x}b_4$
$b_{33}=b_{32}-\bar{x}b_4$
$b_{34}=b_{33}-\bar{x}b_4$ (a4)

$[a_2]_4h^{-2}$:
$b_{21}=b_2-\bar{x}b_{31}$
$b_{22}=b_{21}-\bar{x}b_{32}$
$b_{23}=b_{22}-\bar{x}b_{33}$ (a3)

$[a_1]_4h^{-1}$:
$b_{11}=b_1-\bar{x}b_{21}$
$b_{12}=b_{11}-\bar{x}b_{22}$ (a2)

$[a_0]_4+\bar{y}$:
$b_{01}=b_0-\bar{x}b_{11}$ (a1)   (a0)

$[a_3]_3h^{-3}$:
$[a_2]_3h^{-2}$:
$b_{21}=b_2-\bar{x}b_3$
$b_{22}=b_{21}-\bar{x}b_3$
$b_{23}=b_{22}-\bar{x}b_3$ (a3)

$[a_1]_3h^{-1}$:
$b_{11}=b_1-\bar{x}b_{21}$
$b_{12}=b_{11}-\bar{x}b_{22}$ (a2)

$[a_0]_3+\bar{y}$:
$b_{01}=b_0-\bar{x}b_{11}$ (a1)   (a0)

$[a_2]_2h^{-2}$:
$[a_1]_2h^{-1}$:
$b_{11}=b_1-\bar{x}b_2$
$b_{12}=b_{11}-\bar{x}b_2$ (a2)

$[a_0]_2+\bar{y}$:
$b_{01}=b_0-\bar{x}b_{11}$ (a1)   (a0)

$[a_1]_1h^{-1}$:
$[a_0]_1+\bar{y}$:
$b_{01}=b_0-\bar{x}b_1$ (a1)   (a0)

Example 8.6. Fit the data (x_i, y_i) by a polynomial.

SOLUTION.

x	y	I	X	I	S(Y)	D(Y)	CONSTANTS	
0	.5179	8	0	0	−3.0490	−3.0490	$m = 17$	$A_{13} = 24$
.2	.7049	7	.2	1	−5.8520	2.5360	$h = .2$	$A_{33} = 19$
.4	.9625	6	.4	2	−5.1110	5.1390	$\bar{x} = 1.6$	
.6	1.3090	5	.6	3	−3.8690	7.8730	$\bar{y} = 8.2240$	$A_{24} = 43$
.8	1.7650	4	.8	4	−2.1140	10.8040	$2\bar{y} = 16.4480$	$A_{44} = 342$
1.0	2.3530	3	1.0	5	.1690	13.9990	$S_2 = 204$	
1.2	3.0990	2	1.2	6	3.0015	17.5245	$2S_2 = 408$	$A_{35} = 61$
1.4	4.0300	1	1.4	7	6.4079	21.4461	$p_2 = 122.30882$	$A_{55} = 5928$
1.6	5.1750	0	1.6	8	10.4166	25.8288	$p_3 = 39.9195$	
1.8	6.5660	1			0		$p_4 = 216.5056$	
2.0	8.2380	2					$p_5 = 97.7682$	
2.2	10.2260	3						
2.4	12.5690	4						
2.6	15.3080	5						
2.8	18.4870	6						
3.0	22.1510	7						
3.2	26.3467	8						

i	h^{-i+1}	C_i	K_i	$[\alpha_{i-1}]_4$	$[\alpha_{i-1}]_3$	$[\alpha_{i-1}]_2$	$\alpha[_{i-1}]_1$
1	1	0	0	−3.048999	−3.089736	−3.089736	0
2	5	1.498883	1.498883	1.262598	1.262598	1.498883	1.498883
3	25	2.446048	.128739	.122987	.128739	.128739	
4	125	66.331372	.005495	.005495	.005495		
5	625	149.767474	.942937*	.942937*		$*(10^{-4})$	

b_4	b_3	b_2	b_1	b_0	$-\bar{x}$
.058933	.686875	3.074675	6.312990	5.175001	−1.6
↓	.592582	2.126544	2.910520	.518169	$\leftarrow a_0$
	.498289	1.329282	.783669	$\leftarrow a_1$	quartic fit
	.403996	.682888	$\leftarrow a_2$		
	.309703	$\leftarrow a_3$			
.058933 $\leftarrow a_4$					

	b_3	b_2	b_1	b_0	$-\bar{x}$
	.686875	3.218475	6.312990	5.134264	−1.6
	↓	2.119475	2.921830	.459336	$\leftarrow a_0$
		1.020475	1.289070	$\leftarrow a_1$	cubic fit
		−.078525	$\leftarrow a_2$		
	.686875 $\leftarrow a_3$				

Quartic fit: $.0589x^4 + .3097x^3 + .6829x^2 + .7837x + .5182 = y$.

Cubic fit: $.6869x^3 - .0785x^2 + 1.2891x + .4593 = y$.

Example 8.7. Fit a sixth-degree polynomial to the data.

SOLUTION.

x	y	I	X	$S(Y)$	$D(Y)$	CONSTANTS	
−2.0	175.0	8	0	−25.3	−25.3	$m = 17$	$A_{13} = 24$
−1.5	97.2	7	.5	−39.8	103.2	$h = .5$	$A_{33} = 19$
−1.0	50.8	6	1.0	−11.2	189.6	$\bar{x} = 2.0$	$A_{24} = 43$
−0.5	20.0	5	1.5	23.5	244.9	$\bar{y} = 104.8$	$A_{44} = 342$
0	.5	4	2.0	47.9	256.5	$2\bar{y} = 209.6$	$A_{35} = 61$
0.5	−5.9	3	2.5	48.4	218.0	$S_2 = 204$	$A_{55} = 5928$
1.0	4.4	2	3.0	19.2	127.2	$2S_2 = 408$	$A_{26} = 2191$
1.5	33.3	1	3.5	−25.0	−9.8		$A_{46} = 78\ 1/3$
2.0	79.5	0	4.0	−37.7	−178.1		$A_{66} = 98800$
2.5	136.5	1		check			$A_{37} = 3601$
3.0	194.0	2					$A_{57} = 95$
3.5	239.0	3					$A_{77} = 1573200$
4.0	257.0	4					
4.5	238.0	5					
5.0	178.0	6					
5.5	87.4	7					
6.0	−3.1	8					

i	h^{-i+1}	C_i	K_i	K_i'	α_{i-1}	b_{i-1}
1	1	0	0		−25.381860	79.418140
2	2	6.379657	6.379657		52.907237	105.814474
3	4	−2.066912	−.108785		5.678039	22.712156
4	8	−37.193873	−.9108875	−311.519124	−1.400547	−11.204377
5	16	−356.284558	−.03883315	−230.202926	−.18683232	−2.989317
6	32	−9806.890720	.006251134		.006251134	.200036
7	64	−26861.361024	.001557886		.001557886	.099705

b_6	b_5	b_4	b_3	b_2	b_1	b_0	$-\bar{x}$
.099705	.200036	−2.989317	−11.204377	22.712156	105.814474	79.418140	−2
	.000627	−2.990571	−5.223236	33.158627	39.497220	.423700	
	−.198783	−2.593006	−.037224	33.233075	−26.968930		
	−.398192	−1.796622	3.556020	26.121035			
	−.597601	−.601419	4.758859				
	−.797011	.992602					
	−.996420						
.099705							

$$y = .0997x^6 - .9964x^5 + .9926x^4 + 4.759x^3 + 26.12x^2 - 26.97x + .4237.$$

Note. The application of this method to the linear equation

$$y = a_0 + a_1 x$$

yields the direct solutions

$$a_1 = (2S_2)^{-1} h^{-2} \sum X_j D_j(Y) \quad \text{and} \quad a_0 = \bar{y} - \bar{x} a_1. \qquad (88.16)$$

89. USE OF ORTHOGONAL POLYNOMIALS

The polynomial fitting of data determines the coefficients $a_i (i = 0, \dots, n)$ such that

$$y = a_0 + a_1 x + a_2 x^2 + \cdots + a_n x^n \qquad (89.1)$$

is a good fit. Suppose, instead, we consider fitting the data with

$$y = b_0 P_0 + b_1 P_1(x) + b_2 P_2(x) + \cdots + b_n P_n(x), \qquad (89.2)$$

where

$$P_i(x) = i\text{th degree polynomial in } x.$$

The principle of least squares seeks to minimize the squares of the residuals

$$\sum_{j=0}^{m} (b_0 P_0 + b_1 P_1 + \cdots + b_n P_n - y_j)^2 = R^2(b_i). \qquad (89.3)$$

The normal equations are

$$\begin{aligned}
(\sum P_0^2) b_0 + (\sum P_0 P_1) b_1 + \cdots + (\sum P_0 P_n) b_n - \sum P_0 y_j &= 0, \\
(\sum P_0 P_1) b_0 + (\sum P_1^2) b_1 + \cdots + (\sum P_1 P_n) b_n - \sum P_1 y_j &= 0, \\
\vdots \\
(\sum P_0 P_n) b_0 + (\sum P_1 P_n) b_1 + \cdots + (\sum P_n^2) b_n - \sum P_n y_j &= 0.
\end{aligned} \qquad (89.4)$$

Now if

$$\sum P_i P_j = 0 \quad \text{when} \quad (i \neq j), \qquad (89.5)$$

the normal equations reduce to

$$\begin{aligned}
\sum P_0^2 b_0 - \sum P_0 y_j &= 0, \\
\sum P_1^2 b_1 - \sum P_1 y_j &= 0, \\
\vdots \\
\sum P_n^2 b_n - \sum P_n y_j &= 0,
\end{aligned} \qquad (89.6)$$

from which

$$b_i = \frac{\sum P_i y_j}{\sum P_i^2},$$ (89.7)

and we have the coefficients for (89.2).

A set of polynomials which satisfies the condition (89.5) are the orthogonal polynomials.[5] In particular, we choose the following set:

$$P_0(x) = 1,$$

$$P_1(x) = x - \bar{x},$$

$$\vdots$$ (89.8)

$$P_{i+1}(x) = P_1 P_i - \frac{i^2(m^2 - i^2)}{4(4i^2 - 1)} P_{i-1},$$

where m is the number of observations in the given data (x_i, y_i) and we have transformed x to integral values by (87.2). Let us have a closer look at these polynomials by considering a specific number of observations, say $m = 11$. Then by substituting into Formula 89.8 we have

$$P_0 = 1,$$

$$P_1 = x - \bar{x},$$

$$P_2 = P_1^2 - 10P_0 = (x - \bar{x})^2 - 10,$$

$$P_3 = P_1 P_2 - \frac{117}{15} P_1 = \frac{1}{5}(5P_1 P_2 - 39P_1),$$ (89.9)

$$P_4 = P_1 P_3 - \frac{36}{5} P_2 = \frac{1}{5}(5P_1 P_3 - 36P_2),$$

$$P_5 = P_1 P_4 - \frac{20}{3} P_3 = \frac{1}{3}(3P_1 P_4 - 20P_3),$$

and, since x_i has the values $1, 2, 3, \ldots, 11$, we see that

x_i	1	2	3	4	5	6	7	8	9	10	11	C.F.
$P_0(x_i)$	1	1	1	1	1	1	1	1	1	1	1	
$P_1(x_i)$	-5	-4	-3	-2	-1	0	1	2	3	4	5	
$P_2(x_i)$	15	6	-1	-6	-9	-10	-9	-6	-1	6	15	
$P_3(x_i)$	-30	6	22	23	14	0	-14	-23	-22	-6	30	6/5
$P_4(x_i)$	6	-6	-6	-1	4	6	4	-1	-6	-6	6	12
$P_5(x_i)$	-3	6	1	-4	-4	0	4	4	-1	-6	3	40

[5] See Chapter 1, Section 3H.

where C.F. $\equiv$ common factor which has been removed from each value of $P_j(x_i)$. The condition

$$\sum_{i=1}^{m} P_k P_n(x_i) = 0, \qquad k \neq n,$$

can easily be verified for these numbers.

Since the values of $P_i(x_j)$ for integral values of x are dependent only on the number of observations, these values can be computed once and for all and tabulated. In tabulating them, we note the "symmetry" about x_M and see that we need record only half of the values if we use $S(Y)$ and $D(Y)$. It is also necessary to have $\sum P_i^2$ which can be recorded at the bottom of each column. Since it is convenient to use only integral values for the entries, common factors are factored out so that the entries are really related to the polynomial values by

$$P_i(x_j) = \text{C.F. (entry)}, \tag{89.10}$$

and a transformation to the true value in terms of x is accomplished by replacing P_i' which is obtained from the entry by λP_i where $\lambda = 1/\text{C.F.}$ Values of λ are also recorded for each polynomial. The tabular values for $m = 11$ would then take this form:

X	P_1'	P_2'	P_3'	P_4'	P_5'
0	0	-10	0	6	0
1	1	-9	-14	4	4
2	2	-6	-23	-1	4
3	3	-1	-22	-6	-1
4	4	6	-6	-6	-6
5	5	15	30	6	3
$\sum P_i'^2$	110	858	4290	286	156
λ	1	1	5/6	1/12	1/40

The values of $P_0(x_i) \equiv 1$ and therefore are not recorded. To compute b_i from Formula 89.7, we obtain $S(Y)$ and $D(Y)$ and then

$$b_0 = \frac{1}{m}\sum y_j = \bar{y},$$

$$b_1 = \frac{\sum P_1'(X) D(Y)}{\sum P_1'^2(x)},$$

$$b_2 = \frac{\sum P_2'(X) S(Y)}{\sum P_2'^2(x)},$$

$$b_3 = \frac{\sum P_3'(X) D(Y)}{\sum P_3'^2(x)}, \qquad\qquad (89.11)$$

$$b_4 = \frac{\sum P_4'(X) S(Y)}{\sum P_4'^2(x)},$$

$$b_5 = \frac{\sum P_5'(X) D(Y)}{\sum P_5'^2(x)}.$$

This obtains the polynomial expression

$$y = b_0 + b_1 P_1'(x) + b_2 P_2'(x) + \cdots + b_n P_n'(x). \qquad (89.12)$$

If y is to be expressed as a polynomial in x, we make the further transformation

$$P_i'(x_j) = \lambda P_i(x_j)$$

and calculate the form of $P_i(x_j)$ by (89.8). Let us consider an example.

Example 8.8. Solve Example 8.5. by using the table of orthogonal polynomials.

SOLUTION.

x	y	I	X	I	$S(Y)$	$D(Y)$	b_i
1	108.0	5	0	0	-99.9	-99.9	-32
2	55.9	4	1	1	-179.9	-43.9	-5.201818
3	.1	3	2	2	-120.0	-75.8	9.995337
4	-54.1	2	3	3	-20.0	-84.2	1.198787
5	-100.0	1	4	4	119.9	-55.9	
6	-131.9	0	5	5	299.9	19.9	
7	-143.9	1					
8	-129.9	2					
9	-84.1	3					
10	0	4					
11	127.9	5					

The values of b_i are computed by (89.11) by using the table for $m = 11$. This yields

$$y = 1.198787P_3'(x) + 9.995337P_2'(x) - 5.201818P_1'(x) - 32.$$

To transform these values to a power series in x, we have

$$P_1'(x) = 1P_1(x) = 1(x - \bar{x}) = x - 6,$$

$$P_2'(x) = 1P_2(x) = (x - \bar{x})^2 - 10 = x^2 - 12x + 26,$$

$$P_3'(x) = \tfrac{5}{6}P_3(x) = \tfrac{5}{6}(\tfrac{1}{5})(5P_1P_2 - 39P_1)$$

$$= \tfrac{1}{6}(5x^3 - 90x^2 + 451x - 546),$$

and

$$\boxed{y = .99899x^3 - 7.98647x^2 - 35.03704x + 150}\,.$$

Values of the modified orthogonal polynomials for $m = 4$ to $m = 33$ are given in Table XVII, p. 386.[6]

90.   SMOOTHING OF DATA

The formulas derived in the last sections may be used to obtain smoother data than that given by the observations. This smoothing of data is accomplished by replacing the observed data by calculated data based on fitting the original data by a polynomial. Thus for equidistant data we calculate the values from the approximating polynomial (89.2):

$$y(x) = \sum_{i=0}^{n} b_i P_i(x), \tag{90.1}$$

where

$$b_i = \frac{\sum P_i y_i}{\sum P_i^2}. \tag{90.2}$$

[6]An extensive table up to $m = 75$ may be found in Fisher and Yates, *Statistical Tables.* New York: Hafner, 1949.

At a given value of the argument we may express the value of the function in terms of the observed values of the function. To illustrate clearly, let us consider five equidistant points.

x_0	x_1	x_2	x_3	x_4
y_0	y_1	y_2	y_3	y_4

and fit them with a third-degree polynomial,

$$y(x) = b_0 P_0(x) + b_1 P_1(x) + b_2 P_2(x) + b_3 P_3(x). \tag{90.3}$$

Now let

$$S_i = \sum_{j=0}^{4} P_i^2(x_j), \qquad (i = 0, 1, 2, 3), \tag{90.4}$$

so that

$$b_i = \frac{1}{S_i} \sum_{j=0}^{4} P_i(x_j) y_j$$

$$= \frac{1}{S_i} [P_i(0)y_0 + P_i(1)y_1 + P_i(2)y_2 + P_i(3)y_3 + P_i(4)y_4] \tag{90.5}$$

if the x_i have been transformed to the integers. Then

$$y(x) = \frac{1}{S_0} [P_0(0)y_0 + P_0(1)y_1 + P_0(2)y_2 + P_0(3)y_3 + P_0(4)y_4]P_0(x)$$

$$+ \frac{1}{S_1} [P_1(0)y_0 + P_1(1)y_1 + P_1(2)y_2 + P_1(3)y_3 + P_1(4)y_4]P_1(x)$$

$$+ \frac{1}{S_2} [P_2(0)y_0 + P_2(1)y_1 + P_2(2)y_2 + P_2(3)y_3 + P_2(4)y_4]P_2(x)$$

$$+ \frac{1}{S_3} [P_3(0)y_0 + P_3(1)y_1 + P_3(2)y_2 + P_3(3)y_3 + P_3(4)y_4]P_3(x)$$

$$= c_0 y_0 + c_1 y_1 + c_2 y_2 + c_3 y_3 + c_4 y_4,$$

where

$$c_0(x) = \frac{1}{S_0} P_0(0) P_0(x) + \frac{1}{S_1} P_1(0) P_1(x)$$

$$+ \frac{1}{S_2} P_2(0) P_2(x) + \frac{1}{S_3} P_3(0) P_3(x),$$

$$c_1(x) = \sum_{j=0}^{3} \frac{1}{S_j} P_j(1) P_j(x),$$ \hspace{2cm} (90.6)

$$\vdots$$

$$c_i(x) = \sum_{j=0}^{3} \frac{1}{S_j} P_j(i) P_j(x).$$

Now if we pick a specific point, $x = x_i$, $P_j(x_i)$ can be evaluated and $y(x_j)$ is the sum of known numbers. For the values $x_i = 0, 1, 2, 3, 4$ we have $\bar{x} = 2$ so that by Formula 89.8

$$P_0(x) = 1,$$

$$P_1(x) = x - 2,$$ \hspace{2cm} (90.7)

$$P_2(x) = x^2 - 4x + 2,$$

$$P_3(x) = \tfrac{1}{5}(x - 2)(5x^2 - 20x + 3),$$

and the values are

	$x=0$	$x=1$	$x=2$	$x=3$	$x=4$	S_i
$P_0(x)$	1	1	1	1	1	5
$P_1(x)$	-2	-1	0	1	2	10
$P_2(x)$	2	-1	-2	-1	2	14
$P_3(x)$	$-\dfrac{6}{5}$	$\dfrac{12}{5}$	0	$-\dfrac{12}{5}$	$\dfrac{6}{5}$	$\dfrac{72}{5}$

The values of $c_i(x)$ at $x = x_j$ are easily calculated from (90.6) to yield

	$x=0$	$x=1$	$x=2$	$x=3$	$x=4$
$c_0(x)$	69	2	-3	2	-1
$c_1(x)$	4	27	12	-8	4
$c_2(x)$	-6	12	17	12	-6
$c_3(x)$	4	-8	12	27	4
$c_4(x)$	-1	2	-3	2	69
L.C.D.	70	35	35	35	70

Thus the new values of y_i are given by

$$y_0^* = \tfrac{1}{70}(69y_0 + 4y_1 - 6y_2 + 4y_3 - y_4),$$

$$y_1^* = \tfrac{1}{35}(2y_0 + 27y_1 + 12y_2 - 8y_3 + 2y_4),$$

$$y_2^* = \tfrac{1}{35}(-3y_0 + 12y_1 + 17y_2 + 12y_3 - 3y_4), \qquad (90.8)$$

$$y_3^* = \tfrac{1}{35}(2y_0 - 8y_1 + 12y_2 + 27y_3 + 2y_4),$$

$$y_4^* = \tfrac{1}{70}(-y_0 + 4y_1 - 6y_2 + 4y_3 + 69y_4).$$

The midpoint formula y_2^* is most frequently used when smoothing the data by fitting a cubic to five points, for it can apply to any portion of the data for which $h = 1$.

Example 8.9. Obtain a smoother set of values to (x_i, y_i) given below by a cubic fit to five consecutive points.

SOLUTION. The formulas for y_0^*, y_1^*, and y_2^* of (90.8) are used to calculate these new values. Then the midpoint formula, y_2^*, is used until y_{17}^* is reached. The formulas for y_3^* and y_4^* give y_{18}^* and y_{19}^*.

x	y	y^*
0	0	$-.1$
1	3	3.3
2	7	6.5
3	9	9.5
4	12	11.6
5	13	13.3
6	14	13.9
7	14	14.0
8	13	12.8
9	11	11.1
10	10	10.4
11	11	10.6
12	10	9.9
13	8	8.3
14	7	6.8
15	6	6.1
16	6	6.3
17	7	6.1
18	5	5.6
19	6	5.9

These formulas are based on the idea of fitting the best cubic polynomial through five consecutive points with $h = 1$. It is, of course, easy to derive some other smoothing formula based on different choices of the *degree of the polynomial* and on *the number of points*. The procedure would be identical, but the usual is to keep both the degree of the polynomial and the number of points odd. The results would be a set of multiplying coefficients for the y_i entries, the most important being the midpoint formula. These coefficients are given in Tables 8.2 and 8.3.

TABLE 8.2. SMOOTHING FORMULAS. BASED ON THIRD-DEGREE POLYNOMIAL

NO POINTS	5	7	9	11	13	15	17	19
DENOMINATOR	35	21	231	429	143	1105	323	2261
i								
0	-3	-2	-21	-36	-11	-78	-21	-136
1	12	3	14	9	0	-13	-6	-51
2	17	6	39	44	9	42	7	24
3	12	7	54	69	16	87	18	89
4	-3	6	59	84	21	122	27	144
5		3	54	89	24	147	34	189
6		-2	39	84	25	162	39	224
7			14	69	24	167	42	249
8			-21	44	21	162	43	264
9				9	16	147	42	269
10				-36	9	122	39	264
11					0	87	34	249
12					-11	42	27	224
13						-13	18	189
14						-78	7	144
15							-6	89
16							-21	24
17								-51
18								-136

TABLE 8.3. SMOOTHING FORMULAS. BASED ON FIFTH-DEGREE POLYNOMIAL

i / NO POINTS	7	9	11	13	15	17	19
DENOMINATOR	231	429	429	2431	46189	4199	7429
0	5	15	18	110	2145	195	340
1	−30	−55	−45	−198	−2860	−195	−255
2	75	30	−10	−135	−2937	−260	−420
3	131	135	60	110	−165	−117	−290
4	75	179	120	390	3755	135	18
5	−30	135	143	600	7500	415	405
6	5	30	120	677	10125	660	790
7		−55	60	600	11063	825	1110
8		15	−10	390	10125	883	1320
9			−45	110	7500	825	1393
10			18	−135	3755	660	1320
11				−198	−165	415	1110
12				110	−2937	135	790
13					−2860	−117	405
14					2145	−260	18
15						−195	−290
16						195	−420
17							−255
18							340

Example 8.10. Check the value at $x = 12$ of Example 8.6 by the 11-point formula for both a third-degree and a fifth-degree fit.

SOLUTION.

(a) Third degree:

$$y^*(12) = [-36(14) + 9(13) + 44(11) + 69(10) + 84(11) + 89(10)$$
$$+ 84(8) + 69(7) + 44(6) + 9(6) - 36(7)]/429$$
$$= 8.9.$$

(b) Fifth degree:

$$y^*(12) = [18(14) - 45(13) - 10(11) + 60(10) + 120(11) + 143(10)$$
$$+ 120(8) + 60(7) - 10(6) - 45(6) + 18(7)]/429$$
$$= 9.5.$$

91. WEIGHTED RESIDUALS

For some data more weight may be given to some observations than others, in which case the best fit is that for which the sum of the weighted squares of the residuals is a minimum:

$$\sum wR^2 = w_1 R_1^2 + w_2 R_2^2 + \cdots + w_n R_n^2, \tag{91.1}$$

where w_i is a set of weights. To minimize the function (91.1), we set the partial derivatives equal to zero to obtain a set of weighted normal equations.

Let us consider a simple problem of fitting the data having weights w_j with a quadratic:

$$y = a_0 + a_1 x + a_2 x^2. \tag{91.2}$$

The weighted residuals are

$$w_j R_j = w_j (a_0 + a_1 x_j + a_2 x_j^2 - y_j), \tag{91.3}$$

and the sum of the weighted squares of the residuals is

$$\sum w_j R_j^2 = \sum w_j (a_0 + a_1 x_j + a_2 x_j^2 - y_j)^2, \tag{91.4}$$

the summation being over j from 0 to m for the m observations. Taking the partial derivative of (91.4) with respect to a_i and setting each equal to zero yields the weighted normal equations

$$w_1(a_0 + a_1 x_1 + a_2 x_1^2 - y_1) + \cdots$$
$$+ w_m(a_0 + a_1 x_m + a_2 x_m^2 - y_m) = 0,$$
$$w_1 x_1(a_0 + a_1 x_1 + a_2 x_1^2 - y_1) + \cdots$$
$$+ w_m x_m(a_0 + a_1 x_m + a_2 x_m^2 - y_m) = 0, \tag{91.5}$$
$$w_1 x_1^2(a_0 + a_1 x_1 + a_2 x_1^2 - y_1) + \cdots$$
$$+ w_m x_m^2(a_0 + a_1 x_m + a_2 x_m^2 - y_m) = 0,$$

which may be transformed into

$$(\sum w_j)a_0 + (\sum w_j x_j)a_1 + (\sum w_j x_j^2)a_2 = \sum w_j y_j,$$
$$(\sum w_j x_j)a_0 + (\sum w_j x_j^2)a_1 + (\sum w_j x_j^3)a_2 = \sum w_j x_j y_j, \tag{91.6}$$
$$(\sum w_j x_j^2)a_0 + (\sum w_j x_j^3)a_1 + (\sum w_j x_j^4)a_2 = \sum w_j x_j^2 y_j,$$

and from which we solve for a_i to obtain the fit (91.2).

The weights, w_j, may be arbitrarily assigned from previous knowledge of the observations, or they may be determined by some probable error study. In general, the weights are inversely proportional to the squares of the probable errors. If the data are obtained statistically, the weights are usually chosen to be the reciprocal to the square of the standard deviation.

For the logarithmic function it can be shown[7] that if the weights of y are equal the weights of $\log y$ are given by

$$w_f = \frac{y^2}{M^2},\tag{91.7}$$

where $M = .43429$.

Example 8.11. Fit the following data, given the values of the weights, with the expression

$$\log y = \log k + n \log x$$

x	172	210	320	400
y	66	80	100	120
w	4356	6400	10000	14400

SOLUTION. To determine $\log k$ and n, we write the equation

$$Y = K + nX,$$

where

$$Y = \log y, \qquad K = \log k, \qquad X = \log x,$$

so that the data is changed to

X	2.23553	2.32222	2.50515	2.60206
Y	1.81954	1.90309	2.00000	2.07918
w	4356	6400	10000	14400

---

[7]See J. B. Scarborough, *Numerical Mathematical Analysis*, seconded. Baltimore: Johns Hopkins University Press, 1950, p. 460.

The weighted normal equations [see (91.6)] are easily calculated:

$$35156K + 87121.34n = 70045.88,$$
$$87121.34K + 216538.92n = 174011.92,$$

the solution of which yields

$$K = 0.33346, \qquad n = .66944.$$

The equation is

$$\boxed{\log y = .33346 + .66944 \log x}.$$

92.   EXERCISE XI

1. Obtain the least square linear fit to the data:

(a)

x	-2	-1	0	2	3	5
y	-1.0	0.7	2.3	5.6	7.4	10.7

(b)

x	0	1	2	3	4	5	6	7	8	9	10
y	5.0	4.4	3.9	3.6	3.1	2.4	2.0	1.6	0.9	.06	-0.1

Use (86.1) and (88.16) on (b).

2. Given the data

x	-2	0	1	3	4
y	18.1	3.9	3.0	12.9	24.1

obtain the best fitting quadratic function.

3. Given the data

x	0	1	2	3	4	5	6	7	8	9	10
y	4	88	158	211	240	250	240	210	160	100	0

obtain the best fitting polynomial of degree 4, 3, and 2. Use the Nielsen-Goldstein method and the method of orthogonal polynomials and compare results.

4. Obtain the best cubic fit to the data

x	y	x	y
0	.127462	3.2	2.55362
.2	.133271	3.4	.263251
.4	.139413	3.6	.270285
.6	.145905	3.8	.276221
.8	.152753	4.0	.280822
1.0	.159964	4.2	.283815
1.2	.167528	4.4	.285005
1.4	.175459	4.6	.284214
1.6	.183731	4.8	.281286
1.8	.192319	5.0	.276144
2.0	.201186	5.2	.268764
2.2	.210262	5.4	.259179
2.4	.219482	5.6	.247465
2.6	.228741	5.8	.233738
2.8	.237937	6.0	.218226
3.0	.246848		

5. Fit a fourth-degree polynomial to the data for y_2 in Problem 14, Exercise II.

6. Fit a fifth-degree polynomial to the first 25 values of the data for y_3 in Problem 14, Exercise II (Option: round the data for y_3 to two decimal values before fitting the data.)

7. Apply the principle of least squares to the relation $Ax^2 + Cy^2 = 1$; develop the normal equations and solutions for A and C.

8. Apply the principle of least squares to the general second degree equation

$$Ax^2 + Bxy + Cy^2 + Dx + Ey + 1 = 0.$$

9. Given the circle $x^2 + y^2 = 9$, compute 11 ordered pairs (correct to two decimals) that satisfy this relation. Apply the formulas developed in Problem 7 to fit the calculated data and compare with the given equation.

10. Prove by direct substitution that

$$\sum_{j=1}^{m} X_j^i = 2h^i \sum_{k=1}^{r-1} k^i$$

if $m = 2r - 1 = 17$ and $i = 4$.

11. Prove that

$$\sum_{k=1}^{r} (2k-1)^i = \sum_{k=1}^{2r} k^i - 2^i \sum_{k=1}^{r} k^i.$$

12. Show that in the method of orthogonal polynomials $S(Y)$ may be replaced by $S^*(Y) = y_{M+i} + y_{M-i}$ and $S^*(Y_0) = y_M$ if $m = 11$. Generalize this statement.

13. Given the data

x	y	x	y
0	1	13	15
1	3	14	14
2	4	15	16
3	6	16	15
4	5	17	15
5	7	18	14
6	6	19	13
7	9	20	12
8	10	21	12
9	10	22	10
10	12	23	11
11	11	24	9
12	14	25	7

Smooth the values with (90.8) at the beginning and end and use

(a) an 11-point cubic,
(b) a 9-point fifth degree

wherever possible. Compare values.

14. Fit a quadratic to the weighted observations of

x	0	1	2	3	4	5	6
y	1	3	4	6	6	7	8
w	1	1	.75	.5	.5	1	1

15. Develop the normal equations for fitting a cubic to a set of weighted observations. Calculate 13 pairs of values from the equation $y = x^3$ in the interval $-3 \leq x \leq 3$. Weight the central seven values 2 and the remaining six values 1; then fit this weighted data with a cubic.

93. THE EXPONENTIAL TYPE FUNCTION

Frequently in physical problems a given set of data may be well fitted by a function of the type

$$y = aN^x \tag{93.1}$$

or

$$y = ae^{bx}. \tag{93.2}$$

From the properties of logarithms they may be changed to the forms

$$\log y = \log a + x \log N \qquad (93.3)$$

and

$$\log y = \log a + bx \log e,$$
$$\ln y = \ln a + bx, \qquad (93.4)$$

where $\ln N$ is the natural logarithm of N (to the base e). By a substitution of variables we can let

$$\log y = z,$$
$$\log a = c,$$
$$\log N = d, \qquad (93.5)$$
$$x \log e = w,$$

to obtain

$$z = c + dx \qquad (93.6)$$

and

$$z = c + bw, \qquad (93.7)$$

both of which are linear expressions to which we may apply the principle of least squares to determine b, c, and d.

Another function treated in the same manner is

$$y = ax^n \qquad (93.8)$$

which may be transformed to

$$\log y = \log a + n \log x. \qquad (93.9)$$

In order to determine if the given data are suitable to be fitted by these functions, it is recommended that they be plotted on various graph papers from which we establish the following criterion:

1. If the data appear to lie on a straight line when plotted on *semilogarithmic* graph paper, use the formula

$$y = ae^{bx} \quad \text{or} \quad y = aN^x.$$

2. If the data appear to lie on a straight line when plotted on *logarithmic* graph paper, use the formula

$$y = ax^n.$$

Example 8.12. Determine a functional fit to the data

x	1	2	3	4	5	6	7	8	9	10	11
y	1.00	1.15	1.30	1.50	1.75	2.00	2.30	2.65	3.00	3.50	4.00

SOLUTION. A plot on semilogarithmic paper reveals a straight-line tendency. We therefore fit the data with

$$y = aN^x \quad \text{or} \quad z = c + dx,$$

where $z = \log y$, $c = \log a$, and $d = \log N$. Using a five-place logarithmic table, we have

x	1	2	3	4	5	6	7	8	9	10	11
z	0	.06070	.11394	.17609	.24304	.30103	.36173	.42325	.47712	.54407	.60206

The Nielsen-Goldstein method yields

$$d = (2S_2)^{-1} \sum X_j \, D_j(Y) = (110)^{-1}(6.64633) = .060421,$$

$$c = \bar{y} - \bar{x}d = .300275 - 6(.060421) = -.062251.$$

Therefore

$$a = \text{antilog}\,(-.062251) = \text{antilog}\,(9.93775 - 10) = .86646,$$

$$N = \text{antilog}\,(.06042) \quad = 1.1493,$$

and

$$y = .86646(1.1493)^x.$$

Example 8.13. Determine a functional fit to the data

x	1	2	3	4	5	6	7
y	5.0	7.5	9.5	11.3	13.0	14.5	16.0

SOLUTION. A plot on log paper shows a straight-line tendency. Thus we try

$$y = ax^n \quad \text{or} \quad z = c + nw,$$

where $z = \log y$, $c = \log a$, and $w = \log x$.

The transformed data are

w	0	.30103	.47712	.60206	.69897	.77815	.84510
z	.69897	.87506	.97772	1.05308	1.11394	1.16137	1.20412

The values are no longer given at equidistant values of the independent variable (w), so that we need to obtain the normal equations to apply the principle of least squares. For a linear expression these are [see (86.1)]

$$mc + \sum w_i n = \sum z_i,$$
$$\sum w_i c + \sum w_i^2 n = \sum w_i z_i,$$

and in our our example, using the schematic of Section 61.

c	n	k
7	3.70243	7.08426
3.70243	2.489009	4.063859
3.715075	.69625	.59704

Now

$$a = \text{antilog} (.69625) = 4.9688,$$

so that we have

$$y = 4.9688x^{.59704}.$$

94.   THE METHOD OF DIFFERENTIAL CORRECTION

In the preceding sections we discussed the fitting of empirical data by some well-known functions that adapt themselves to simple procedures. Thus we can usually transform the functions to a polynomial and then apply the method of least squares. This is the most desirable procedure since it is advantageous to deal with well-known functions. Occasionally, however, certain empirical data can be fitted only by complicated functions, or the data may be the result of a physical experiment which dictates certain parameters that can be given physical significance. It is then necessary to have a general method for handling these cases, one that we call the *method of differential correction*.

Let us suppose that we want a formula which is to relate the two variables x and y and which will have a number of undetermined constants; for simplicity let us choose three, a, b, and c. Symbolically, we write

$$y = f(x, a, b, c). \tag{94.1}$$

This formula is to be a good fit to the data $(x_i, y_i)(i = 1, \ldots, m)$. The residuals are given by

$$R_1 = f(x_1, a, b, c) - y_1,$$
$$R_2 = f(x_2, a, b, c) - y_2, \tag{94.2}$$
$$\vdots$$
$$R_m = f(x_m, a, b, c) - y_m,$$

where $y_i(i = 1, \ldots, m)$ are the given (observed) values from the original data. Let us make a plot of the given data and from it determine approximate values to the constants, a, b, c, and call them a_0, b_0, c_0; or let us simply pick a form for f based on our past experience perhaps and then make an educated guess on some initial values for the parameters. It is desired to correct these approximate values by some incremental amount α, β, γ such that

$$a = a_0 + \alpha,$$
$$b = b_0 + \beta, \tag{94.3}$$
$$c = c_0 + \gamma$$

will yield better values and the formula will fit the data.

If we substitute the values in (94.3) into the residuals in (94.2) and transpose the y_i, we have

$$R_i + y_i = f(x_i, a_0 + \alpha, b_0 + \beta, c_0 + \gamma). \tag{94.4}$$

We may expand the right-hand side by Taylor's theorem for a function of several variables (see Formula 3.21) to obtain the set of equations

$$R_i + y_i = f(x_i, a_0, b_0, c_0) + \alpha \left(\frac{\partial f_i}{\partial a}\right)_0 + \beta \left(\frac{\partial f_i}{\partial b}\right)_0 + \gamma \left(\frac{\partial f_i}{\partial c}\right)_0 \tag{94.5}$$

$$+ \text{ higher order terms in } \alpha, \beta, \gamma,$$

where

$$\left(\frac{\partial f_i}{\partial u}\right)_0 \equiv \text{ the value of the partial derivative } \partial f/\partial u \text{ at } x = x_i,$$

$$a = a_0, b = b_0, \text{ and } c = c_0 \tag{94.6}$$

$$\equiv f_{iu}.$$

A first approximation is obtained from

$$y^* = f(x, a_0, b_0, c_0),$$

so that we have

$$f(x_i, a_0, b_0, c_0) = y_i^* \tag{94.7}$$

and these first approximations can be put into (94.5). For simplicity let

$$r_i = y_i^* - y_i. \tag{94.8}$$

If we ignore the high-order terms, we then have a set of residual equations of the form

$$R_i = \alpha \left(\frac{\partial f_i}{\partial a}\right)_0 + \beta \left(\frac{\partial f_i}{\partial b}\right)_0 + \gamma \left(\frac{\partial f_i}{\partial c}\right)_0 + r_i, \tag{94.9}$$

which are linear in α, β, γ. Thus we may determine the corrections by the method of least squares. We minimize

$$\sum R_i^2 = g(\alpha, \beta, \gamma) \tag{94.10}$$

from which the normal equations are

$$\left(\sum f_{ia}^2\right)\alpha + \left(\sum f_{ia}f_{ib}\right)\beta + \left(\sum f_{ia}f_{ic}\right)\gamma + \sum f_{ia}r_i = 0,$$
$$\left(\sum f_{ia}f_{ib}\right)\alpha + \left(\sum f_{ib}^2\right)\beta + \left(\sum f_{ib}f_{ic}\right)\gamma + \sum f_{ib}r_i = 0, \tag{94.11}$$
$$\left(\sum f_{ic}f_{ia}\right)\alpha + \left(\sum f_{ic}f_{ib}\right)\beta + \left(\sum f_{ic}^2\right)\gamma + \sum f_{ic}r_i = 0.$$

Example 8.14. Find a functional representation for the data

x	1	2	3	4	5	6	7
y	.5	1.6	2.4	3.2	3.9	4.6	5.2

SOLUTION. A plot of the function shows a logarithmic tendency with something added. A simple expression is

$$y = ax + b \log x.$$

Since $y = .5$ when $x = 1$ and log x (at 1) $= 0$, we choose $a_0 = .5$ and guess $b_0 = 1$; the first approximation is

$$y^* = .5x + \log x.$$

Furthermore,

$$\frac{\partial y}{\partial a} = x \quad \text{and} \quad \frac{\partial y}{\partial b} = \log x.$$

We then calculate

x	y	y^*	r	$\dfrac{\partial y}{\partial a}$	$\dfrac{\partial y}{\partial b}$
1	.5	.5	0	1	0
2	1.6	1.30103	−.29897	2	.30103
3	2.4	1.97712	−.42288	3	.47712
4	3.2	2.60206	−.59794	4	.60206
5	3.9	3.19897	−.70103	5	.69897
6	4.6	3.77815	−.82185	6	.77815
7	5.2	4.34510	−.85490	7	.84510

Using (97.11), we calculate the normal equations,

$$140\alpha + 18.52111\beta = 18.67889,$$

$$18.5211\alpha + 2.48901\beta = 2.50376,$$

with $D = 5.42988$, from which we get

$$\alpha = .022, \quad \beta = .842,$$

and

$$a = .5 + .022 = .522,$$

$$b = 1 + .842 = 1.842;$$

our function then becomes

$$\boxed{y = .522x + 1.842 \log x}.$$

Although the correction β is large, it turns out that in this example no improvement in our degree of accuracy is made by finding another set of corrections, using the foregoing expression as a second approximation. There are times, though, when this may be necessary, and it is simple to do if a and b are not involved in the partial derivatives, for then we simply calculate new values for r_i and the constant terms in the normal equations.

The answer yields a set of residuals for which

$$\sum r_i^2 = .0038.$$

95.   PERIODIC FUNCTIONS

We now consider empirical data that exhibits the characteristic of a periodic function. However, before turning to this case, let us review briefly the concept of trigonometric approximations to periodic functions.

A function for which

$$f(x + p) = f(x)$$

is said to be a periodic function with period p. The period can always be changed to 2π by the transformation

$$x = \left(\frac{p}{2\pi}\right)x', \tag{95.1}$$

and consequently we can limit our attention to functions of period 2π.

A trigonometric series is one of the form

$$\tfrac{1}{2}a_0 + \sum_{n=1}^{\infty} (a_n \cos nx + b_n \sin nx), \tag{95.2}$$

where a_n and b_n are constants.

Any periodic function $f(x)$ can be represented by the trigonometric series (94.2), and if we choose

$$a_n = \frac{1}{\pi} \int_{-\pi}^{\pi} f(x)\cos nx\, dx,$$

$$b_n = \frac{1}{\pi} \int_{-\pi}^{\pi} f(x)\sin nx\, dx, \tag{95.3}$$

we have the well-known Fourier series.[8]

This series will have additional characteristics if $f(x)$ is an even or an odd function. We recall the definition of those functions:

    (a) $f(x)$ is said to be an even function if $f(-x) \equiv f(x)$;
    (b) $f(x)$ is said to be an odd function if $f(-x) \equiv -f(x)$.

For even functions we have $b_n = 0$ and $a'_n = 2a_n$; for odd functions we have $a_n = 0$ and $b'_n = 2b_n$.

---

[8] See H. W. Reddick and F. H. Miller, *Advanced Mathematics for Engineers* second ed. New York: Wiley, 1950, Chapter 5.

The representation of a function in a given interval by a Fourier series is a trigonometric approximation that is easily accomplished provided a_n and b_n may be determined. Consider the following classical example.

Example 8.15. Find the Fourier series representation of the function

$$f(x) = -x \quad \text{for} \quad -\pi < x \leq 0,$$

$$f(x) = x \quad \text{for} \quad 0 < x < \pi.$$

SOLUTION.

$$a_0 = \frac{1}{\pi} \int_{-\pi}^{\pi} f(x)\, dx = \frac{1}{\pi} \int_{-\pi}^{0} (-x)\, dx + \frac{1}{\pi} \int_{0}^{\pi} x\, dx = \frac{1}{2}(\pi + \pi) = \pi,$$

$$a_n = \frac{1}{\pi} \int_{-\pi}^{\pi} f(x) \cos nx\, dx$$

$$= \frac{1}{\pi} \left[\int_{-\pi}^{0} (-x) \cos nx\, dx + \int_{0}^{\pi} x \cos nx\, dx \right]$$

$$= \frac{2}{\pi n^2} (\cos n\pi - 1),$$

$$b_n = \frac{1}{\pi} \int_{-\pi}^{\pi} f(x) \sin nx\, dx$$

$$= \frac{1}{\pi} \left[\int_{-\pi}^{0} (-x) \sin nx\, dx + \int_{0}^{\pi} x \sin nx\, dx \right]$$

$$= \frac{1}{n} (\cos n\pi - \cos n\pi) = 0.$$

Thus the series is

$$f(x) = \frac{1}{2}\pi - \frac{4}{\pi}\left(\cos x + \frac{1}{3^2}\cos 3x + \frac{1}{5^2}\cos 5x + \cdots \right).$$

96.   HARMONIC ANALYSIS

The problem of finding the coefficients a_n, b_n of the trigonometric series when we are given only the equidistant values of the function within an interval is called *harmonic analysis*. Let us divide the interval from $-\pi$ to π into $2k$ equal parts so that

$$x_j = \frac{j}{k}\pi.$$

We now seek to minimize the residual equation

$$\sum R^2 = \sum_{j=-k}^{k-1}\left[y_j - \sum_{n=0}^{m}(a_n\cos nx_j + b_n\sin nx_j)\right]^2. \qquad (96.1)$$

Take the partial derivatives with respect to a_n and b_n and set them equal to zero to obtain the normal equations

$$\sum_{n=0}^{m}\left[a_n\sum_{j=-k}^{k-1}\cos nx_j\cos rx_j + b_n\sum_{j=-k}^{k-1}\sin nx_j\cos rx_j\right]$$

$$= \sum_{j=-k}^{k-1}y_j\cos rx_j,$$

$$\sum_{n=0}^{m}\left[a_n\sum_{j=-k}^{k-1}\cos nx_j\sin rx_j + b_n\sum_{j=-k}^{k-1}\sin nx_j\sin rx_j\right] \qquad (96.2)$$

$$= \sum_{j=-k}^{k-1}y_j\sin rx_j,$$

with $(r = 0, \ldots, m)$.

By the use of trigonometric identities and remembering that we have $2k$ divisions of the interval $(-\pi, \pi)$ with $x_{-i} = -x_i$, we can show that

$$\sum_{j=-k}^{k-1}\sin nx_j\cos rx_j = 0,$$

$$\sum_{j=-k}^{k-1}\cos nx_j\cos rx_j = \begin{cases}0, & \text{if } n \neq r, \\ k, & \text{if } n = r \neq 0, k, \\ 2k, & \text{if } n = r = 0, k,\end{cases} \qquad (96.3)$$

$$\sum_{j=-k}^{k-1}\sin nx_j\sin rx_j = \begin{cases}0, & \text{if } n \neq r, \\ k, & \text{if } n = r \neq 0, k, \\ 0, & \text{if } n = r = 0, k,\end{cases}$$

so that the normal equations in (96.2) take the form

$$2ka_0 = \sum_{j=-k}^{k-1} y_j,$$

$$ka_1 = \sum_{j=-k}^{k-1} y_j \cos x_j,$$

$$ka_r = \sum_{j=-k}^{k-1} y_j \cos rx_j,$$ (96.4)

$$kb_r = \sum_{j=-k}^{k-1} y_j \sin rx_j.$$

The calculation of these coefficients may be simplified somewhat by first deriving $S(y_j)$ and $D(y_j)$ as in the last chapter. Thus let us define

$$F_j = f(x_j) + f(-x_j), \qquad (j = 1, \ldots, k-1),$$

$$G_j = f(x_j) - f(-x_j), \qquad (j = 1, \ldots, k-1),$$ (96.5)

$$F_0 = f(0) \quad \text{and} \quad F_k = f(x_k).$$

Then

$$a_0 = \frac{1}{2k} \sum_{j=0}^{k} F_j,$$

$$a_r = \frac{1}{k} \sum_{j=-k}^{k-1} y_j \cos rx_j = \frac{1}{k} \sum_{j=0}^{k} F_j \cos rx_j,$$ (96.6)

$$a_k = \frac{1}{2k} \sum_{j=-k}^{k-1} F_j \cos kx_j,$$

$$b_r = \frac{1}{k} \sum_{j=-k}^{k-1} y_j \sin rx_j = \frac{1}{k} \sum_{j=1}^{k-1} G_j \sin rx_j,$$

$(r = 1, \ldots, k-1)$. The computation may be arranged in a schematic for $k = 6$, that is, the interval $(-\pi, \pi)$ divided into twelve parts.

x	F	$\cos x$	$\cos 2x$	$\cos 3x$	$\cos 4x$	$\cos 5x$	$\cos 6x$
0	$F_0 = y_0$	1	1	1	1	1	1
$\dfrac{\pi}{6}$	$F_1 = y_1 + y_{-1}$	$\dfrac{1}{2}\sqrt{3}$	$\dfrac{1}{2}$	0	$-\dfrac{1}{2}$	$-\dfrac{1}{2}\sqrt{3}$	-1
$\dfrac{2\pi}{6}$	$F_2 = y_2 + y_{-2}$	$\dfrac{1}{2}$	$-\dfrac{1}{2}$	-1	$-\dfrac{1}{2}$	$\dfrac{1}{2}$	1
$\dfrac{3\pi}{6}$	$F_3 = y_3 + y_{-3}$	0	-1	0	1	0	-1
$\dfrac{4\pi}{6}$	$F_4 = y_4 + y_{-4}$	$-\dfrac{1}{2}$	$-\dfrac{1}{2}$	1	$-\dfrac{1}{2}$	$-\dfrac{1}{2}$	-1
$\dfrac{5\pi}{6}$	$F_5 = y_5 + y_{-5}$	$-\dfrac{1}{2}\sqrt{3}$	$\dfrac{1}{2}$	0	$-\dfrac{1}{2}$	$\dfrac{1}{2}\sqrt{3}$	-1
$\dfrac{6\pi}{6}$	$F_6 = y_6$	-1	1	-1	1	-1	1
		a_0	a_1	a_2	a_3	a_4	a_5	a_6

x	G	$\sin x$	$\sin 2x$	$\sin 3x$	$\sin 4x$	$\sin 5x$	$\sin 6x$
$\dfrac{\pi}{6}$	$G_1 = y_1 - y_{-1}$	$\dfrac{1}{2}$	$\dfrac{1}{2}\sqrt{3}$	1	$\dfrac{1}{2}\sqrt{3}$	$\dfrac{1}{2}$	0
$\dfrac{2\pi}{6}$	$G_2 = y_2 - y_{-2}$	$\dfrac{1}{2}\sqrt{3}$	$\dfrac{1}{2}\sqrt{3}$	0	$-\dfrac{1}{2}\sqrt{3}$	$-\dfrac{1}{2}\sqrt{3}$	0
$\dfrac{3\pi}{6}$	$G_3 = y_3 - y_{-3}$	1	0	-1	0	1	0
$\dfrac{4\pi}{6}$	$G_4 = y_4 - y_{-4}$	$\dfrac{1}{2}\sqrt{3}$	$-\dfrac{1}{2}\sqrt{3}$	0	$\dfrac{1}{2}\sqrt{3}$	$-\dfrac{1}{2}\sqrt{3}$	0
$\dfrac{5\pi}{6}$	$G_5 = y_5 - y_{-5}$	$\dfrac{1}{2}$	$-\dfrac{1}{2}\sqrt{3}$	1	$-\dfrac{1}{2}\sqrt{3}$	$\dfrac{1}{2}$	0
		b_1	b_2	b_3	b_4	b_5	b_6

The coefficients are now obtained according to Formula 96.6 by summing the products of the elements in F column with the corresponding elements in appropriate $\cos rx$ column and similarly for the $\sin rx$. A closer look at the table of values for the trigonometric functions will indicate some advantageous grouping. Thus

$$a_0 = \tfrac{1}{12}(F_0 + F_1 + \cdots + F_6),$$

$$a_1 = \tfrac{1}{6}[F_0 - F_6 + \tfrac{1}{2}\sqrt{3}(F_1 - F_5) + \tfrac{1}{2}(F_2 - F_4)],$$

$$a_2 = \tfrac{1}{6}[F_0 - F_3 + F_6 + \tfrac{1}{2}(F_1 - F_2 - F_4 + F_5)],$$

$$a_3 = \tfrac{1}{6}(F_0 - F_2 + F_4 - F_6),\qquad\qquad\qquad (96.7)$$

$$a_4 = \tfrac{1}{6}[F_0 + F_3 + F_6 - \tfrac{1}{2}(F_1 + F_2 + F_4 + F_5)],$$

$$a_5 = \tfrac{1}{6}[F_0 - F_6 - \tfrac{1}{2}\sqrt{3}(F_1 - F_5) + \tfrac{1}{2}(F_2 - F_4)],$$

$$a_6 = \tfrac{1}{12}(F_0 - F_1 + F_2 - F_3 + F_4 - F_5 + F_6)$$

and

$$b_1 = \tfrac{1}{6}[G_3 + \tfrac{1}{2}(G_1 + G_5) + \tfrac{1}{2}\sqrt{3}(G_2 + G_4)],$$

$$b_2 = \tfrac{1}{6}[\tfrac{1}{2}\sqrt{3}(G_1 + G_2 - G_4 - G_5)],$$

$$b_3 = \tfrac{1}{6}(G_1 - G_3 + G_5),\qquad\qquad\qquad (96.8)$$

$$b_4 = \tfrac{1}{6}[\tfrac{1}{2}\sqrt{3}(G_1 - G_2 + G_4 - G_5)],$$

$$b_5 = \tfrac{1}{6}[G_3 + \tfrac{1}{2}(G_1 + G_5) - \tfrac{1}{2}\sqrt{3}(G_2 + G_4)].$$

Such grouping is extremely advantageous when the computing equipment is rather limited. However, with an automatic desk calculator it may be just as rapid to place the F and G columns with a stencil of the table of values and sum the products of two terms. We therefore present a six-place table which may be used.

TABLE 8.4. HARMONIC ANALYSIS—12 OBSERVATIONS

x	$\cos x$	$\cos 2x$	$\cos 3x$	$\cos 4x$	$\cos 5x$	$\cos 6x$
0	1	1.0	1	1.0	1	1
30	.866025	0.5	0	−0.5	−.866025	−1
60	.500000	−0.5	−1	−0.5	.500000	1
90	0	−1.0	0	1.0	0	−1
120	−.500000	−0.5	1	−0.5	−.500000	1
150	−.866025	0.5	0	−0.5	.866025	−1
180	−1	1.0	−1	1.0	−1	1

TABLE 8.4. (cont'd)

	SIN x	SIN $2x$	SIN $3x$	SIN $4x$	SIN $5x$
30	.500000	.866025	1	.866025	.500000
60	.866025	.866025	0	−.866025	−.866025
90	1	0	−1	0	1
120	.866025	−.866025	0	.866025	−.866025
150	.500000	−.866025	1	−.866025	.500000

Example 8.16. Obtain the trigonometric approximation to

x^0	−150	−120	−90	−60	−30	0	30	60	90	120	150	180
y	10	16	18	24	38	32	16	5	−7	−13	−14	−5

SOLUTION.

x	F	G		
0	32		$a_0 = 10$	
30	54	−22	$a_1 = 16.705$	$b_1 = 14.928$
60	29	−19	$a_2 = 4.167$	$b_2 = 1.732$
90	11	−25	$a_3 = 1.833$	$b_3 = -3.500$
120	3	−29	$a_4 = -.500$	$b_4 = -1.155$
150	−4	−24	$a_5 = -.038$	$b_5 = -1.072$
180	−5		$a_6 = -.167$	

$$y = 10 + 16.705 \cos x + 4.167 \cos 2x + 1.833 \cos 3x - .5 \cos 4x$$
$$- .038 \cos 5x - .167 \cos 6x$$
$$+ 14.928 \sin x + 1.732 \sin 2x - 3.5 \sin 3x - 1.155 \sin 4x$$
$$- 1.072 \sin 5x.$$

CHECK

x^0	−150	−120	−90	−60	−30	0	30	60	90	120	150	180
y (given)	10	16	18	24	38	32	16	5	−7	−13	−14	−5
y (calc.)	10.89	16.25	18.17	23.42	37.45	31.17	15.44	4.42	−6.83	−12.75	−13.11	−4.33

Another convenient division of the interval $(-\pi, \pi)$ is into 24 equal subdivision ($k = 12$). The multipliers of F_i and G_i now become

TABLE 8.5. HARMONIC ANALYSIS—24 OBSERVATIONS

x	cos x	cos 2x	cos 3x	cos 4x	cos 5x	cos 6x	cos 7x	cos 8x	cos 9x	cos 10x	cos 11x	cos 12x
0	1	1	1	1.0	1	1	1	1	1	1	1	1
15	.965926	.866025	.707107	.5	.258819	0	-.258819	-.5	-.707107	-.866025	-.965926	-1
30	.866025	.500000	0	-.5	-.866025	-1	-.866025	-.5	0	.500000	.866025	1
45	.707107	0	-.707107	-1.0	-.707107	0	.707107	1	.707107	0	-.707107	-1
60	.500000	-.500000	-1	-.5	.500000	1	.500000	-.5	-1	-.500000	.500000	1
75	.258819	-.866025	-.707107	.5	.965926	0	-.965926	-.5	.707107	.866025	-.258819	-1
90	0	-1	0	1.0	0	-1	0	1	0	-1	0	1
105	-.258819	-.866025	.707107	.5	-.965926	0	.965926	-.5	-.707107	.866025	.258819	-1
120	-.500000	-.500000	1	-.5	-.500000	1	-.500000	-.5	1	-.500000	-.500000	1
135	-.707107	0	.707107	-1.0	.707107	0	-.707107	1	-.707107	0	.707107	-1
150	-.866025	.500000	0	-.5	.866025	-1	.866025	-.5	0	.500000	-.866025	1
165	-.965926	.866025	-.707107	.5	-.258819	0	.258819	-.5	.707107	-.866025	.965926	-1
180	-1	1	-1	1.0	-1	1	-1	1	-1	1	-1	1

x	sin x	sin 2x	sin 3x	sin 4x	sin 5x	sin 6x	sin 7x	sin 8x	sin 9x	sin 10x	sin 11x
15	.258819	.500000	.707107	.866025	.965926	1	.965926	.866025	.707107	.500000	.258819
30	.500000	.866025	1	.866025	.500000	0	-.500000	-.866025	-1	-.866025	-.500000
45	.707107	1	.707107	0	-.707107	-1	-.707107	0	.707107	1	.707107
60	.866025	.866025	0	-.866025	-.866025.	0	.866025	.866025	0	-.866025	-.866025
75	.965926	.500000	-.707107	-.866025	.258819	1	.258819	-.866025	-.707107	.500000	.965926
90	1	0	-1	0	1	0	-1	0	1	0	-1
105	.965926	-.500000	-.707107	.866025	.258819	-1	.258819	.866025	-.707107	-.500000	.965926
120	.866025	-.866025	0	.866025	-.866025	0	.866025	-.866025	0	.866025	-.866025
135	.707107	-1	.707107	0	-.707107	1	-.707107	0	.707107	-1	.707107
150	.500000	-.866025	1	-.866025	.500000	0	-.500000	.866025	-1	.866025	-.500000
165	.258819	-.500000	.707107	-.866025	.965926	-1	.965926	-.866025	.707107	-.500000	.258819

Example 8.17. Obtain the trigonometric approximation to the following data.

SOLUTION.

x	y	x	y	F	G	i	a_i	b_i
0	32			32		0	10.167	
−15	37	15	25	62	−12	1	16.581	−14.915
−30	38	30	16	54	−22	2	4.321	1.908
−45	32	45	10	42	−22	3	1.506	−3.518
−60	24	60	5	29	−19	4	−.208	−.938
−75	20	75	0	20	−20	5	.019	−.739
−90	18	90	−7	11	−25	6	−.167	.333
−105	17	105	−11	6	−28	7	−.057	.332
−120	16	120	−13	3	−29	8	−.292	.217
−135	14	135	−15	−1	−29	9	.327	−.018
−150	10	150	−14	−4	−24	10	−.154	.176
−165	5	165	−10	−5	−15	11	.124	.013
		180	−5	−5		12	−.167	

$$y = 10.167 + 16.581 \cos x + 4.321 \cos 2x + 1.506 \cos 3x - .208 \cos 4x$$
$$+ .019 \cos 5x - .167 \cos 6x - .057 \cos 7x - .292 \cos 8x$$
$$+ .327 \cos 9x - .154 \cos 10x + .124 \cos 11x - .167 \cos 12x$$
$$- 14.915 \sin x + 1.908 \sin 2x - 3.518 \sin 3x - .938 \sin 4x$$
$$- .739 \sin 5x + .333 \sin 6x + .332 \sin 7x + .217 \sin 8x$$
$$- .018 \sin 9x + .176 \sin 10x + .013 \sin 11x.$$

CHECK

x	−120	−90	−30	0	30	90	120	180
y (given)	16	18	38	32	16	−7	−13	−5
y (calc.)	16.00	17.97	38.00	32.00	16.00	−7.00	−13.00	−5.00

97.   CONSTRAINED FITTING

There is still another type of fitting known as constrained fitting. In this case we wish not only to fit the data but to do so in a particular manner, that is, to put an additional constraint on the formula. This is accomplished by the use of Lagrangian multipliers (see Section 55). To illustrate, let us consider the fitting of a set of data by a linear expression,

$$y = mx + b, \tag{97.1}$$

by the principle of least squares, and, furthermore, let us constrain the expression so that the slope is a minus twice the y-intercept,

$$g(m, b) = m + 2b = 0. \tag{97.2}$$

The principle of least squares minimizes the sum of the squares of the residuals,

$$f(m, b) = (mx_i + b - y_i)^2, \tag{97.3}$$

with

$$\frac{\partial f}{\partial m} = 2m \sum x_i^2 + 2 \sum x_i b - 2 \sum x_i y_i,$$

$$\frac{\partial f}{\partial b} = 2m \sum x_i + 2nb - 2 \sum y_i \tag{97.4}$$

for n observations $(x_i y_i)(i = 1, \ldots, n)$. Furthermore,

$$\frac{\partial g}{\partial m} = 1 \quad \text{and} \quad \frac{\partial g}{\partial b} = 2, \tag{97.5}$$

so that the equations in (55.4) become

$$(2 \sum x_i^2)m + (2 \sum x_i)b - 2 \sum x_i y_i + \lambda = 0,$$
$$(\sum x_i)m + nb - \sum y_i + \lambda = 0, \tag{97.6}$$
$$m + 2b = 0,$$

and we have three linear equations in the three unknowns, $m, b,$ and λ. The solutions are

$$\lambda = 2k_2 + (4S_2 - 2S_1)b,$$

$$b = \frac{k_1 - 2k_2}{n + 4S_2 - 4S_1}, \tag{97.7}$$

$$m = -2b,$$

where

$$S_1 = \sum x_i, \qquad S_2 = \sum x_i^2, \qquad k_1 = \sum y_i, \qquad k_2 = \sum x_i y_i.$$

Example 8.18. Fit a straight line to the following data such that the slope is a minus twice the y-intercept.

x	1	2	3	4	5	6	7
y	.4	1.1	1.5	2.2	2.6	3.1	3.8

SOLUTION. We have

$$n = 7, \qquad S_1 = 28, \qquad S_2 = 140, \qquad k_1 = 14.7, \qquad k_2 = 74.1.$$

Consequently

$$b = \frac{14.7 - 2(74.1)}{7 + 4(140) - 4(28)} = -.2934,$$

$$m = .5868,$$

and

$$\boxed{y = .5868x - .2934}\,.$$

CHECK

x	1	2	3	4	5	6	7
y	.2934	.8802	1.467	2.0538	2.6406	3.2274	3.8142

This, of course, is not the best fitting straight line; it is the best fitting straight line for which $m = -2b$.

98.   SUMMARY OF DATA FITTING

Analysis of data forms a large part of modern scientific work. It is therefore desirable to establish some kind of criteria for determining the best mathematical expression that will represent a set of experimental data. Unfortunately, there is no clear-cut method. It is, however, possible to set down some logical steps to follow, and we recommend this procedure.

(a) Plot the data on ordinary rectangular coordinate graph paper. A study of the graph will yield certain clues to the type of mathematical formula that may be used to fit the data.

(i) If it is fairly smooth, try a polynomial fit, using a polynomial as simple as possible. It is recommended that the Nielsen-Goldstein method be used and that all the polynomials of degree 1 to 4 be computed simultaneously.

An indication of the "goodness" of the fit may be seen by comparing the calculated values for $[\alpha_{i-1}]_n$ and $Y_0 = Y_M - \bar{y}$; the closer they agree the better the fit. The degree of the polynomial can also be indicated by a table of differences if the data are given at equidistant values of x. Compute a table of differences and look for a column that has a tendency to be constant; then try a polynomial fit of degree equal to the order of this difference. Consider the possibility of $y = [P(x)]^{-1}$ by making a transformation on y;

$$u = \frac{1}{y} = P(x).$$

Consider also the possibility of a transformation on x; for example,

$$y = a + bx^{-1} = a + bt \quad \text{with} \quad t = x^{-1}.$$

(ii) If the graph shows a tendency to be periodic, investigate the data for a trigonometric formula and possibly a harmonic analysis.

(iii) If the graph shows a logarithmic or exponential tendency, ignore this graph and consider the plots below.

(iv) If the graph is highly irregular, attempt to determine its critical region and consider the possibility of obtaining more data at certain portions or of smoothing the data by some smoothing formulas.

(b) Plot the data on logarithmic paper, and if the graph is nearly a straight line consider the formula

$$y = ax^n.$$

(c) Plot the data on semilogarithmic paper, and if the graph is nearly a straight line consider the formula

$$y = ae^{bx} \quad \text{or} \quad y = aN^x.$$

(d) If this procedure does not yield the desired formulation, choose a formula and obtain the best possible fit to it by any of the foregoing methods or the method of differential correction.

Some typical formulas for the method of differential corrections are

$$y = ae^{bx} + c, \qquad y = (1 + ax^{-2})(x - b),$$
$$y = ae^{bx} + ce^{dx}, \qquad y = ax^n + bx^m,$$
$$y = a(10)^{bx/c+x}, \qquad y = \frac{x}{a + bx} + c.$$

(e) If the fit is constrained by a given condition, use the Lagrangian multipliers. This case is becoming more prominent in what is known as operations or cost analysis.

99.   THE AUTOCORRELATION FUNCTION

We close this chapter with a discussion of a special type of analysis of experimental data. It is concerned with the generation of a function that has become prominent in modern electrical engineering and is known as the autocorrelation function. It is of special interest in the theory of servomechanisms and in general analysis of "noise" data.[9] We are not concerned with the theory at all, which is beyond the scope of this book. We shall explain only how an autocorrelation function can be calculated from a finite set of discrete data. It is usually associated with functions that have time as the independent variable, and the general definition is that the *autocorrelation function of a function $y(t)$ is the time average of $y(t)y(t + r)$*. Mathematically, this may be expressed by

$$R(\tau) = \lim_{T \to \infty} \frac{1}{2T} \int_{-T}^{T} y(t)\, y(t + \tau)\, dt. \qquad (99.1)$$

To obtain an autocorrelation function from experimental data, we have a record of $y(t)$ for a finite interval of time, $0 \le t \le T$. It should be obtained at equidistant values so that we have values y_i at t_i with $t_i = t_1 + (i - 1)h$ and $(i = 1, 2, \ldots, N)$, where $N = T/h$. The time interval h should be chosen quite small, at least small enough so that the function $y(t)$ does not vary significantly in the interval h. The autocorrelation function may then be approximated by

$$R(m) \doteq \frac{1}{N - m} \sum_{i=1}^{N-m} y_i y_{i+m}, \qquad (m > 0). \qquad (99.2)$$

For this calculation we must be careful in choosing m; according to Phillips, m should not exceed $\frac{1}{5}N$.

For the computation it is advantageous first to centralize the data about the mean value so that we first calculate a new set of data. $Y_i = y_i - \bar{y}$, where

$$\bar{y} = \frac{1}{N} \sum_{1}^{N} y_i \qquad (99.3)$$

and consider

$$R'(m) \doteq \frac{1}{N - m} \sum_{i=1}^{N-m} Y_i Y_{i+m}. \qquad (99.4)$$

To illustrate the calculations, we shall consider a simple example. In practice, a large amount of data is obtained, and the calculations are

[9]For a good discussion of its application see H. M. James, N. B. Nichols, and R. S. Phillips, *Theory of Servomechanisms*. New York: McGraw-Hill, 1947, Chapter 6.

performed on large-scale calculating machines. The following naïve example, however, indicates the procedure for the calculation of an auto-correlation function.

Example 8.19. Obtain the autocorrelation function for the data given in the table.

SOLUTION. For this data we have $N = 61$, $\bar{y} = .1$; we shall calculate $R'(m)$ for $(m = 0, \ldots, 10)$ by Formula 99.4.

t	y	Y	t	y	Y	m	$R'(m)$
0	-2.0	-2.1	.31	-1.5	-1.6	0	1.368
.01	-1.7	-1.8	.32	$-.8$	$-.9$	1	1.236
.02	-1.4	-1.5	.33	$-.5$	$-.6$	2	1.001
.03	-1.2	-1.2	.34	$-.1$	$-.2$	3	.709
.04	$-.7$	$-.8$	.35	$-.1$	$-.2$	4	.390
.05	$-.3$	$-.4$	.36	.4	.3	5	.082
.06	$-.2$	$-.3$	.37	1.0	.9	6	$-.178$
.07	$-.3$	$-.4$	.38	2.0	1.9	7	$-.385$
.08	$-.6$	$-.7$	.39	2.8	2.7	8	$-.545$
.09	$-.9$	-1.0	.40	2.7	2.6	9	$-.679$
.10	-1.2	-1.3	.41	2.9	2.8	10	$-.784$
.11	$-.6$	$-.7$	.42	2.5	2.4		
.12	$-.2$	$-.3$	.43	1.0	0.9		
.13	$-.3$	$-.4$	.44	0	$-.1$		
.14	.2	.1	.45	$-.4$	$-.5$		
.15	.8	.7	.46	$-.5$	$-.6$		
.16	.5	.4	.47	$-.3$	$-.4$		
.17	1.4	1.3	.48	.1	0		
.18	1.3	1.2	.49	0	$-.1$		
.19	2.2	2.1	.50	.2	.1		
.20	2.0	1.9	.51	.5	.4		
.21	1.8	1.7	.52	0	$-.1$		
.22	1.5	1.4	.53	$-.5$	$-.6$		
.23	1.0	.9	.54	$-.1$	$-.2$		
.24	.3	.2	.55	.3	.2		
.25	$-.3$	$-.4$	.56	.1	0		
.26	-1.0	-1.1	.57	$-.2$	$-.3$		
.27	-1.0	-1.1	.58	0	$-.1$		
.28	-1.1	-1.2	.59	.2	.1		
.29	-1.6	-1.7	.60	0	$-.1$		
.30	-2.0	-2.1					

When performing calculations on a desk calculator, it is strongly recommended that a stencil be employed as m gets large.

100.   EXERCISE XII

1. Determine a functional fit to the data

	(a)		(b)		(c)
x	y	x	y	x	y
1	2.10	1	5.00	1	1.10
2	2.71	2	6.51	2	1.62
3	3.42	3	7.63	3	2.15
4	4.35	4	8.48	4	2.63
5	5.60	5	8.93	5	3.05
6	7.15	6	8.76	6	3.49
7	9.00	7	7.72	7	3.87
8	12.85	8	5.61	8	4.26
9	14.30	9	3.87	9	4.59
10	17.50	10	3.00	10	4.89
11	24.00	11	2.65	11	5.10
		12	2.41		
		13	2.52		

2. Fit the following data by

$$y = ax + b \ln cx.$$

x	1	2	3	4	5	6	7
y	4.24	8.48	12.29	15.92	19.45	26.38	29.81

3. Fit the following data by $y = ax^n + bx^m$.

x	0	1	2	3	4	5	6
y	0	1.833	7.256	14.72	23.80	205.55	275.62

(*Hint.* Let $a_0 = 3$, $b_0 = -2$, $n_0 = 1$, $m_0 = 1$.)

4. Obtain the trigonometric approximations to

x^0	-150	-120	-90	-60	-30	0	30	60	90	120	150	180
y	102	161	179	235	360	312	170	53	-53	-110	-135	-120

5. Obtain the trigonometric approximation to

x^0	y	x^0	y
-165	2.0	15	4.6
-150	3.0	30	3.3
-135	3.5	45	1.9
-120	3.0	60	.6
-105	1.0	75	-1.0
-90	-1.0	90	-1.0
-75	-1.6	105	.9
-60	-1.1	120	1.8
-45	.4	135	1.4
-30	2.1	150	.3
-15	4.2	165	$-.5$
0	6.1	180	$-.5$

6. Divide the interval $(-\pi, \pi)$ into 12 equal parts and prove

(a) $\displaystyle\sum_{j=-6}^{5} \sin x_j \cos 2x_j = 0,$

(c) $\displaystyle\sum_{j=-6}^{5} \sin^2 2x_j = 6,$

(b) $\displaystyle\sum_{j=-6}^{5} \cos^2 x_j = 6,$

(d) $\displaystyle\sum_{j=-6}^{5} \sin x_j \sin 2x_j = 0.$

7. Fit the following data with a straight line such that the slope is three times the y-intercept.

x	1	2	3	4	5	6	7	8	9	10
y	1.36848	2.39484	3.42120	4.44756	5.47292	6.50028	7.52664	8.55300	9.57936	10.60572

8. Fit the following data with a quadratic $(y = ax^2 + bx + c)$ such that it passes through the point $x = 1, y = 2$.

x	-3	-2	-1	0	1	2	3
y	17.48	8.36	2.74	.62	2.00	6.88	15.26

9. Find the autocorrelation function for the data

t	y	t	y	t	y
0	1.0	.31	2.4	.61	.7
.01	1.2	.32	2.7	.62	.5
.02	1.5	.33	1.0	.63	.1
.03	1.9	.34	−1.0	.64	0
.04	2.2	.35	−3.0	.65	−.3
.05	2.8	.36	−2.2	.66	−.7
.06	2.9	.37	−1.6	.67	−1.0
.07	2.5	.38	−2.5	.68	−1.0
.08	2.2	.39	−2.3	.69	−.5
.09	1.9	.40	−1.9	.70	0
.10	1.4	.41	−1.4	.71	.1
.11	.7	.42	−.7	.72	.3
.12	.3	.43	−.1	.73	.6
.13	−.2	.44	.5	.74	.6
.14	−1.0	.45	1.1	.75	.4
.15	−1.0	.46	1.7	.76	.2
.16	−1.5	.47	2.2	.77	0
.17	−3.1	.48	1.9	.78	−.3
.18	−3.1	.49	1.4	.79	−.6
.19	−3.0	.50	.9	.80	−.7
.20	−2.0	.51	.1	.81	−.8
.21	−1.0	.52	−1.0	.82	−.8
.22	0	.53	−1.5	.83	−.7
.23	.2	.54	−1.7	.84	−.6
.24	2.0	.55	−1.4	.85	−.4
.25	2.6	.56	−1.2	.86	−.1
.26	2.8	.57	−.7	.87	.1
.27	2.6	.58	−.1	.88	.3
.28	2.0	.59	.5	.89	.5
.29	1.7	.60	.8	.90	.5
.30	1.9				

10. Develop the differential correction formulas for

$$y = \frac{x}{a + bx} + c.$$

Choose fractional values for a, b, c, (e.g. $a = \frac{3}{4}$, $b = -\frac{2}{3}$, $c = \frac{5}{7}$) and calculate a set (x_i, y_i) for $0 \leq x \leq 9$. Fit the set (x_i, y_i), letting the initial values be the nearest integer to the chosen fractions (e.g., $a_0 = 1, b_0 = -1, c_0 = 1$).

9

Linear Programming

101. INTRODUCTION

The application of mathematics to business and managerial problems has resulted in the extensive use of a technique known as *linear programming*. The task is one of finding a solution which will make a certain function a maximum (or minimum) under a set of constraints or restrictions. When the given function and the constraints are linear in the variables, we have a linear problem. If it is solvable by some mathematical program, then we refer to its formulation and solution as linear programming. Much has been written on this technique, for it has been successful in the solution of industrial problems. We shall develop the mathematical concept and discuss a method of solution. Although simple academic problems can be solved by a small amount of computation, a typical business problem is sufficiently complex to require large-scale computers.

102. SYSTEM OF LINEAR INEQUALITIES

The constraints for a linear programming problem are usually given as a system of linear inequalities. Let us consider a simple system in two variables:

$$a_1 x + b_1 y \leq c_1,$$

$$a_2 x + b_2 y \geq c_2, \qquad\qquad (102.1)$$

$$a_3 x + b_3 y \leq c_3.$$

Each equation in this system defines (in the xy-plane) a straight line that divides the plane into two half planes. All points in one of these half planes will satisfy the inequality.[1] When the equality is also stated, we can include the boundary (*i.e.*, the line itself) and call it a *closed half plane*. The set of points (x, y) which will satisfy the system of inequalities is the intersection of the closed half planes defined by each inequality.

We shall use the following definition and the associated theorem.

Definition. The intersection of closed half planes is called a *polygonal convex set*.

Theorem 9.1. The points that are simultaneous solutions of a system of inequalities which also include the equalities form a polygonal convex set.

In a system involving two variables this set can be described graphically in the plane of the variables.

Example 9.1. Find the set of points that satisfies the system

$$4x + 5y \leq 33, \qquad x + 4y \geq 11, \qquad 2x - 3y \geq -11.$$

SOLUTION. The first inequality is satisfied by the closed half plane to the left of the line $4x + 5y = 33$; the second, by the closed half plane to the right of the line $x + 4y = 11$; the third, by the closed half plane to the right of $2x - 3y = -11$. The intersection of these half planes form the set of points in the interior and on the boundary of the triangle with vertices $P_1(-1, 3), P_2(7, 1)$, and $P_3(2, 5)$. See Figure 9.1.

In the foregoing example the polygonal convex set has a finite area consisting of the interior of the triangle and its boundary. If the polygonal convex set which satisfies a system of inequalities has a finite area, we refer to it as a *convex polygon*. A convenient manner of describing the convex polygon is to define the polygon in terms of its vertices. These vertices can be found at the points of intersection of the lines, taken two at a time. We shall see in the next section that these vertices (corners) are important in the linear programming problem.

The solution to a system of inequalities may be a polygonal convex set with an infinite area, as we show in the next example.

---

[1] If the coefficient of x is positive, all points to the *right* of the line satisfy the $>$ inequality and all points to the *left* of the line satisfy the $<$ inequality. For a horizontal line points *above* satisfy $>$ and points *below* satisfy $<$.

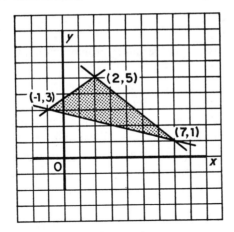

Figure 9.1

Example 9.2. Find the solution set to the system

$$y \geq 0, \qquad y \leq 3, \qquad x + y \geq 3.$$

SOLUTION.

$y \geq 0$: set (x, y) above the x-axis.
$y \leq 3$: set (x, y) below $y = 3$.
$x + y \geq 3$: set (x, y) to the right of $x + y = 3$.

The solution set is the polygonal convex set of infinite area shown in the shaded region of Figure 9.2.

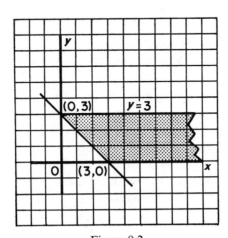

Figure 9.2

103.   TWO-VARIABLE PROBLEM

The simple two-variable linear programming problem can be stated as follows:

Find the maximum and/or minimum value of the linear function $ax + by + c$, constrained by a system of inequalities in x and y. The constants a, b, and c are specified. The function may be an expression for profit, in which case we would like to obtain the maximum, or it could be a cost function which we would like to minimize. We could also find the minimum profit or the maximum cost. If the solution set to the system of inequalities which constrains our function is a convex polygon, we have the following theorem:

Theorem 9.2. The function $ax + by + c$ defined over a convex polygon takes on its maximum (minimum) value at a vertex point of the convex polygon.

The solution of this simple linear programming problem can then be obtained by

(a) finding the vertices of the convex polygon;
(b) substituting the coordinates of each vertex into the function.

The largest value of the function is, of course, the maximum, the smallest value, the minimum.

Example 9.3. Find the extrema of the function $f(x, y) = 2x - 3y + 7$ defined over the convex polygon given in Example 9.1.

SOLUTION. The vertices of the polygon are $(-3, 3)$, $(2, 5)$, and $(7, 1)$.

At $P_1(-1, 3)$: $f(-1.3) = -2 - 9 + 7 = -4$ (minimum).
At $P_2(2, 5)$: $f(2, 5) = 4 - 15 + 7 = -4$ (minimum).
At $P_3(7, 1)$: $f(7, 1) = 14 - 3 + 7 = 18$ (maximum).

An integral part of a linear programming problem is to establish the expression for the function to be investigated and the inequalities of the constraints placed on this function. Since we wish to concentrate on the method of solution, we shall not discuss this point of the problem in detail. However, to indicate its general nature, let us consider a simple case.

A company manufactures two products, x and y, by machining a material. It has three machines capable of making either product, but because of their location and type the time for making a complete product varies for each machine. Let the conditions be

MACHINE	TIME PER PIECE		TOTAL TIME AVAILABLE
	x	y	
A	1.75	3.75	40
B	2.00	3.50	40
C	2.50	3.00	39

Since x and y must be positive or zero, we have five constraints,

$$1.75x + 3.75y \leq 40,$$

$$2.00x + 3.50y \leq 40,$$

$$2.50x + 3.00y \leq 39,$$

$$x \geq 0,$$

$$y \geq 0.$$

Let the profit on the x product be \$15.85 and on y, \$16.15; the profit function is

$$P(x, y) = 15.85x + 16.15y.$$

The convex polygon satisfying all the constraints has vertices

$$V_0(0,0); \quad V_1(15.6,0); \quad V_2(6.\overline{36},7.\overline{69}); \quad V_3(0,10.\overline{6}),$$

where V_2 is the point of intersection between the two lines with the smallest x- and y-intercepts. Substitution of these vertices into the profit function gives

$$P_{max}(6.36, 7.69) = \$225.17,$$

which is the optimum solution for maximum profit and is the best mixing schedule for the machines to utilize their available time; that is, each machine should make 6.36 units of product x and 7.69 units of product y.

104.   THE GENERAL PROBLEM

The application of linear programming to industrial problems usually involves many variables, and the construction of the convex polygon can not be easily accomplished. Before proceeding to other methods of solution, let us state the general problem and associated terminology.

The function we wish to investigate for extrema is usually called the *object function* and is represented by a linear combination

$$f = c_1 x_1 + c_2 x_2 + \cdots + c_n x_n = \sum_{j=1}^{n} c_j x_j, \qquad (104.1)$$

where the c_j are given constants (*object coefficients*) and x_j are the variables whose values are sought. The variables are further constrained by a system of m inequalities

$$\sum_{j=1}^{n} a_{ij} x_j \le b_i, \qquad (i = 1, \ldots, m), \qquad (104.2)$$

and the restriction that $x_j \ge 0$ for all j. The a_{ij} and b_i are given constants. The system (104.2) may also include inequalities of the form

$$\sum_{j=1}^{n} a_{ij} x_j \ge b_i \qquad (104.3)$$

or equations

$$\sum_{j=1}^{n} a_{ij} x_j = b_i. \qquad (104.4)$$

For convenience we change the form of the constraints by multiplying the inequality by -1 whenever necessary so that all $b_i \ge 0$. Furthermore, all inequalities are changed to equalities by the algebraic addition of new variables with unit coefficients; that is,

$$a_{i1} x_1 + a_{i2} x_2 + \cdots + a_{in} x_n \pm x_{n+i} = b_i, \qquad (i = 1, \ldots, m).$$

These new variables, called *slack variables*, have the nonnegative characteristic ($x_{n+i} \ge 0$) and do not contribute to the value of the object function; that is, their coefficients c_j are taken to be zero.

We can now state the problem. Find nonnegative values of x_j which satisfy the system

$$\sum_{j=1}^{n} a_{ij} x_j \pm x_{n+i} = b_i, \qquad (i = 1, \ldots, m), \qquad (104.5)$$

where $b_i \ge 0$ and which make the object function

$$f = \sum_{j=1}^{n+m} c_j x_j \quad \text{a maximum (minimum).} \qquad (104.6)$$

We shall need the following definitions:

A *feasible solution* contains a set x_j, all nonnegative and satisfying the system in (104.5), but which do not necessarily make the object function a maximum (or minimum).

A *basic feasible solution* is a feasible solution with not more than m non-zero values of x_j.

An *extremal solution* is a set x_j which satisfies all the conditions of the problem; that is, a nonnegative set which satisfies the system in (104.5) and makes the value of f an extrema (either maximum or minimum, depending on the requirement).

A *basic extremal solution* is an extremal solution with not more than m nonzero values of x_j.

The mathematical solution to the problem seeks to establish a systematic procedure (program) to find a basic extremal solution founded on the following theorems:

Theorem 9.3. If a feasible solution exists, a basic feasible solution exists.

Theorem 9.4. If the object function remains finite for all feasible solutions, a basic extremal solution exists.

Since the object is to find the extrema of f, the problem can be stated in two ways:

1. *Maximum.* Find the set x_j which makes

$$f = \sum_{j=1}^{n} c_j x_j$$

a maximum under the constraints

$$\sum_{j=1}^{n} a_{ij}x_j \le b_i \quad \text{and} \quad x_j \ge 0, \qquad (i = 1, \ldots, m).$$

2. *Minimum.* Find the set y_j which makes

$$F = \sum_{j=1}^{n} d_j y_j$$

a minimum under the constraints

$$\sum_{j=1}^{n} a_{ij}y_j \ge b_i \quad \text{and} \quad y_j \ge 0, \qquad (i = 1, \ldots, m).$$

These problems are said to be the *dual* of each other, and it can be proved that if a finite solution exists for one a finite solution also exists for the other under the same conditions properly interpreted.[2] We now consider a method of solution of the general problem.

---

[2] For a complete discussion of the dual theorem, see A. Charnes and W. W. Cooper, *Management Models and Industrial Applications of Linear Programming.* New York: Wiley, 1961, p. 179.

105.   THE SIMPLEX METHOD

For simplicity we specify a maximum problem. The simplex method is a systematic procedure of trials which arrives at the optimal solution through the iterative steps:

1. Construct a basic feasible solution.
2. Replace the first basic feasible solution by another which improves the function f toward the maximal solution.
3. Continue the process until f_{max} is obtained, which will be indicated by a computer criterion, or until the computations indicate that $f_{max} = \infty$.

The computations are accomplished by iterating in a matrix which is also called the *simplex tableau*. Let us consider the maximum problem with $n = 4$ and $m = 3$. The constraints are

$$a_{11}x_1 + a_{12}x_2 + a_{13}x_3 + a_{14}x_4 \leq b_1,$$
$$a_{21}x_1 + a_{22}x_2 + a_{23}x_3 + a_{24}x_4 \leq b_2, \qquad (105.1)$$
$$a_{31}x_1 + a_{32}x_2 + a_{33}x_3 + a_{34}x_4 \leq b_3.$$

Introduce the slack variables x_5 (in the first inequality), x_6 (in the second), and x_7 (in the third) with unit coefficients so that the inequalities in (105.1) become a system of linear equations. The object function now becomes

$$\sum_{j=1}^{n+m} c_j x_j = c_1 x_1 + c_2 x_2 + c_3 x_3 + c_4 x_4 + c_5 x_5 + c_6 x_6 + c_7 x_7, \qquad (105.2)$$

with $c_5 = c_6 = c_7 = 0$, for the slack variables do not contribute to the value of the object function. The initial tableau is the matrix shown in Table 9.1.

TABLE 9.1   FIRST SIMPLEX TABLEAU

			c_1	c_2	c_3	c_4	0	0	0
			x_1	x_2	x_3	x_4	x_5	x_6	x_7
0	x_5	b_1	a_{11}	a_{12}	a_{13}	a_{14}	1	0	0
0	x_6	b_2	a_{21}	a_{22}	a_{23}	a_{24}	0	1	0
0	x_7	b_3	a_{31}	a_{32}	a_{33}	a_{34}	0	0	1
		g_0	g_1	g_2	g_3	g_4	g_5	g_6	g_7

The first two columns form the stub, with the second column indicating variables x_j under consideration; for the initial matrix we choose them as the slack variables. The first column contains c_j, corresponding to the x_j in the second column.

The third column is composed of the constants $b_i \geq 0$.

The first row contains the coefficients of the object function and has no entries in the stub and constants column. It is usually called the *objective row* and is used only in the first tableau.

The second row is the *variable row* and indicates the columnar positions of the variables. There are no entries in the first three columns.

The submatrix (a_{ij}), is called the *body* or *trunk* and is formed from the coefficients in (105.1) in the usual matrix formulation.

The submatrix connected with the slack variables is the identity matrix because their coefficients are unity or zero.

The last row is called the *index row* or *base row* and is the focal point for computation. The general formulas for the elements are

$$g_j = \sum_{i=1}^{m} c_i a_{ij} - c_j, \qquad (j = 1, \ldots, n + m) \quad \text{and} \quad g_0 = 0. \qquad (105.3)$$

Since the initial matrix is formed with the slack variables in the stub, the $c_i = 0$ and the elements of the index row for the *first* matrix are

$$g_0 = 0, \qquad g_j = -c_j, \qquad (j = 1, \ldots, n + m). \qquad (105.4)$$

Example 9.4. Set up the initial simplex matrix for the problem

$$f(x_i) = 3.10x_1 + 4.75x_2 + 5.80x_3 + 6.15x_4$$

constrained by

$$10x_1 + 18x_2 + 27x_3 + 8x_4 \leq 750$$
$$5x_1 + 11x_2 + 23x_3 + 7x_4 \leq 675$$
$$9x_1 + 7x_2 + 13x_3 + 12x_4 \leq 480.$$

SOLUTION

			3.10	4.75	5.80	6.15	0	0	0
			x_1	x_2	x_3	x_4	x_5	x_6	x_7
0	x_5	750	10	18	27	8	1	0	0
0	x_6	675	5	11	23	7	0	1	0
0	x_7	480	9	7	13	12	0	0	1
		0	-3.10	-4.75	-5.80	-6.15	0	0	0

We prepare for the computation of the second matrix by first determining a key column and a key row in the initial matrix.

The *key column* contains the smallest number (i.e., the most negative number) in the *index row*. Mark this column and identify the elements by $e_{ik}(i = 1, \ldots, m + 1)$. This is the "come in" vector.

Now calculate the ratios

$$r_i = \frac{b_i}{e_{ik}}, \qquad (i = 1, \ldots, m). \tag{105.5}$$

The row with the smallest nonnegative value of these ratios is the *key row*. The elements of this row are designated by e_{kj} $(j = 0, \ldots, n + m)$; this is the "remove" vector.

The entry that lies in the key row and key column is called the *key number* and is designated by e_{kk}.

Add a column for the computation of r_i to the initial matrix and mark the key items in this matrix. The diagram in Figure 9.3 shows the key elements and a characteristic entry of the initial matrix.

			KEY COLUMN		$r_i = b_i/e_{ik}$
...	...	...	...	...	...
...	e_{ij}		e_{ik}		r_i
...	...	...	...	...	...
KEY ROW ...	e_{kj}	...	e_{kk}	...	$r_k = \min r_i$
...	...	...	...	...	

Figure 9.3

The iteration is now started by computing a second matrix in the following manner.

STEP I.

Calculate the *main row* of the second matrix. This row is located in the *second* matrix in the same position as the *key row* in the *initial* matrix and has the following elements:

1. The stub: replace the element in the variable (second) column by the variable in the key column and replace the c_i (in the first column) by the c_k from the key column.

2. The remaining elements are calculated by dividing the entries in the key row by the key number; that is,

$$_2 b_k = \frac{_1 b_k}{e_{kk}} \quad \text{and} \quad a_{kj} = \frac{e_{kj}}{e_{kk}}, \qquad (j = 1, \ldots, m + n), \tag{105.6}$$

where the presubscript denotes the matrix to which the entry belongs.

STEP 2.

All entries in the second matrix are calculated by the formula

$$\text{new entry} = e_{ij} - \frac{e_{ik} e_{kj}}{e_{kk}}; \tag{105.7}$$

that is, the entry in the new matrix is equal to the entry in the old matrix, minus the product of the corresponding elements in the key column and key row divided by the key number.

We note that the elements in the new matrix, which replace the elements from the key column, become zero. The exception is the entry at the key number which has already been computed in the main row and will always be one. This can be seen directly from the formula

$$\text{new entry} = e_{ik} - \frac{e_{ik} e_{kk}}{e_{kk}} = e_{ik} - e_{ik} = 0, \qquad (i \neq k).$$

CHECK COLUMN

The computations can be verified by means of a check column. The original elements of this column are formed by summing the elements of each row; that is,

$$e_{ic} = b_i + \sum_{j=1}^{n+m} a_{ij}, \qquad (i = 1, \ldots, m + 1).$$

The elements for the check column in the second matrix are computed in the same manner as the others in this matrix, and each entry should equal the sum of the elements in its row for the rest of the matrix (not including the stub). The check is accurate to within round-off errors.

Example 9.5. Compute the second matrix for Example 9.4.

SOLUTION. Let us first compute the check column for the initial matrix

$$750 + 10 + 18 + 27 + 8 + 1 + 0 + 0 = 814, \text{ etc.}$$

The smallest number in the index row is -6.15 (the check column is not used in deciding key elements) and it occurs in the column headed by x_4; this is the key column. Compute the ratio column

$$r_1 = \frac{b_1}{e_{1k}} = \frac{750}{8} = 93.75; \qquad r_2 = \frac{b_2}{e_{2k}} = \frac{675}{7} = 96.43; \qquad r_3 = \frac{480}{12} = 40.$$

The minimum value is r_3, which occurs in the x_7 row; this is the key row. The key number is $e_{kk} = 12$. We mark the complete initial matrix.

			3.10	4.75	5.80	6.16	0	0	0	CHECK	r_i
			x_i	x_2	x_3	x_4	x_5	x_6	x_7		
0	x_5	750	10	18	27	8	1	0	0	814	93.75
0	x_6	675	5	11	23	7	0	1	0	722	96.43
0	x_7	480	9	7	13	12	0	0	1	522	40.00
		0	-3.10	-4.75	-5.80	-6.15	0	0	0	-19.80	

Compute the main row of the second matrix. x_7 is replaced by x_4 and $c_7 = 0$ is replaced by $c_4 = 6.15$. The remaining elements are

$$\frac{b_3}{e_{kk}} = \frac{480}{12} = r_3 = 40.00, \qquad \frac{a_{31}}{e_{kk}} = \frac{9}{12} = .75, \qquad \frac{a_{32}}{e_{kk}} = \frac{7}{12} = .583, \text{ etc.}$$

Enter the elements in the second matrix for the old key column; these will be 0, except the entry in the main row which has already been calculated. Calculate the remaining elements by Formula 105.7; for example,

$$b_1 = \frac{(750)(12) - (8)(480)}{12} = 430.$$

$$a_{11} = \frac{(12)(10) - (8)(9)}{12} = 4., \text{ etc.}$$

The second matrix is

0	x_5	430	4.000	13.333	18.333	0	1	0	$-.667$	466.000
0	x_6	395	$-.250$	6.917	15.417	0	0	1	$-.583$	417.500
6.15	x_4	40	.750	.583	1.083	1	0	0	.083	43.500
		246	1.512	-1.612	.862	0	0	0	.512	247.725

Since this is usually placed directly under the initial matrix the first two rows are not repeated.

The iteration is now continued by computing a third matrix by the same procedure; that is, determine the new key column, compute r_i, determine the new key row, and calculate the entries based on the new key items.

The optimal is reached when all entries in the index row are nonnegative.

The solutions for x_i are listed in the b_i column in the final matrix and are associated with the x_i in the stub of this matrix. If an x_i does not occur there, its value is zero. If a slack variable remains in the stub of the final matrix, its value is ignored, for it has no value in the object function. The maximum value of the object function appears in the final index row in the b_i column, and its value can be checked by summing the products of the entries in the first column in the stub with the entries in the third (b_i) column.

Example 9.6. Complete the problem in Example 9.4.

SOLUTION. The third matrix for this example is

4.75	x_2	32.250	.300	1	1.375	0	.075	0	−.050	34.950
0	x_6	171.926	−2.325	0	5.906	0	−.519	1	−.237	175.750
6.15	x_4	21.187	.575	0	.281	1	−.044	0	.112	23.112
		283.475	1.860	0	2.459	0	.087	0	.453	288.337

The final solution is

$$x_1 = 0, \qquad x_2 = 32.25, \qquad x_3 = 0, \qquad x_4 = 21.187, \qquad f_{max} = 283.48.$$

(Although the entries in the final matrix are recorded to only three decimal values, the computation was performed with six decimal values.)

In the calculations of each successive matrix it is advantageous to work the new index row after the main row; if all the terms are nonnegative, it is not necessary to compute all the remaining entries but only the b_i column. The simplex method may be summarized in a flow diagram such as that shown in Figure 9.4.

In the next example we illustrate a complete solution to a linear programming problem by the simplex method.

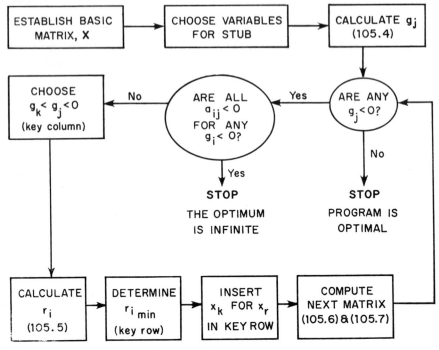

Figure 9.4 Flow Diagram

Example 9.7. Find the maximum value of $f = 2.00x_1 + 5.00x_2 + 4.74x_3$ constrained by

$$7x_1 + 25x_2 + 23x_3 \leq 650$$
$$5x_1 + 22x_2 + 13x_3 \leq 550$$
$$7x_1 + 11x_2 + 9x_3 \leq 350.$$

SOLUTION. The solution is shown in the following sequence of matrices. The calculations were performed to six decimals, but only three are recorded below.

| | | | 2.00 | 5.00 | 4.75 | 0 | 0 | 0 | check | r_i |
			x_1	x_2	x_3	x_4	x_5	x_6		
0	x_4	650	7	25	23	1	0	0	706	26
0	x_5	550	5	22	13	0	1	0	591	25
0	x_6	350	7	11	9	0	0	1	378	31+
		0	−2.00	−5.00	−4.75	0	0	0	−11.75	

			x_1	x_2	x_3	x_4	x_5	x_6	check	r_i
0	x_4	25	1.318	0	8.227	1	−1.136	0	34.409	3.+
5.00	x_2	25	2.27	1	.591	0	.045	0	26.864	42.+
0	x_6	75	4.5	0	2.5	0	−.5	1	82.5	30.+
		125	−.864	0	−1.795	1	.227	0	122.568	
4.75	x_3	3.039	.160	0	1	.122	−.138	0	4.182	18.+
5.00	x_2	23.204	.133	1	0	−.072	.127	0	24.392	175 +
0	x_6	67.403	4.099	0	0	−.304	−.155	1	72.044	16.+
		130.456	−.576	0	0	.218	−.021	0	130.077	
4.75	x_3	.404	0	0	1	.133	−.132	−.039	1.367	
5.00	x_2	21.024	0	1	0	−.062	.132	−.032	23.062	
2.00	x_1	16.442	1	0	0	−.074	−.038	.244	17.574	
		139.926	0	0	0	.176	−.042	.140	140.199	

$$x_1 = 16.442, \qquad x_2 = 21.024, \qquad x_3 = .404, \qquad f_{max} = 139.926.$$

There are other methods for solving linear programming problems, such as the distribution method, the modi method, the ratio-analysis method, and the index method. This author prefers the simplex method, and the foregoing introduction should suffice to familiarize the reader with the general problem. A more thorough discussion can be found in the following books: A. Charnes and W. W. Cooper, *Management Models and Industrial Applications of Linear Programming.* New York: Wiley, 1961; R. O. Ferguson and L. F. Sargent, *Linear Programming.* New York: McGraw-Hill, 1958; and N. V. Reinfeld and W. R. Vogel, *Mathematical Programming.* Engelwood Cliffs, N. J.: Prentice-Hall, 1958.

106.   EXERCISE XIII

1. Find the convex polygon containing the set of points (x, y) which satisfies the system:

(a)
$$3x + 2y \geq 0,$$
$$x + 8y \leq 22,$$
$$5x - 4y \leq 22.$$

(b)
$$5x - 2y - 27 \leq 0,$$
$$2x + 3y - 6 \geq 0,$$
$$3x - 5y + 13 \geq 0,$$
$$y - 4 \leq 0,$$
$$y \geq 0, \quad \text{and} \quad x \leq 0.$$

2. Find the maximum and minimum values of

$$f = 12.75x + 11.15y - 3.45$$

defined over each of the convex polygons in Problem 1.

3. Find the maximum value of

$$f = 9.75x + 11.35y - 3.10$$

defined over the convex polygon with vertices $(0, 2), (8, 0)$, $(7, 4.2)$, $(6.07, 5)$, and $(3, 7)$.

4. Find the maximum value of

$$f = 2.60x_1 + 3.00x_2 + 2.75x_3 + 2.90x_4$$

constrained by

$$20x_1 + 18x_2 + 19x_3 + 22x_4 \le 800,$$
$$18x_1 + 15x_2 + 21x_3 + 18x_4 \le 820,$$
$$21x_1 + 16x_2 + 20x_3 + 15x_4 \le 780,$$
$$22x_1 + 20x_2 + 18x_3 + 17x_4 \le 810,$$
$$23x_1 + 18x_2 + 18x_3 + 19x_4 \le 790.$$

5. Find the maximum value of

$$f = 2.10x_1 + 4.85x_2 + 4.75x_3$$

constrained by

$$8x_1 + 22x_2 + 19x_3 \le 650,$$
$$5x_1 + 20x_2 + 11x_3 \le 550,$$
$$7x_1 + 9x_2 + 7x_3 \le 350.$$

Bibliography

I. BOOKS

Allen, D. N. de G. *Relaxation Methods*. New York: McGraw-Hill, 1954.

Bateman, Harry. *Higher Transcendental Functions*. New York: McGraw-Hill, 1953, Vol. 2, Chapter 10.

Bennett, A. A., W. E. Milne, and H. Bateman. *Numerical Integration of Differential Equations*. New York: Dover, 1956.

Booth, A. D. *Numerical Methods*. New York: Academic, 1958.

Buckingham, R. A. *Numerical Methods*. London: Sir Isaac Pitman & Sons, 1957.

Churchill, R. V. *Fourier Series and Boundary Value Problems*. New York: McGraw-Hill, 1941.

Collatz, L. *The Numerical Treatment of Differential Equations*. Berlin: Springer-Verlag, 1960.

Deming, C. W. E. *The Statistical Adjustment of Data*. New York: Wiley, 1943.

Dwyer, P. S. *Linear Computations*. New York: Wiley, 1951.

Frazer, R. A., W. J. Duncan, and A. R. Collar. *Elementary Matrices*. Cambridge: The University Press, 1950.

Freeman, H. *Mathematics for Actuarial Students*. London: Cambridge University Press, 1948.

Hartree, D. R. *Numerical Analysis*. London: Oxford University Press, 1952.

Hildebrand, F. B. *Introduction to Numerical Analysis*. New York: McGraw-Hill, 1956.

Householder, A. S. *Principles of Numerical Analysis*. New York: McGraw-Hill, 1953.

James, H. M., N. B. Nichols, and R. S. Phillips. *Theory of Servomechanisms*. New York: McGraw-Hill, 1947.

Kopal, Z. *Numerical Analysis*. New York: Wiley, 1955.

Levy, H., and E. A. Baggott. *Numerical Studies in Differential Equations*. New York: Dover, 1950.

Milne, W. E. *Numerical Calculus*. Princeton: Princeton University Press, 1949.

Milne, W. E. *Numerical Solutions of Differential Equations*. New York: Wiley, 1953.

Milne-Thomson, L. M. *The Calculus of Finite Differences.* New York: Macmillan, 1933.

Murnaghan, F. D. *Introduction to Applied Mathematics.* New York: Wiley, 1948.

Salvadori, M. G., and M. L. Baron. *Numerical Methods in Engineering.* Englewood Cliffs, N. J.: Prentice-Hall, 1952.

Scarborough, J. B. *Numerical Mathematical Analysis,* second ed. Baltimore: Johns Hopkins University Press, 1950.

Southwell, R. V. *Relaxation Methods in Theoretical Physics.* London: Oxford University Press, 1946.

Todd, J., Ed. *Survey of Numerical Analysis.* New York: McGraw-Hill, 1962.

Whittaker, E. T., and G. Robinson. *The Calculus of Observations.* London: Blackie, 1948.

Willers, F. A. *Practical Analysis.* New York: Dover, 1948.

II. TABLES

Mathematical tables are important to the numerical analyst, and an ever-increasing number is being published. These tables are reviewed in standard reviewing journals, but we recommend, in particular, the quarterly journal published by the U. S. National Research Council, Washington, D. C., which until 1959 was called *Mathematical Tables and Other Aids to Computation* and then renamed *Mathematics of Computation.* We also recommend A. Fletcher, J. C. P. Miller, and L. Rosenhead, *An Index of Mathematical Tables.* New York: McGraw-Hill, 1946. (A revised edition may now be available.)

A number of organizations have published series of tables, and we suggest that they be approached directly for a list of their current mathematical tables:

British Association for the Advancement of Science and Their Royal Society Tables Committee.
Harvard University Computation Laboratory.
National Physical Laboratory.
U. S. National Bureau of Standards (more than 50 excellent tables).

Some individual tables and handbooks are the following:

Adams, E. P. *Smithsonian Mathematical Formulae.* Washington: Smithsonian Institution, 1947.

Burington, R. S. *Handbook of Mathematical Tables and Formulas.* Sandusky: Handbook Publishers, 1943.

Comrie, L. J. *Barlow's Tables of Squares, Cubes, Square Roots, Cube Roots, and Reciprocals.* New York: Chemical Publishing, 1944.

Fisher, R. A., and F. Yates. *Statistical Tables.* New York: Hafner, 1949.

Hodgman, C. D. *Mathematical Tables,* seventh ed. Cleveland: Chemical Rubber Publishing, 1941.

Nielsen, K. L. *Logarithmic and Trigonometric Tables.* New York: Barnes & Noble, 1961.

Peters, J. *Seven-Place Values of Trigonometric Functions.* Princeton, N. J.: Van Nostrand, 1942.

Thompson, A. J. *Table of Coefficients of Everett's Central Difference Interpolation Formula,* second ed. London: Cambridge University Press, 1943.

III. ARTICLES

The literature on numerical analysis is extensive. The following articles pertain directly to the material in this book:

Aitken, A. C. "On Interpolation by Iteration of Proportional Parts without the Use of Differences," *Edinburgh Mathematical Society Proceedings*, 3 (Ser. 2, 1932), 56–76.

Blanch, Gertrude. "On Modified Divided Differences, I," *Mathematical Tables and Other Aids to Computation*, 8 (January 1954), 1–11.

Crout, P. D. "A Short Method for Evaluating Determinants and Solving Systems of Linear Equations with Real and Complex Coefficients," *Transactions of the A.I.E.E.*, **60** (1941), 1235–1241.

Emmons, H. W. "The Numerical Solution of Partial Differential Equations," *Quarterly of Applied Mathematics*, 2, No. 3 (October 1944), 173–195.

Forsythe, G. E., and R. A. Leiber. "Matrix Inversion by a Monte Carlo Method," *Mathematical Tables and Other Aids to Computation*, 4 (1950), 127–129.

Freeman, G. F. "On the Iterative Solution of Linear Simultaneous Equations," *Philosophical Magazine*, **34** (1943), 409–416.

Friedman, B. "Note on Approximating Complex Zeros of a Polynomial," *Communications on Pure and Applied Mathematics*, II, No. 2–3 (1949), 195–208.

Geiringer, A. "On the Solution of Systems of Linear Equations by Certain Iteration Methods" (Ann Arbor, Mich.), *Reissner Anniversary Volume* (1949), 365–393.

Goldstein, H. H., and J. von Neumann. "Numerical Inverting of Matrices of High Order," *Bulletin of the American Mathematical Society*, **53** (1947), 1021–1099.

Guest, P. G. "Note on the Fitting of Polynomials to Equally Spaced Observations," *Journal of Mathematics and Physics*, **32**, No. 1 (1953), 68–71.

Hankam, E. V. "Linear Equations and Matrix Inversion," *IBM Technical Newsletter*, No. 3 (1951), 26–34.

Householder, A. S. "Some Numerical Methods for Solving Systems of Linear Equations," *American Mathematical Monthly*, **57** (1950), 453–459.

Kincaid, W. M. "Solution of Equations by Interpolation," *The Annals of Mathematical Statistics*, **19** (1948), 207–219.

Ku, Y. H. "A Method for Solving Third and Higher Order Nonlinear Differential Equations," *Journal of Franklin Institute*, **256** (September 1953).

Laderman, J. "The Square Root Method for Solving Simultaneous Linear Equations," *Mathematical Tables and Other Aids to Computation*, 3 (1948), 13–16.

Lanczos, C. "Trigonometric Interpolation of Empirical and Analytical Functions," *Journal Mathematics and Physics*, **17** (1938), 123–198.

Lowan, A. N., N. Davids, and A. Levenson. "Tables of Zeros of the Legendre Polynomials of Order 1–16 and the Weight Coefficients for Gauss' Mechanical Quadrature Formula," *Bulletin of the American Mathematical Society*, **48**, No. 10 (1942), 739–743.

Luke, Y. L., and D. Ufford. "On the Roots of Algebraic Equations," *Journal of Mathematics and Physics*, **30**, No. 2 (1951), 94–101.

Merson, R. H. "The Stability of the Runge-Kutta Method of Solution of Linear Differential Euqations," *Royal Aircraft Establishment* (Farnborough, England), Tech. Note G.W. 320 (June 1954).

Milne, W. E. "Numerical Integration of Ordinary Differential Equations," *American Mathematical Monthly*, **33** (1926), 455–460.

Moulton, F. R. "On the Solutions of Linear Equations Having Small Determinants," *American Mathematical Monthly*, **20** (1913), 242–249.

Neville, E. H. "Iterative Interpolation," *Indian Mathematical Society (Madras) Journal*, **20** (1933), 87–120.

Nielsen, K. L., and L. Goldstein. "An Algorithm for Least Squares," *Journal of Mathematics and Physics*, **26**, No. 2 (1947), 120–132.

Sterne, T. E. "The Accuracy of Numerical Solutions of Ordinary Differential Equations," *Mathematical Tables and Other Aids to Computation*, **7**, No. 43 (July 1953), 159–164.

Synge, J. L. "A Geometric Interpretation of the Relaxation Method," *Quarterly of Applied Mathematics*, **2** (1944), 87–89.

Tuckerman, L. B. "On the Mathematical Significant Figures in the Solution of Simultaneous Linear Equations," *The Annals of Mathematical Statistics*, **12** (1941), 307–316.

Tweedie, M. C. K. "A Modification of the Aitken-Neville Linear Iterative Procedures for Polynomial Interpolation," *Mathematical Tables and Other Aids to Computation*, **8**, No. 45 (January 1954), 13–16.

Tables

TABLE I. BINOMIAL COEFFICIENTS $\binom{n}{i}$

n	$\binom{n}{0}$	$\binom{n}{1}$	$\binom{n}{2}$	$\binom{n}{3}$	$\binom{n}{4}$	$\binom{n}{5}$	$\binom{n}{6}$	$\binom{n}{7}$	$\binom{n}{8}$	$\binom{n}{9}$	$\binom{n}{10}$
0	1										
1	1	1									
2	1	2	1								
3	1	3	3	1							
4	1	4	6	4	1						
5	1	5	10	10	5	1					
6	1	6	15	20	15	6	1				
7	1	7	21	35	35	21	7	1			
8	1	8	28	56	70	56	28	8	1		
9	1	9	36	84	126	126	84	36	9	1	
10	1	10	45	120	210	252	210	120	45	10	1
11	1	11	55	165	330	462	462	330	165	55	11
12	1	12	66	220	495	792	924	792	495	220	66
13	1	13	78	286	715	1287	1716	1716	1287	715	286
14	1	14	91	364	1001	2002	3003	3432	3003	2002	1001
15	1	15	105	455	1365	3003	5005	6435	6435	5005	3003
16	1	16	120	560	1820	4368	8008	11440	12870	11440	8008
17	1	17	136	680	2380	6188	12376	19448	24310	24310	19448
18	1	18	153	816	3060	8568	18564	31824	43758	48620	43758
19	1	19	171	969	3876	11628	27132	50388	75582	92378	92378
20	1	20	190	1140	4845	15504	38760	77520	125970	167960	184756

$$\binom{n}{k} = \binom{n}{n-k}$$

TABLE II. STIRLING NUMBERS OF THE FIRST KIND

$$S_i^{(n+1)} = S_i^{(n)} - nS_{i-1}^{(n)}$$

n	$S_0^{(n)}$	$S_1^{(n)}$	$S_2^{(n)}$	$S_3^{(n)}$	$S_4^{(n)}$	$S_5^{(n)}$	$S_6^{(n)}$	$S_7^{(n)}$	$S_8^{(n)}$	$S_9^{(n)}$	$S_{10}^{(n)}$	$S_{11}^{(n)}$
1	1											
2	1	−1										
3	1	−3	2									
4	1	−6	11	−6								
5	1	−10	35	−50	24							
6	1	−15	85	−225	274	−120						
7	1	−21	175	−735	1624	−1764	720					
8	1	−28	322	−1960	6769	−13132	13068	−5040				
9	1	−36	546	−4536	22449	−67284	118124	−109584	40320			
10	1	−45	870	−9450	63273	−269325	723680	−1172700	1026576	−362880		
11	1	−55	1320	−18150	157773	−902055	3416930	−8409500	12753576	−10628640	3628800	
12	1	−66	1925	−32670	357423	−2637558	13339535	−45995730	105258076	−150917976	120543840	−39916800

TABLE III. NEWTON'S INTERPOLATION COEFFICIENTS

u or $-u$	$N_{21} = N_{22}$	$N_{31} = -N_{32}$	$N_{41} = N_{42}$	$N_{51} = -N_{52}$	$N_{61} = N_{62}$	u or $-u$
.01	-0.0049500	0.0032835	-0.0024544	0.0019586	-0.0016289	.01
.02	$-.0098000$	$.0064680$	$-.0048187$	$.0038357$	$-.0031836$	.02
.03	$-.0145500$	$.0095545$	$-.0070942$	$.0056328$	$-.0046658$	.03
.04	$-.0192000$	$.0125440$	$-.0092826$	$.0073518$	$-.0060775$	.04
.05	$-.2375000$	$.0154375$	$-.0113852$	$.0089943$	$-.0074203$	.05
.06	$-.0282000$	$.0182360$	$-.0134035$	$.0105619$	$-.0086960$	.06
.07	$-.0325500$	$.0209405$	$-.0153389$	$.0120564$	$-.0099063$	.07
.08	$-.0368000$	$.0235520$	$-.0171930$	$.0134793$	$-.0110530$	.08
.09	$-.0409500$	$.0260715$	$-.0189670$	$.0148322$	$-.0121377$	.09
.10	$-.0450000$	$.0285000$	$-.0206625$	$.0161168$	$-.0131620$	.10
.11	$-.0489500$	$.0308385$	$-.0222808$	$.0173345$	$-.0141276$	.11
.12	$-.0528000$	$.0330880$	$-.0238234$	$.0184869$	$-.0150360$	.12
.13	$-.0565500$	$.0352495$	$-.0252915$	$.0195756$	$-.0158889$	.13
.14	$-.0602000$	$.0373240$	$-.0266867$	$.0206021$	$-.0166877$	.14
.15	$-.0637500$	$.0393125$	$-.0280102$	$.0215678$	$-.0174340$	.15
.16	$-.0672000$	$.0412160$	$-.0292634$	$.0224743$	$-.0181292$	.16
.17	$-.0705500$	$.0430355$	$-.0304476$	$.0233229$	$-.0187749$	.17
.18	$-.0738000$	$.0447720$	$-.0315643$	$.0241151$	$-.0193725$	.18
.19	$-.0769500$	$.0464265$	$-.0326146$	$.0248523$	$-.0199233$	.19
.20	$-.0800000$	$.0480000$	$-.0336000$	$.0255360$	$-.0204288$	.20
.21	$-.0829500$	$.0494935$	$-.0345217$	$.0261675$	$-.0208904$	.21
.22	$-.0858000$	$.0509080$	$-.0353811$	$.0267481$	$-.0213093$	.22
.23	$-.0885500$	$.0522445$	$-.0361793$	$.0272792$	$-.0216870$	.23
.24	$-.0912000$	$.0535040$	$-.0369178$	$.0277622$	$-.0220246$	.24
.25	$-.0937500$	$.0546875$	$-.0375977$	$.0281982$	$-.0223236$	.25
.26	$-.0962000$	$.0557960$	$-.0382203$	$.0285888$	$-.0225851$	.26
.27	$-.0985500$	$.0568305$	$-.0387868$	$.0289350$	$-.0228104$	.27
.28	$-.1008000$	$.0577920$	$-.0392986$	$.0292381$	$-.0230007$	.28
.29	$-.1029500$	$.0586815$	$-.0397567$	$.0294995$	$-.0231571$	.29
.30	$-.1050000$	$.0595000$	$-.0401625$	$.0297202$	$-.0232809$	.30
.31	$-.1069500$	$.0602485$	$-.0405171$	$.0299016$	$-.0233731$	.31
.32	$-.1088000$	$.0609280$	$-.0408218$	$.0300448$	$-.0234350$	.32
.33	$-.1105500$	$.0615395$	$-.0410776$	$.0301510$	$-.0234675$	.33
.34	$-.1122000$	$.0620840$	$-.0412859$	$.0302212$	$-.0234718$	.34
.35	$-.1137500$	$.0625625$	$-.0414477$	$.0302568$	$-.0234490$	.35
.36	$-.1152000$	$.0629760$	$-.0415642$	$.0302587$	$-.0234001$	.36
.37	$-.1165500$	$.0633255$	$-.0416365$	$.0302281$	$-.0233260$	.37
.38	$-.1178000$	$.0636120$	$-.0416659$	$.0301661$	$-.0232279$	.38
.39	$-.1189500$	$.0638365$	$-.0416533$	$.0300737$	$-.0231066$	.39
.40	$-.1200000$	$.0640000$	$-.0416000$	$.0299520$	$-.0229632$	.40
.41	$-.1209500$	$.0641035$	$-.0415070$	$.0298020$	$-.0227986$	.41
.42	$-.1218000$	$.0641480$	$-.0413755$	$.0296248$	$-.0226136$	.42
.43	$-.1225500$	$.0641345$	$-.0412064$	$.0294214$	$-.0224093$	.43
.44	$-.1232000$	$.0640640$	$-.0410010$	$.0291927$	$-.0221864$	.44
.45	$-.1237500$	$.0639375$	$-.0407602$	$.0289397$	$-.0219459$	.45
.46	$-.1242000$	$.0637560$	$-.0404851$	$.0286634$	$-.0216887$	.46
.47	$-.1245500$	$.0635205$	$-.0401767$	$.0283648$	$-.0214154$	.47
.48	$-.1248000$	$.0632320$	$-.0398362$	$.0280447$	$-.0211270$	.48
.49	$-.1249500$	$.0628915$	$-.0394644$	$.0277040$	$-.0208242$	.49
.50	$-.1250000$	$.0625000$	$-.0390625$	$.0273438$	$-.0205078$	.50

TABLE III (continued). NEWTON'S INTERPOLATION COEFFICIENTS

u or $-u$	$N_{21} = N_{22}$	$N_{31} = -N_{32}$	$N_{41} = N_{42}$	$N_{51} = -N_{52}$	$N_{61} = N_{62}$	u or $-u$
.51	−0.1249500	0.0620585	−0.0386314	0.0269647	−0.0201786	.51
.52	−.1248000	.0615680	−.0381722	.0265678	−.0198373	.52
.53	−.1245500	.0610295	−.0376857	.0261539	−.0194846	.53
.54	−.1242000	.0604440	−.0371731	.0257238	−.0191213	.54
.55	−.1237500	.0598125	−.0366352	.0252783	−.0187480	.55
.56	−.1232000	.0591360	−.0360730	.0248182	−.0183655	.56
.57	−.1225500	.0584155	−.0354874	.0243444	−.0179743	.57
.58	−.1218000	.0576520	−.0348795	.0238576	−.0175751	.58
.59	−.1209500	.0568465	−.0342500	.0233585	−.0171685	.59
.60	−.1200000	.0560000	−.0336000	.0228480	−.0167552	.60
.61	−.1189500	.0551135	−.0329303	.0223268	−.0163357	.61
.62	−.1178000	.0541880	−.0322419	.0217955	−.0159107	.62
.63	−.1165500	.0532245	−.0315355	.0212549	−.0154807	.63
.64	−.1152000	.0522240	−.0308122	.0207058	−.0150462	.64
.65	−.1137500	.0511875	−.0300727	.0201487	−.0146078	.65
.66	−.1122000	.0501160	−.0293179	.0195843	−.0141660	.66
.67	−.1105500	.0490105	−.0285486	.0190134	−.0137213	.67
.68	−.1088000	.0478720	−.0277658	.0184365	−.0132743	.68
.69	−.1069500	.0467015	−.0269701	.0178542	−.0128253	.69
.70	−.1050000	.0455000	−.0261625	.0172673	−.0123749	.70
.71	−.1029500	.0442685	−.0253437	.0166762	−.0119235	.71
.72	−.1008000	.0430080	−.0245146	.0160816	−.0114715	.72
.73	−.0985500	.0417195	−.0236758	.0154840	−.0110194	.73
.74	−.0962000	.0404040	−.0228283	.0148841	−.0105677	.74
.75	−.0937500	.0390625	−.0219727	.0142822	−.0101166	.75
.76	−.0912000	.0376960	−.0211098	.0136791	−.0096666	.76
.77	−.0885500	.0363055	−.0202403	.0130752	−.0092180	.77
.78	−.0858000	.0348920	−.0193651	.0124711	−.0087713	.78
.79	−.0829500	.0334565	−.0184847	.0118672	−.0083268	.79
.80	−.0800000	.0320000	−.0176000	.0112640	−.0078848	.80
.81	−.0769500	.0305235	−.0167116	.0106620	−.0074456	.81
.82	−.0738000	.0290280	−.0158203	.0100617	−.0070096	.82
.83	−.0705500	.0275145	−.0149266	.0094635	−.0065771	.83
.84	−.0672000	.0259840	−.0140314	.0088678	−.0061484	.84
.85	−.0637500	.0244375	−.0131352	.0082751	−.0057236	.85
.86	−.0602000	.0228760	−.0122387	.0076859	−.0053033	.86
.87	−.0565500	.0213005	−.0113425	.0071004	−.0048875	.87
.88	−.0528000	.0197120	−.0104474	.0065192	−.0044765	.88
.89	−.0489500	.0181115	−.0095538	.0059425	−.0040706	.89
.90	−.0450000	.0165000	−.0086625	.0053708	−.0036700	.90
.91	−.0409500	.0148785	−.0077740	.0048043	−.0032750	.91
.92	−.0368000	.0132480	−.0068890	.0042436	−.0028856	.92
.93	−.0325500	.0116095	−.0060079	.0036889	−.0025023	.93
.94	−.0282000	.0099640	−.0051315	.0031405	−.0021250	.94
.95	−.0237500	.0083125	−.0042602	.0025987	−.0017541	.95
.96	−.0192000	.0066560	−.0033946	.0020639	−.0013897	.96
.97	−.0145500	.0049955	−.0025352	.0015363	−.0010319	.97
.98	−.0098000	.0033320	−.0016827	.0010163	−.0006809	.98
.99	−.0049500	.0016665	−.0008374	.0005041	−.0003369	.99
1.00	0	0	0	0	0	1.00

TABLE III (continued). NEWTON'S INTERPOLATION COEFFICIENTS

u or $-u$	$N_{21} = N_{22}$	$N_{31} = -N_{32}$	$N_{41} = N_{42}$	$N_{51} = -N_{52}$	$N_{61} = N_{62}$	u or $-u$
1.01	0.0050500	−0.0016665	0.0008291	−0.0004958	0.0003297	1.01
1.02	.0102000	−.0033120	.0016394	−.0009771	.0006481	1.02
1.03	.0154500	−.0049955	.0024603	−.0014614	.0009670	1.03
1.04	.0208000	−.0066560	.0032614	−.0019307	.0012743	1.04
1.05	.0262500	−.0083125	.0040523	−.0023909	.0015740	1.05
1.06	.0318000	−.0099640	.0048325	−.0028415	.0018659	1.06
1.07	.0374500	−.0116095	.0056016	−.0032825	.0021500	1.07
1.08	.0432000	−.0132480	.0063590	−.0037137	.0024263	1.08
1.09	.0490500	−.0148785	.0071045	−.0041348	.0026954	1.09
1.10	.0550000	−.0165000	.0078375	−.0045458	.0029548	1.10
1.11	.0610500	−.0181115	.0085577	−.0049464	.0032069	1.11
1.12	.0672000	−.0197120	.0092646	−.0053364	.0034509	1.12
1.13	.0734500	−.0213005	.0099580	−.0057159	.0036867	1.13
1.14	.0798000	−.0228760	.0106373	−.0060846	.0039144	1.14
1.15	.0862500	−.0244375	.0113023	−.0064423	.0041338	1.15
1.16	.0928000	−.0259840	.0119526	−.0067891	.0043450	1.16
1.17	.0994500	−.0275145	.0125879	−.0071247	.0045480	1.17
1.18	.1062000	−.0290280	.0132077	−.0074492	.0047427	1.18
1.19	.1130500	−.0305235	.0138119	−.0077623	.0049290	1.19
1.20	.1200000	−.0320000	.0144000	−.0080640	.0051072	1.20
1.21	.1270500	−.0334565	.0149718	−.0083543	.0052771	1.21
1.22	.1342000	−.0348920	.0155269	−.0086330	.0054388	1.22
1.23	.1414500	−.0363055	.0160652	−.0089001	.0055922	1.23
1.24	.1488000	−.0376960	.0165862	−.0091556	.0057375	1.24
1.25	.1562500	−.0390625	.0170898	−.0093994	.0058746	1.25
1.26	.1638000	−.0404040	.0175757	−.0096315	.0060036	1.26
1.27	.1714500	−.0422910	.0182909	−.0099868	.0062085	1.27
1.28	.1792000	−.0430080	.0184934	−.0100604	.0062375	1.28
1.29	.1870500	−.0442685	.0189248	−.0102572	.0063424	1.29
1.30	.1950000	−.0455000	.0193375	−.0104423	.0064394	1.30
1.31	.2030500	−.0467015	.0197314	−.0106155	.0065285	1.31
1.32	.2112000	−.0478720	.0201062	−.0107769	.0066099	1.32
1.33	.2194500	−.0490105	.0204619	−.0109266	.0066835	1.33
1.34	.2278000	−.0501160	.0207981	−.0110646	.0067494	1.34
1.35	.2362500	−.0511875	.0211148	−.0111909	.0068078	1.35
1.36	.2448000	−.0522240	.0214118	−.0113055	.0068587	1.36
1.37	.2534500	−.0532245	.0216890	−.0114084	.0069021	1.37
1.38	.2622000	−.0541880	.0219461	−.0114998	.0069382	1.38
1.39	.2710500	−.0551135	.0221832	−.0115796	.0069671	1.39
1.40	.2800000	−.0460000	.0224000	−.0116480	.0069888	1.40
1.41	.2890500	−.0568465	.0225965	−.0117050	.0070035	1.41
1.42	.2982000	−.0576520	.0227725	−.0117506	.0070112	1.42
1.43	.3074500	−.0584155	.0229281	−.0117850	.0070121	1.43
1.44	.3168000	−.0591360	.0230630	−.0118083	.0070062	1.44
1.45	.3262500	−.0598125	.0231773	−.0118204	.0069937	1.45
1.46	.3358000	−.0604440	.0232709	−.0118216	.0069748	1.46
1.47	.3454500	−.0610295	.0233438	−.0118120	.0069494	1.47
1.48	.3552000	−.0615680	.0233958	−.0117915	.0069177	1.48
1.49	.3650500	−.0620585	.0234271	−.0117604	.0068798	1.49
1.50	.3750000	−.0625000	.0234375	−.0117188	.0068359	1.50

TABLE III (continued).   NEWTON'S INTERPOLATION COEFFICIENTS

u or $-u$	$N_{21} = N_{22}$	$N_{31} = -N_{32}$	$N_{41} = N_{42}$	$N_{51} = -N_{52}$	$N_{61} = N_{62}$	u or $-u$
1.51	0.3850500	−0.0628915	0.0234271	−0.0116667	0.0067861	1.51
1.52	.3952000	−.0632320	.0233958	−.0116043	.0067305	1.52
1.53	.4054500	−.0635205	.0233438	−.0115318	.0066692	1.53
1.54	.4158000	−.0637560	.0232709	−.0114493	.0066024	1.54
1.55	.4262500	−.0639375	.0231773	−.0113569	.0065302	1.55
1.56	.4368000	−.0640640	.0230630	−.0112548	.0064527	1.56
1.57	.4474500	−.0641345	.0229281	−.0111430	.0063701	1.57
1.58	.4582000	−.0641480	.0227725	−.0110219	.0062825	1.58
1.59	.4690500	−.0641035	.0225965	−.0108915	.0061900	1.59
1.60	.4800000	−.0640000	.0224000	−.0107520	.0060928	1.60
1.61	.4910500	−.0638365	.0221832	−.0106036	.0059910	1.61
1.62	.5022000	−.0636120	.0219461	−.0104464	.0058848	1.62
1.63	.5134500	−.0633255	.0216890	−.0102806	.0057743	1.63
1.64	.5248000	−.0629760	.0214118	−.0101064	.0056596	1.64
1.65	.5362500	−.0625625	.0211148	−.0099240	.0055409	1.65
1.66	.5478000	−.0620840	.0207981	−.0097335	.0054183	1.66
1.67	.5594500	−.0615395	.0204619	−.0095352	.0052921	1.67
1.68	.5712000	−.0609280	.0201062	−.0093293	.0051622	1.68
1.69	.5830500	−.0602485	.0197314	−.0091159	.0050289	1.69
1.70	.5950000	−.0595000	.0193375	−.0088953	.0048924	1.70
1.71	.6070500	−.0586815	.0189248	−.0086676	.0047527	1.71
1.72	.6192000	−.0577920	.0184934	−.0084330	.0046100	1.72
1.73	.6314500	−.0568305	.0180437	−.0081918	.0044645	1.73
1.74	.6438000	−.0557960	.0175757	−.0079442	.0043164	1.74
1.75	.6562500	−.0546875	.0170898	−.0076904	.0041656	1.75
1.76	.6688000	−.0535040	.0165862	−.0074306	.0040125	1.76
1.77	.6814500	−.0522445	.0160652	−.0071651	.0038572	1.77
1.78	.6942000	−.0509080	.0155269	−.0068940	.0036998	1.78
1.79	.7070500	−.0494935	.0149718	−.0066175	.0035404	1.79
1.80	.7200000	−.0480000	.0144000	−.0063360	.0033792	1.80
1.81	.7330500	−.0464265	.0138119	−.0060496	.0032164	1.81
1.82	.7462000	−.0447720	.0132077	−.0057586	.0030520	1.82
1.83	.7594500	−.0430355	.0125879	−.0054631	.0028864	1.83
1.84	.7728000	−.0412160	.0119526	−.0051635	.0027195	1.84
1.85	.7862500	−.0393125	.0113023	−.0048600	.0025515	1.85
1.86	.7998000	−.0373240	.0106373	−.0045528	.0023826	1.86
1.87	.8134500	−.0352495	.0099580	−.0042421	.0022130	1.87
1.88	.8272000	−.0330880	.0092646	−.0039282	.0020427	1.88
1.89	.8410500	−.0308385	.0085577	−.0036113	.0018719	1.89
1.90	.8550000	−.0285000	.0078375	−.0032918	.0017007	1.90
1.91	.8690500	−.0260715	.0071045	−.0029697	.0015294	1.91
1.92	.8832000	−.0235520	.0063590	−.0026454	.0013580	1.92
1.93	.8974500	−.0209405	.0056016	−.0023191	.0011866	1.93
1.94	.9118000	−.0182360	.0048325	−.0019910	.0010154	1.94
1.95	.9262500	−.0154375	.0040523	−.0016615	.0008446	1.95
1.96	.9408000	−.0125440	.0032614	−.0013307	.0006742	1.96
1.97	.9554500	−.0095545	.0024603	−.0009989	.0005044	1.97
1.98	.9702000	−.0064680	.0016493	−.0006663	.0003354	1.98
1.99	.9850500	−.0032835	.0008291	−.0003333	.0000167	1.99
2.00	1.0000000	.0000000	.0000000	.0000000	.0000000	2.00

TABLE IV. STIRLING'S INTERPOLATION COEFFICIENTS

u	S_2	S_3	S_4	S_5	S_6	u
.01	.0000500	−.0016665	−.0000042	.0003333	.0000006	.01
.02	.0002000	−.0033320	−.0000167	.0006663	.0000022	.02
.03	.0004500	−.0049955	−.0000375	.0009989	.0000050	.03
.04	.0008000	−.0066560	−.0000666	.0013307	.0000089	.04
.05	.0012500	−.0083125	−.0001039	.0016615	.0000138	.05
.06	.0018000	−.0099640	−.0001495	.0019910	.0000199	.06
.07	.0024500	−.0116095	−.0002032	.0023191	.0000271	.07
.08	.0032000	−.0132480	−.0002650	.0026454	.0000353	.08
.09	.0040500	−.0148785	−.0003348	.0029697	.0000445	.09
.10	.0050000	−.0165000	−.0004125	.0032918	.0000549	.10
.11	.0060500	−.0181115	−.0004981	.0036113	.0000662	.11
.12	.0072000	−.0197120	−.0005914	.0039282	.0000786	.12
.13	.0084500	−.0213005	−.0006923	.0042421	.0000919	.13
.14	.0098000	−.0228760	−.0008007	.0045528	.0001062	.14
.15	.0112500	−.0244375	−.0009164	.0048600	.0001215	.15
.16	.0128000	−.0259840	−.0010394	.0051635	.0001377	.16
.17	.0144500	−.0275145	−.0011694	.0054631	.0001548	.17
.18	.0162000	−.0290280	−.0013063	.0057586	.0001728	.18
.19	.0180500	−.0305235	−.0014499	.0060496	.0001916	.19
.20	.0200000	−.0320000	−.0016000	.0063360	.0002112	.20
.21	.0220500	−.0334565	−.0017565	.0066175	.0002316	.21
.22	.0242000	−.0348920	−.0019191	.0068940	.0002528	.22
.23	.0264500	−.0363055	−.0020876	.0071651	.0002747	.23
.24	.0288000	−.0376960	−.0022618	.0074306	.0002972	.24
.25	.0312500	−.0390625	−.0024414	.0076904	.0003204	.25
.26	.0338000	−.0404040	−.0026263	.0079442	.0003443	.26
.27	.0364500	−.0417195	−.0028161	.0081918	.0003686	.27
.28	.0392000	−.0430080	−.0030106	.0084330	.0003935	.28
.29	.0420500	−.0442685	−.0032095	.0086676	.0004189	.29
.30	.0450000	−.0455000	−.0034125	.0088952	.0004448	.30
.31	.0480500	−.0467015	−.0036194	.0091159	.0004710	.31
.32	.0512000	−.0478720	−.0038298	.0093293	.0004976	.32
.33	.0544500	−.0490105	−.0040434	.0095352	.0005244	.33
.34	.0578000	−.0501160	−.0042599	.0097335	.0005516	.34
.35	.0612500	−.0511875	−.0044798	.0099259	.0005790	.35
.36	.0648000	−.0522240	−.0047002	.0101064	.0006064	.36
.37	.0684500	−.0532245	−.0049233	.0102806	.0006340	.37
.38	.0722000	−.0541880	−.0051479	.0104464	.0006616	.38
.39	.0760500	−.0551135	−.0053736	.0106036	.0006892	.39
.40	.0800000	−.0560000	−.0056000	.0107520	.0007168	.40
.41	.0840500	−.0568465	−.0058268	.0108915	.0007443	.41
.42	.0882000	−.0576520	−.0060535	.0110219	.0007715	.42
.43	.0924500	−.0584155	−.0062797	.0111430	.0007986	.43
.44	.0968000	−.0591360	−.0065050	.0112548	.0008253	.44
.45	.1012500	−.0598125	−.0067289	.0113569	.0008518	.45
.46	.1058000	−.0604440	−.0069511	.0114493	.0008778	.46
.47	.1104500	−.0610295	−.0071710	.0115318	.0009033	.47
.48	.1152000	−.0615680	−.0073882	.0116043	.0009283	.48
.49	.1200500	−.0620585	−.0076022	.0116667	.0009528	.49
.50	.1250000	−.0625000	−.0078125	.0117188	.0009766	.50

TABLE IV (continued). STIRLING'S INTERPOLATION COEFFICIENTS

u	S_2	S_3	S_4	S_5	S_6	u
.51	.1300500	−.0628915	−.0080187	.0117604	.0009996	.51
.52	.1352000	−.0632320	−.0082202	.0117915	.0010219	.52
.53	.1404500	−.0635205	−.0084165	.0118120	.0010434	.53
.54	.1458000	−.0637560	−.0086071	.0118216	.0010639	.54
.55	.1512500	−.0639375	−.0087914	.0118204	.0010835	.55
.56	.1568000	−.0640640	−.0089690	.0118083	.0011021	.56
.57	.1624500	−.0641345	−.0091392	.0117850	.0011196	.57
.58	.1682000	−.0641480	−.0093015	.0117506	.0011359	.58
.59	.1740500	−.0641035	−.0094553	.0117050	.0011510	.59
.60	.1800000	−.0640000	−.0096000	.0116480	.0011648	.60
.61	.1860500	−.0638365	−.0097351	.0115796	.0011773	.61
.62	.1922000	−.0636120	−.0098599	.0114998	.0011883	.62
.63	.1984500	−.0633255	−.0099738	.0114084	.0011979	.63
.64	.2048000	−.0629760	−.0100762	.0113055	.0012059	.64
.65	.2112500	−.0625625	−.0101664	.0111909	.0012123	.65
.66	.2178000	−.0620840	−.0102439	.0110646	.0012171	.66
.67	.2244500	−.0615395	−.0103079	.0109266	.0012201	.67
.68	.2312000	−.0609280	−.0103578	.0107769	.0012214	.68
.69	.2380500	−.0602485	−.0103929	.0106155	.0012208	.69
.70	.2450000	−.0595000	−.0104125	.0104423	.0012183	.70
.71	.2520500	−.0586815	−.0104160	.0102572	.0012138	.71
.72	.2592000	−.0577920	−.0104026	.0100604	.0012073	.72
.73	.2664500	−.0568305	−.0103716	.0098519	.0011986	.73
.74	.2738000	−.0557960	−.0103223	.0096315	.0011879	.74
.75	.2812500	−.0546875	−.0102539	.0093994	.0011749	.75
.76	.2888000	−.0535040	−.0101658	.0091556	.0011597	.76
.77	.2964500	−.0522445	−.0100571	.0089001	.0011422	.77
.78	.3042000	−.0509080	−.0099271	.0086330	.0011223	.78
.79	.3120500	−.0494935	−.0097750	.0083543	.0011000	.79
.80	.3200000	−.0480000	−.0096000	.0080640	.0010752	.70
.81	.3280500	−.0464265	−.0094014	.0077623	.0010479	.81
.82	.3362000	−.0447720	−.0091783	.0074492	.0010181	.82
.83	.3444500	−.0430355	−.0089299	.0071247	.0009856	.83
.84	.3528000	−.0412160	−.0086554	.0067891	.0009505	.84
.85	.3612500	−.0393125	−.0083539	.0064423	.0009127	.85
.86	.3698000	−.0373240	−.0080247	.0060846	.0008721	.86
.87	.3784500	−.0352495	−.0076668	.0057159	.0008288	.87
.88	.3872000	−.0330880	−.0072794	.0053364	.0007827	.88
.89	.3960500	−.0308385	−.0068616	.0049463	.0007337	.89
.90	.4050000	−.0285000	−.0064125	.0045458	.0006819	.90
.91	.4140500	−.0260715	−.0059313	.0041348	.0006271	.91
.92	.4232000	−.0235520	−.0054170	.0037137	.0005694	.92
.93	.4324500	−.0209405	−.0048687	.0032825	.0005088	.93
.94	.4418000	−.0182360	−.0042855	.0028415	.0004452	.94
.95	.4512500	−.0154375	−.0036664	.0023909	.0003786	.95
.96	.4608000	−.0125440	−.0030106	.0019308	.0003089	.96
.97	.4704500	−.0095545	−.0023170	.0014614	.0002363	.97
.98	.4802000	−.0064680	−.0015847	.0009830	.0001606	.98
.99	.4900500	−.0032835	−.0008127	.0004958	.0000818	.99
1.00	.5000000	.0000000	.0000000	.0000000	.0000000	1.00

TABLE V. COEFFICIENTS E_{ij} FOR EVERETT'S FORMULA

u	E_{1j}	E_{2j}	E_{3j}	u
.01	$-.0016665$	.0003333	$-.0000714$	.01
.02	$-.0033320$	.0006663	$-.0001428$	.02
.03	$-.0049955$	.0009989	$-.0002140$	.03
.04	$-.0066560$	.0013307	$-.0002851$	.04
.05	$-.0083125$	.0016615	$-.0003560$	.05
.06	$-.0099640$	.0019910	$-.0004265$	.06
.07	$-.0116095$	.0023191	$-.0004967$	.07
.08	$-.0132480$	.0026454	$-.0005665$	.08
.09	$-.0148785$	.0029697	$-.0006358$	.09
.10	$-.0165000$	.0032918	$-.0007046$	.10
.11	$-.0181115$	.0036113	$-.0007728$	.11
.12	$-.0197120$	.0039282	$-.0008404$	.12
.13	$-.0213005$	.0042421	$-.0009073$	.13
.14	$-.0228760$	.0045528	$-.0009735$	.14
.15	$-.0244375$	.0048600	$-.0010388$	.15
.16	$-.0259840$	.0051635	$-.0011033$	.16
.17	$-.0275145$	.0054631	$-.0011669$	.17
.18	$-.0290280$	.0057586	$-.0012295$	.18
.19	$-.0305235$	.0060496	$-.0012911$	.19
.20	$-.0320000$	.0063360	$-.0013517$	.20
.21	$-.0334565$	.0066175	$-.0014111$	.21
.22	$-.0348920$	.0068940	$-.0014693$	.22
.23	$-.0363055$	.0071651	$-.0015264$	.23
.24	$-.0376960$	.0074306	$-.0015821$	.24
.25	$-.0390625$	.0076904	$-.0016365$	.25
.26	$-.0404040$	.0079442	$-.0016895$	.26
.27	$-.0417195$	.0081918	$-.0017412$	.27
.28	$-.0430080$	.0084330	$-.0017913$	.28
.29	$-.0442685$	.0086676	$-.0018400$	.29
.30	$-.0455000$	.0088952	$-.0018871$	.30
.31	$-.0467015$	.0091159	$-.0019325$	.31
.32	$-.0478720$	.0093293	$-.0019764$	.32
.33	$-.0490105$	.0095352	$-.0020185$	.33
.34	$-.0501160$	.0097335	$-.0020590$	.34
.35	$-.0511875$	.0099259	$-.0020980$	.35
.36	$-.0522240$	.0101064	$-.0021345$	.36
.37	$-.0532245$	.0102806	$-.0021695$	.37
.38	$-.0541880$	.0104464	$-.0022026$	.38
.39	$-.0551135$	.0106036	$-.0022338$	.39
.40	$-.0560000$	.0107520	$-.0022630$	.40
.41	$-.0568465$	.0108915	$-.0022903$	.41
.42	$-.0576520$	.0110219	$-.0023155$	.42
.43	$-.0584155$	.0111430	$-.0023387$	.43
.44	$-.0591360$	.0112548	$-.0023599$	.44
.45	$-.0598125$	.0113569	$-.0023789$	.45
.46	$-.0604440$	.0114493	$-.0023957$	.46
.47	$-.0610295$	.0115318	$-.0024104$	.47
.48	$-.0615680$	.0116043	$-.0024230$	.48
.49	$-.0620585$	.0116667	$-.0024333$	.49
.50	$-.0625000$	.0117188	$-.0024414$	.50

TABLE V (continued).   COEFFICIENTS E_{ij} FOR EVERETT'S FORMULA

u	E_{1j}	E_{2j}	E_{3j}	u
.51	− .0628915	.0117604	− .0024473	.51
.52	− .0632320	.0117915	− .0024508	.52
.53	− .0635205	.0118120	− .0024521	.53
.54	− .0637560	.0118216	− .0024511	.54
.55	− .0639375	.0118204	− .0024478	.55
.56	− .0640640	.0118083	− .0024422	.56
.57	− .0641345	.0117850	− .0024342	.57
.58	− .0641480	.0117506	− .0024239	.58
.59	− .0641035	.0117050	− .0024112	.59
.60	− .0640000	.0116480	− .0023962	.60
.61	− .0638365	.0115796	− .0023788	.61
.62	− .0636120	.0114998	− .0023590	.62
.63	− .0633255	.0114084	− .0023368	.73
.64	− .0629760	.0113055	− .0023124	.64
.65	− .0625625	.0111909	− .0022855	.65
.66	− .0620840	.0110640	− .0022562	.66
.67	− .0615395	.0109266	− .0022246	.67
.68	− .0609280	.0107769	− .0021907	.68
.69	− .0602485	.0106155	− .0021544	.69
.70	− .0595000	.0104423	− .0021158	.70
.71	− .0586815	.0102572	− .0020749	.71
.72	− .0577920	.0100604	− .0020316	.72
.73	− .0568305	.0098519	− .0019861	.73
.74	− .0557960	.0096315	− .0019383	.74
.75	− .0546875	.0093994	− .0018883	.75
.76	− .0535040	.0091556	− .0018360	.76
.77	− .0522445	.0089001	− .0017815	.77
.78	− .0509080	.0086330	− .0017249	.78
.79	− .0494935	.0083543	− .0016661	.79
.80	− .0480000	.0080640	− .0016051	.80
.81	− .0464265	.0077623	− .0015421	.81
.82	− .0447720	.0074492	− .0014770	.82
.83	− .0430355	.0071247	− .0014099	.83
.84	− .0412160	.0067891	− .0013408	.84
.85	− .0393125	.0064423	− .0012697	.85
.86	− .0373240	.0060846	− .0011967	.86
.87	− .0352495	.0057159	− .0011218	.87
.88	− .0330880	.0053364	− .0010451	.88
.89	− .0308385	.0049463	− .0009666	.89
.90	− .0285000	.0045458	− .0008864	.90
.91	− .0260715	.0041348	− .0008045	.91
.92	− .0235520	.0037137	− .0007210	.92
.93	− .0209405	.0032825	− .0006358	.93
.94	− .0182360	.0028415	− .0005491	.94
.95	− .0154375	.0023909	− .0004610	.95
.96	− .0125440	.0019308	− .0003714	.96
.97	− .0095545	.0014614	− .0002804	.97
.98	− .0064680	.0009830	− .0001882	.98
.99	− .0032835	.0004958	− .0000947	.99
1.00	.0000000	.0000000	.0000000	1.00

TABLE VI. BESSEL'S INTERPOLATION COEFFICIENTS

For $.50 < u \leq .99$ use headings at bottom of page.
Numbers with less than 7 decimal places are exact.

u	B_1	B_2	B_3	B_4	$-B_5$	$-B_6$	u
.01	−.49	−.00495	.0008085	.0008291	.0000813	.0001661	.99
.02	−.48	−.00980	.0015680	.0016493	.0001583	.0003309	.98
.03	−.47	−.01455	.0022795	.0024603	.0002313	.0004944	.97
.04	−.46	−.01920	.0029440	.0032614	.0003000	.0006582	.96
.05	−.45	−.02375	.0035625	.0040523	.0003647	.0008169	.95
.06	−.44	−.02820	.0041360	.0048325	.0004253	.0009756	.94
.07	−.43	−.03255	.0046655	.0056016	.0004817	.0011325	.93
.08	−.42	−.03680	.0051520	.0063590	.0005342	.0012874	.92
.09	−.41	−.04095	.0055965	.0071045	.0005826	.0014403	.91
.10	−.40	−.04500	.0060000	.0078375	.0006270	.0015910	.90
.11	−.39	−.04895	.0063635	.0085577	.0006675	.0017395	.89
.12	−.38	−.05280	.0066880	.0092646	.0007041	.0018855	.88
.13	−.37	−.05655	.0069745	.0099580	.0007369	.0020291	.87
.14	−.36	−.06020	.0072240	.0106373	.0007659	.0021702	.86
.15	−.35	−.06375	.0074375	.0113023	.0007912	.0023085	.85
.16	−.34	−.06720	.0076160	.0119526	.0008128	.0024441	.84
.17	−.33	−.07055	.0077605	.0125879	.0008308	.0025768	.83
.18	−.32	−.07380	.0078720	.0132077	.0008453	.0027065	.82
.19	−.31	−.07695	.0079515	.0138119	.0008563	.0028332	.81
.20	−.30	−.08000	.0080000	.0144000	.0008640	.0029568	.80
.21	−.29	−.08295	.0080185	.0149718	.0008684	.0030772	.79
.22	−.28	−.08580	.0080080	.0155269	.0008695	.0031942	.78
.23	−.27	−.08855	.0079695	.0160652	.0008675	.0033079	.77
.24	−.26	−.09120	.0079040	.0165862	.0008625	.0034181	.76
.25	−.25	−.09375	.0078125	.0170898	.0008545	.0035248	.75
.26	−.24	.−09620	.0076960	.0175757	.0008436	.0036279	.74
.27	−.23	−.09855	.0075555	.0180437	.0008300	.0037273	.73
.28	−.22	−.10080	.0073920	.0184937	.0008137	.0038230	.72
.29	−.21	−.10295	.0072065	.0189248	.0007948	.0039148	.71
.30	−.20	−.10500	.0070000	.0193375	.0007735	.0040029	.70
.31	−.19	−.10695	.0067735	.0197314	.0007498	.0040870	.69
.32	−.18	−.10880	.0065280	.0201062	.0007238	.0041671	.68
.33	−.17	−.11055	.0062645	.0204619	.0006957	.0042432	.67
.34	−.16	−.11220	.0059840	.0207981	.0006655	.0043152	.66
.35	−.15	−.11375	.0056875	.0211148	.0006334	.0043831	.65
.36	−.14	−.11520	.0053760	.0214118	.0005995	.0044468	.64
.37	−.13	−.11655	.0050505	.0216890	.0005639	.0045063	.63
.38	−.12	−.11780	.0047120	.0219461	.0005267	.0045616	.62
.39	−.11	−.11895	.0043615	.0221832	.0004880	.0046126	.61
.40	−.10	−.12000	.0040000	.0224000	.0004480	.0046592	.60
.41	−.09	−.12095	.0036285	.0225965	.0004067	.0047015	.59
.42	−.08	−.12180	.0032480	.0227725	.0003644	.0047394	.58
.43	−.07	−.12255	.0028595	.0229281	.0003210	.0047729	.57
.44	−.06	−.12320	.0024640	.0230630	.0002768	.0048020	.56
.45	−.05	−.12375	.0020625	.0231773	.0002318	.0048267	.55
.46	−.04	−.12420	.0016560	.0232709	.0001862	.0048469	.54
.47	−.03	−.12455	.0012455	.0233438	.0001401	.0048626	.53
.48	−.02	−.12480	.0008320	.0233958	.0000936	.0048738	.52
.49	−.01	−.12495	.0004165	.0234271	.0000469	.0048806	.51
.50	.00	−.12500	.0000000	.0234375	.0000000	.0048828	.50
u	$-B_1$	B_2	$-B_3$	B_4	B_5	$-B_6$	u

TABLE VII. GAUSS'S QUADRATURE COEFFICIENTS

i	v_i	g_i
	$n = 2$	
1	0.57735 02692	1.00000 00000
	$n = 3$	
0	0.00000 00000	0.88888 88889
1	0.77459 66692	0.55555 55556
	$n = 4$	
1	0.33998 10436	0.65214 51549
2	0.86113 63116	0.34785 48451
	$n = 5$	
0	0.00000 00000	0.56888 88889
1	0.53846 93101	0.47862 86705
2	0.90617 98459	0.23692 68851
	$n = 6$	
1	0.23861 91861	0.46791 39346
2	0.66120 93865	0.36076 15730
3	0.93246 95142	0.17132 44924
	$n = 7$	
0	0.00000 00000	0.41795 91837
1	0.40584 51514	0.38183 00505
2	0.74153 11856	0.27970 53915
3	0.94910 79123	0.12948 49662
	$n = 8$	
1	0.18343 46425	0.36268 37834
2	0.52553 24099	0.31370 66459
3	0.79666 64774	0.22238 10345
4	0.96028 98565	0.10122 85363
	$n = 9$	
0	0.00000 00000	0.33023 93550
1	0.32425 34234	0.31234 70770
2	0.61337 14327	0.26061 06964
3	0.83603 11073	0.18064 81607
4	0.96816 02395	0.08127 43884
	$n = 10$	
1	0.14887 43390	0.29552 42247
2	0.43339 53941	0.26926 67193
3	0.67940 95683	0.21908 63625
4	0.86506 33667	0.14945 13492
5	0.97390 65285	0.06667 13443

i	v_i	g_i
	$n = 11$	
0	0.00000 00000	0.27292 50868
1	0.26954 31560	0.26280 45445
2	0.51909 61291	0.23319 37646
3	0.73015 20056	0.18629 02109
4	0.88706 25998	0.12558 03695
5	0.97822 86581	0.05566 85671
	$n = 12$	
1	0.12533 34085	0.24914 70458
2	0.36783 14989	0.23349 25365
3	0.58731 79543	0.20316 74267
4	0.76990 26742	0.16007 83285
5	0.90411 72564	0.10693 93260
6	0.98156 06342	0.04717 53364
	$n = 13$	
0	0.00000 00000	0.23255 15532
1	0.23045 83160	0.22628 31803
2	0.44849 27510	0.20781 60475
3	0.64234 93394	0.17814 59808
4	0.80157 80907	0.13887 35102
5	0.91759 83992	0.09212 14998
6	0.98418 30547	0.04048 40048
	$n = 14$	
1	0.10805 49487	0.21526 38535
2	0.31911 23689	0.20519 84637
3	0.51524 86364	0.18553 83975
4	0.68729 29048	0.15720 31672
5	0.82720 13151	0.12151 85707
6	0.92843 48837	0.08015 80872
7	0.98628 38087	0.03511 94603
	$n = 15$	
0	0.00000 00000	0.20257 82419
1	0.20119 40940	0.19843 14853
2	0.39415 13471	0.18616 10000
3	0.57097 21726	0.16626 92058
4	0.72441 77314	0.13957 06779
5	0.84820 65834	0.10715 92205
6	0.93727 33924	0.07036 60475
7	0.98799 25180	0.03075 32420
	$n = 16$	
1	0.09501 25098	0.18945 06105
2	0.28160 35508	0.18260 34150
3	0.45801 67777	0.16915 65194
4	0.61787 62444	0.14959 59888
5	0.75540 44084	0.12462 89713
6	0.86563 12024	0.09515 85117
7	0.94457 50231	0.06225 35239
8	0.98940 09350	0.02715 24594

TABLE VIII. LAGRANGIAN INTERPOLATION COEFFICIENTS

p	A_{-2}	$-A_{-1}$	A_0	A_1	$-A_2$	p
0.00	.0000000	.0000000	1.0000000	.0000000	.0000000	0.00
.01	.0008291	.0065998	.9998750	.0067332	.0008374	.01
.02	.0016493	.0130654	.9995000	.0135986	.0016827	.02
.03	.0024603	.0193956	.9988752	.0205954	.0025352	.03
.04	.0032614	.0255898	.9980006	.0277222	.0033946	.04
0.05	.0040523	.0316469	.9968766	.0349781	.0042602	0.05
.06	.0048325	.0375662	.9955032	.0423618	.0051315	.06
.07	.0056016	.0433468	.9938810	.0498722	.0060079	.07
.08	.0063590	.0489882	.9920102	.0575078	.0068890	.08
.09	.0071045	.0544894	.9898914	.0652676	.0077740	0.09
0.10	.0078375	.0598500	.9875250	.0731500	.0086625	0.10
.11	.0085577	.0650692	.9849116	.0811538	.0095538	.11
.12	.0092646	.0701466	.9820518	.0892774	.0104474	.12
.13	.0099580	.0750814	.9789464	.0975196	.0113425	.13
.14	.0106373	.0798734	.9755960	.1058786	.0122387	.14
0.15	.0113023	.0845219	.9720016	.1143531	.0131352	0.15
.16	.0119526	.0890266	.9681638	.1229414	.0140314	.16
.17	.0125879	.0933870	.9640838	.1316420	.0149266	.17
.18	.0132077	.0976030	.9597624	.1404530	.0158203	.18
.19	.0138119	.1016740	.9552008	.1493730	.0167116	.19
0.20	.0144000	.1056000	.9504000	.1584000	.0176000	0.20
.21	.0149718	.1093806	.9453612	.1675324	.0184847	.21
.22	.0155269	.1130158	.9400856	.1767682	.0193651	.22
.23	.0160652	.1165052	.9345746	.1861058	.0202403	.23
.24	.0165862	.1198490	.9288294	.1955430	.0211098	.24
0.25	.0170898	.1230469	.9228516	.2050781	.0219727	0.25
.26	.0175757	.1260990	.9166424	.2147090	.0228283	.26
.27	.0180437	.1290052	.9102036	.2244338	.0236758	.27
.28	.0184934	.1317658	.9035366	.2342502	.0245146	.28
.29	.0189248	.1343806	.8966432	.2441564	.0253437	.29
0.30	.0193375	.1368500	.8895250	.2541500	.0261625	0.30
.31	.0197314	.1391740	.8821838	.2642290	.0269701	.31
.32	.0201062	.1413530	.8746214	.2743910	.0277658	.32
.33	.0204619	.1433870	.8668398	.2846340	.0285486	.33
.34	.0207981	.1452766	.8588408	2949554	.0293179	.34
0.35	.0211148	.1470219	.8506266	.3053531	.0300727	.35
.36	.0214118	.1486234	.8421990	.3158246	.0308122	.36
.37	.0216890	.1500814	.8335604	.3263676	.0315355	.37
.38	.0219461	.1513966	.8247128	.3369794	.0322419	.38
.39	.0221832	.1525692	.8156586	.3476578	.0329303	.39
0.40	.0224000	.1536000	.8064000	.3584000	.0336000	0.40
.41	.0225965	.1544894	.7969394	.3692036	.0342500	.41
.42	.0227725	.1552382	.7872792	.3800658	.0348795	.42
.43	.0229281	.1558468	.7774220	.3909842	.0354874	.43
.44	.0230630	.1563162	.7673702	.4019558	.0360730	.44
0.45	.0231773	.1566469	.7571266	.4129781	.0366352	.45
.46	.0232709	.1568398	.7466936	.4240482	.0371731	.46
.47	.0233438	.1568956	.7360742	.4351634	.0376857	.47
.48	.0233958	.1568154	.7252710	.4463206	.0381722	.48
.49	.0234271	.1565998	.7142870	.4575172	.0386314	.49
0.50	.0234375	.1562500	.7031250	.4687500	.0390625	0.50
$-p$	A_2	$-A_1$	A_0	A_{-1}	$-A_{-2}$	$-p$

TABLE VIII (continued). LAGRANGIAN INTERPOLATION COEFFICIENTS

5-Points

p	A_{-2}	$-A_{-1}$	A_0	A_1	$-A_2$	p
0.50	.0234375	.1562500	.7031250	.4687500	.0390625	0.50
.51	.0234271	.1557668	.6917880	.4800162	.0394644	.51
.52	.0233958	.1551514	.8602790	.4913126	.0398362	.52
.53	.0233438	.1544046	.6686012	.5026364	.0401767	.53
.54	.0232709	.1535278	.6567576	.5139842	.0404851	.54
0.55	.0231773	.1525219	.6447516	.5253531	.0407602	0.55
.56	.0230630	.1513882	.6325862	.5367398	.0410010	.56
57	.0229281	.1501278	.6202650	.5481412	.0412064	.57
58	.0227725	.1487422	.6077912	.5595538	.0413755	.58
.59	.0225965	.1472324	.5951684	.5709746	.0415070	.59
0.60	.0224000	.1456000	.5824000	.5824000	.0416000	0.60
.61	.0221832	.1438462	.5694896	.5938268	.0416533	.61
.62	.0219461	.1419726	.5564408	.6052514	.0416659	.62
.63	.0216890	.1399804	.5432574	.6166706	.0416363	.63
.64	.0214118	.1378714	.5299430	.6280806	.0415642	.64
0.65	.0211148	.1356469	.5165016	.6394781	.0414477	0.65
.66	.0207981	.1333086	.5029368	.6508594	.0412859	.66
.67	.0204619	.1308580	.4892528	.6622210	.0410776	.67
.68	.0201062	.1282970	.4754534	.6735590	.0408218	.68
.69	.0197314	.1256270	.4615428	.6848700	.0405171	.69
0.70	.0193375	.1228500	.4475250	.6961500	.0401625	0.70
.71	.0189248	.1199676	.4334042	.7073954	.0397567	.71
.72	.0184934	.1169818	.4191846	.7186022	.0392986	.72
.73	.0180437	.1138942	.4048706	.7297668	.0387868	.73
.74	.0175757	.1107070	.3904664	.7408850	.0382203	.74
0.75	.0170898	.1074219	.3759766	.7519531	.0375977	0.75
.76	.0165862	.1040410	.3614054	.7629670	.0369178	.76
.77	.0160652	.1005662	.3467576	.7739228	.0361793	.77
.78	.0155269	.0969998	.3320376	.7848162	.0353811	.78
.79	.0149718	.0933436	.3172502	.7956434	.0345217	.79
0.80	.0144000	.0896000	.3024000	.8064000	.0336000	0.30
.81	.0138119	.0857710	.2874918	.8170820	.0326146	.81
.82	.0132077	.0818590	.2725304	.8276850	.0315643	.82
.83	.0125879	.0778660	.2575208	.8382050	.0304476	.83
.84	.0119526	.0737946	.2424678	.8486374	.0292634	.84
0.85	.0113023	.0696469	.2273766	.8589781	.0280102	0.85
.86	.0106373	.0654254	.2122520	.8692226	.0266867	.86
.87	.0099580	.0611324	.1970994	.8793666	.0252915	.87
.88	.0092646	.0567706	.1819238	.8894054	.0238234	.88
.89	.0085577	.0523422	.1667306	.8993348	.0222808	.89
0.90	.0078375	.0478500	.1515250	.9091500	.0206625	0.90
.91	.0071045	.0432964	.1363124	.9188466	.0189670	.91
.92	.0063590	.0386842	.1210982	.9284198	.0171930	.92
.93	.0056016	.0340158	.1058880	.9378652	.0153389	.93
.94	.0048325	.0292942	.0906872	.9471778	.0134035	.94
0.95	.0040523	.0245219	.0755016	.9563531	.0113852	0.95
.96	.0032614	.0197018	.0603366	.9653862	.0092826	.96
.97	.0024603	.0148366	.0451982	.9742724	.0070942	.97
.98	.0016493	.0099294	.0300920	.9830066	.0048187	.98
.99	.0008291	.0049828	.0150240	.9915842	.0024544	.99
1.00	.0000000	.0000000	.0000000	1.0000000	.0000000	1.00
$-p$	A_2	$-A_1$	A_0	A_{-1}	$-A_{-2}$	$-p$

TABLE VIII (continued).   LAGRANGIAN INTERPOLATION COEFFICIENTS

5-Points

p	A_{-2}	$-A_{-1}$	A_0	A_1	$-A_2$	p
1.00	.0000000	.0000000	.0000000	1.000000	.0000000	1.00
.01	.0008374	.0050162	.0149740	1.0082492	.0025461	.01
.02	.0016827	.0100626	.0298920	1.0163266	.0051853	.02
.03	.0025352	.0151364	.0447478	1.0242274	.0079193	.03
.04	.0033946	.0202342	.0595354	1.0319462	.0107494	.04
1.05	.0042602	.0253531	.0742484	1.0394781	.0136773	1.05
.06	.0051315	.0304898	.0888808	1.0468178	.0167045	.06
.07	.0060079	.0356412	.1034260	1.0539602	.0198326	.07
.08	.0068890	.0408038	.1178778	1.0608998	.0230630	.08
.09	.0077740	.0459746	.1322296	1.0676316	.0263975	.09
1.10	.0086625	.0511500	.1464750	1.0741500	.0298375	1.10
.11	.0095538	.0563268	.1606074	1.0804498	.0333847	.11
.12	.0104474	.0615014	.1746202	1.0865254	.0370406	.12
.13	.0113425	.0666706	.1885066	1.0923716	.0408070	.13
.14	.0122387	.0718306	.2022600	1.0979826	.0446853	.14
1.15	.0131352	.0769781	.2158734	1.1033531	.0486773	1.15
.16	.0140314	.0821094	.2293402	1.1084774	.0527846	.16
.17	.0149266	.0872210	.2426532	1.1133500	.0570089	.17
.18	.0158203	.0923090	.2558056	1.1179650	.0613517	.18
.19	.0167116	.0973700	.2687902	1.1223170	.0658149	.19
1.20	.0176000	.1024000	.2816000	1.1264000	.0704000	1.20
.21	.0184847	.1073954	.2942278	1.1302084	.0751088	.21
.22	.0193651	.1123522	.3066664	1.1337362	.0799429	.22
.23	.0202403	.1172668	.3189084	1.1369778	.0849042	.23
.24	.0211098	.1221350	.3309466	1.1399270	.0899942	.24
1.25	.0219727	.1269531	.3427734	1.1425781	.0952148	1.25
.26	.0228283	.1317170	.3543816	1.1449250	.1005677	.26
.27	.0236758	.1364228	.3657634	1.1469618	.1060547	.27
.28	.0245146	.1410662	.3769114	1.1486822	.1116774	.28
.29	.0253437	.1456434	.3878178	1.1500804.	.1174378	.29
1.30	.0261625	.1501500	.3984752	1.1511500	.1233375	1.30
.31	.0269701	.1545820	.4088752	1.1518850	.1293784	.31
.32	.0277658	.1589350	.4190106	1.1522790	.1355622	.32
.33	.0285486	.1632050	.4288732	1.1523260	.1418909	.33
.34	.0293179	.1673874	.4384552	1.1520194	.1483661	.34
1.35	.0300727	.1714781	.4477484	1.1513531	.1549898	1.35
.36	.0308122	.1754726	.4567450	1.1503206	.1617638	.36
.37	.0315355	.1793666	.4654366	1.1489156	.1686900	.37
.38	.0322419	.1831554	.4738152	1.1471314	.1757701	.38
.39	.0329303	.1868348	.4818724	1.1449618	.1830062	.39
1.40	.0336000	.1904000	.4896000	1.1424000	.1904000	.140
.41	.0342500	.1938466	.4969896	1.1394396	.1979535	.41
.42	.0348795	.1971698	.5040328	1.1360738	.2056685	.42
.43	.0354874	.2003652	.5107210	1.1322962	.2135471	.43
.44	.0360730	.2034278	.5170458	1.1280998	.2215910	.44
1.45	.0366352	.2063531	.5229984	1.1234781	.2298023	1.45
.46	.0371731	.2091362	.5285704	1.1184242	.2381829	.46
.47	.0376857	.2117724	.5337528	1.1129314	.2467348	.47
.48	.0381722	.2142566	.5385370	1.1069926	.2554598	.48
.49	.0386314	.2165842	.5429140	1.1006012	.2643601	.49
1.50	.0390625	.2187500	.5468750	1.0937500	.2734375	1.50
$-p$	$-A_2$	A_1	$-A_0$	A_{-1}	A_{-2}	$-p$

TABLE VIII (continued). LAGRANGIAN INTERPOLATION COEFFICIENTS

5-Points

p	A_{-2}	$-A_{-1}$	A_0	A_1	$-A_2$	p
1.50	.0390625	.2187500	.5468750	1.0937500	.2734375	1.50
.51	.0394644	.2207492	.5504110	1.0864322	.2826941	.51
.52	.0398362	.2225766	.5535130	1.0786406	.2921318	.52
.53	.0401767	.2242274	.5561718	1.0703684	.3017528	.53
.54	.0404851	.2256962	.5583784	1.0616082	.3115589	.54
1.55	.0407602	.2269781	.5601234	1.0523531	.3215523	1.55
.56	.0410010	.2280678	.5613978	1.0425958	.3317350	.56
.57	.0412064	.2289602	.5621920	1.0323292	.3421091	.57
.58	.0413755	.2296498	.5624968	1.0215458	.3526765	.58
.59	.0415070	.2301316	.5623026	1.0102386	.3634395	.59
1.60	.0416000	.2304000	.5616000	.9984000	.3744000	1.60
.61	.0416533	.2304498	.5603794	.9860228	.3855602	.61
.62	.0416659	.2302754	.5586312	.9730994	.3969221	.62
.63	.0416365	.2298716	.5563456	.9596226	.4084880	.63
.64	.0415642	.2292326	.5535130	.9455846	.4202598	.64
1.65	.0414477	.2283531	.5501234	.9309781	.4322398	1.65
.66	.0412859	.2272274	.5461672	.9157954	.4444301	.66
.67	.0410776	.2258500	.5416342	.9000290	.4568329	.67
.68	.0408218	.2242150	.5365146	.8836710	.4694502	.68
.69	.0405171	.2223170	.5307982	.8667140	.4822844	.69
1.70	.0401625	.2201500	.5244750	.8491500	.4953375	1.70
.71	.0397567	.2177084	.5175348	.8309714	.5086118	.71
.72	.0392986	.2149862	.5099674	.8121702	.5221094	.72
.73	.0387868	.2119778	.5017624	.7927388	.5358327	.73
.74	.0382203	.2086770	.4929096	.7726690	.5497837	.74
1.75	.0375977	.2050781	.4833984	.7519531	.5639648	1.75
.76	.0369178	.2011750	.4732186	.7305830	.5783782	.76
.77	.0361793	.1969618	.4623594	.7085508	.5930262	.77
.78	.0353811	.1924322	.4508104	.6858482	.6079109	.78
.79	.0345217	.1875804	.4385608	.6624674	.6230348	.79
1.80	.0336000	.1824000	.4256000	.6384000	.6384000	1.80
.81	.0326146	.1768850	.4119172	.6136380	.6540089	.81
.82	.0315643	.1710290	.3975016	.5881730	.6698637	.82
.83	.0304476	.1648260	.3823422	.5619970	.6859669	.83
.84	.0292634	.1582694	.3664282	.5351014	.7023206	.84
1.85	.0280102	.1513531	.3497484	.5074781	.7189273	1.85
.86	.0266867	.1440706	.3322920	.4791186	.7357893	.86
.87	.0252915	.1364156	.3140476	.4500146	.7529090	.87
.88	.0238234	.1283814	.2950042	.4201574	.7702886	.88
.89	.0222808	.1199618	.2751504	.3895388	.7879307	.89
1.90	.0206625	.1111500	.2544750	.3581500	.8058375	1.90
.91	.0189670	.1019396	.2329666	.3259826	.8240115	.91
.92	.0171930	.0923238	.2106138	.2930278	.8424550	.92
.93	.0153389	.0822962	.1874050	.2592772	.8611706	.93
.94	.0134035	.0718498	.1633288	.2247218	.8801605	.94
1.95	.0113852	.0609781	.1383734	.1893531	.8994273	1.95
.96	.0092826	.0496742	.1125274	.1531622	.9189734	.96
.97	.0070942	.0379314	.0857788	.1161404	.9388013	.97
.98	.0048187	.0257426	.0581160	.0782786	.9589133	.98
.99	.0024544	.0131012	.0295270	.0395682	.9793121	.99
2.00	.0000000	.0000000	.0000000	.0000000	1.0000000	2.00
$-p$	$-A_2$	A_1	$-A_0$	A_{-1}	A_{-2}	$-p$

TABLE IX. DIFFERENTIAL COEFFICIENTS—FRACTIONAL FORM

$$A'_{ki} = \frac{dA_i}{du}\bigg|_{u=k}$$

i\k	A'_{k0}	A'_{k1}	A'_{k2}	A'_{k3}	A'_{k4}	A'_{k5}	A'_{k6}	A'_{k7}	A'_{k8}	A'_{k9}	k
						$n = 2$ (3 points) $D_n = 2$					
0	-3	4	-1								2
1	-1	0	1								
						$n = 3$ (4 points) $D_n = 6$					
0	-11	18	-9	2							3
1	-2	-3	6	-1							2
						$n = 4$ (5 points) $D_n = 12$					
0	-25	48	-36	16	-3						4
1	-3	-10	18	-6	1						3
2	1	-8	0	8	-1						
						$n = 5$ (6 points) $D_n = 60$					
0	-137	300	-300	200	-75	12					5
1	-12	-65	120	-60	20	-3					4
2	3	-30	-20	60	-15	2					3

$n = 6$ (7 points) $D_n = 60$

								k
								6
								5
								4

k	$-A_{k,n}$	$-A_{k,n-1}$	$-A_{k,n-2}$	$-A_{k,n-3}$	$-A_{k,n-4}$	$-A_{k,n-5}$	$-A_{k,n-6}$
0	-147	360	-450	400	-225	72	-10
1	-10	-77	150	-100	50	-15	2
2	2	-24	-35	80	-30	8	-1
3	-1	9	-45	0	45	-9	1

$n = 7$ (8 points) $D_n = 420$

top k labels: 7, 6, 5, 4

k	$-A_{k,n}$	$-A_{k,n-1}$	$-A_{k,n-2}$	$-A_{k,n-3}$	$-A_{k,n-4}$	$-A_{k,n-5}$	$-A_{k,n-6}$	$-A_{k,n-7}$
0	-1089	2940	-4410	4900	-3675	1764	-490	60
1	-60	-609	1260	-1050	700	-315	84	-10
2	10	-140	-329	700	-350	140	-35	4
3	-4	42	-252	-105	420	-42	28	-3

$n = 8$ (9 points) $D_n = 840$

top k labels: 8, 7, 6, 5

k	$-A_{k,n}$	$-A_{k,n-1}$	$-A_{k,n-2}$	$-A_{k,n-3}$	$-A_{k,n-4}$	$-A_{k,n-5}$	$-A_{k,n-6}$	$-A_{k,n-7}$	$-A_{k,n-8}$
0	-2283	6720	-11760	15680	-14700	9804	-3920	960	-105
1	-105	-1338	2940	-2940	2540	-1470	588	-140	15
2	15	-240	-798	1680	-1050	560	-210	48	-5
3	-5	60	-420	-378	1050	-420	140	-30	3
4	3	-32	168	-672	0	672	-168	32	-3

$n = 9$ (10 points) $D_n = 2520$

top k labels: 9, 8, 7, 6, 5

k	$-A_{k,n}$	$-A_{k,n-1}$	$-A_{k,n-2}$	$-A_{k,n-3}$	$-A_{k,n-4}$	$-A_{k,n-5}$	$-A_{k,n-6}$	$-A_{k,n-7}$	$-A_{k,n-8}$	$-A_{k,n-9}$
0	-7129	22680	-45360	70560	-79380	63504	-35280	12960	-2835	280
1	-280	-4329	10080	-11760	11760	-8820	4704	-1680	360	-35
2	35	-630	-2754	5880	-4410	2940	-1470	504	-105	10
3	-10	135	-1080	-1554	3780	-1890	840	-270	54	-5
4	5	-60	360	-1680	-504	2520	-840	240	-45	4

TABLE X. DIFFERENTIATION COEFFICIENTS—DECIMAL FORM

$$A'_{ki} = \frac{dA_i}{du}\bigg|_{u=k}$$

$$A'_{ki} = -A'_{n-k,\,n-i}$$
$$k > \tfrac{1}{2}n$$

k \\ i	A'_{k0}	A'_{k1}	A'_{k2}	A'_{k3}	A'_{k4}	A'_{k5}	A'_{k6}	A'_{k7}	A'_{k8}	A'_{k9}
n = 2										
0	-1.5	2.0	-.5							
1	-.5	0	.5							
n = 3										
0	-1.833333	3.000000	-1.500000	.333333						
1	-.333333	-.500000	1.000000	-.166667						
n = 4										
0	-2.083333	4.000000	-3.000000	1.333333	-.250000					
1	-.250000	-.833333	1.500000	-.500000	.083333					
2	.083333	-.666667	0	.666667	-.083333					
n = 5										
0	-2.283333	5.000000	-5.000000	3.333333	-1.250000	.200000				
1	-.200000	-1.083333	2.000000	-1.000000	.333333	-.050000				
2	.050000	-.500000	-.333333	1.000000	-.250000	.033333				

$$A'_{ki} = \frac{dA_i}{du}\Big|_{u=k}$$

$n = 6$

k							
0	-2.450000	6.000000	-7.500000	6.666667	-3.750000	1.200000	-.166667
1	-.166667	-1.283333	2.500000	-1.666667	.833333	.250000	.033333
2	-.033333	-.400000	-.583333	1.333333	-.500000	.133333	-.016667
3	-.016667	.150000	-.750000	0	.750000	-.150000	.016667

$n = 7$

k								
0	-2.592857	7.000000	-10.500000	11.666667	-8.750000	4.200000	-1.166667	.142857
1	.142857	-1.450000	3.000000	-2.500000	1.666667	-.750000	.200000	-.023810
2	.023810	-.333333	-.783333	1.666667	-1.250000	.333333	-.083333	.009524
3	-.009524	.100000	-.600000	-.250000	1.000000	-.100000	.066667	-.007143

$n = 8$

k									
0	-2.717857	8.000000	-14.000000	18.666667	-17.500000	11.200000	-4.666667	1.142857	-.125000
1	-.125000	-1.592857	3.500000	-3.500000	2.916667	-1.750000	.700000	-.166667	.017857
2	-.017857	-.285714	-.950000	2.000000	-1.250000	.666667	-.250000	.057143	-.005952
3	-.005952	.071429	-.500000	-.450000	1.250000	.500000	.166667	-.035714	.003571
4	.003571	-.038095	.200000	-.800000	0	.800000	-.200000	.038095	-.003571

$n = 9$

k										
0	-2.828968	9.000000	-18.000000	28.000000	-31.500000	25.200000	-14.000000	5.142857	-1.125000	.111111
1	-.111111	-1.717857	4.000000	-4.666667	4.666667	-3.500000	1.866667	-.666667	.142857	-.013889
2	.013889	-.250000	-1.092857	2.333333	-1.750000	1.166667	-.583333	-.200000	-.041667	.003968
3	-.003968	.053571	-.428571	-.616667	1.500000	.750000	-.333333	-.107143	.021429	-.001984
4	.001984	-.023810	.142857	-.666667	-.200000	1.000000	-.333333	.095238	-.017857	.001587

TABLE XI. SECOND DERIVATIVE COEFFICIENTS

$$A_{ki}'' = \frac{dA_{ki}'}{du}\bigg|_{u=k}$$

k	A_{k0}''	A_{k1}''	A_{k2}''	A_{k3}''	A_{k4}''	A_{k5}''	A_{k6}''	A_{k7}''
			$n = 2$ (3 Points) $D_n = 1$					
All	1	-2	1					
			$n = 3$ (4 Points) $D_n = 1$					
0	2	-5	4	-1				
1	1	-2	1	0				
2	0	1	-2	1				
3	-1	4	-5	2				
			$n = 4$ (5 Points) $D_n = 12$					
0	35	-104	114	-56	11			
1	11	-20	6	4	-1			
2	-1	16	-30	16	-1			
3	-1	4	6	-20	11			
4	11	-56	114	-104	35			
			$n = 5$ (6 Points) $D_n = 12$					
0	45	-154	214	-156	61	-10		
1	10	-15	-4	14	-6	1		
2	-1	16	-30	16	-1	0		
3	0	-1	16	-30	16	-1		
4	1	-6	14	-4	-15	10		
5	-10	61	-156	214	-154	45		
			$n = 6$ (7 Points) $D_n = 180$					
0	812	-3132	5265	-5080	2970	-972	137	
1	137	-207	-255	470	-285	93	-13	
2	-13	228	-420	200	15	-12	2	
3	2	-27	270	-490	270	-27	2	
4	2	-12	15	200	-420	228	-13	
5	-13	93	-285	470	-255	-207	137	
6	137	-972	2970	-5080	5265	-3132	812	
			$n = 7$ (8 Points) $D_n = 180$					
0	938	-4014	7911	-9490	7380	-3618	1019	-126
1	126	-70	-486	855	-670	324	-90	11
2	-11	214	-378	130	85	-102	16	-2
3	2	-27	270	-490	270	-27	2	0
4	0	2	-27	270	-490	270	-27	2
5	-2	16	-102	85	130	-378	214	-11
6	11	-90	324	-670	855	-486	-70	126
7	-126	1019	-3618	7380	-9490	7911	-4014	938

TABLE XII. THIRD DERIVATIVE COEFFICIENTS

$$A_{ki}''' = \frac{dA_{ki}''}{du}\Bigg|_{u=k}$$

k	A_{k0}'''	A_{k1}'''	A_{k2}'''	A_{k3}'''	A_{k4}'''	A_{k5}'''	A_{k6}'''	A_{k7}'''
			$n = 3$ (4 Points) $D_n = 1$					
All	-1	3	-3	1				
			$n = 4$ (5 Points) $D_n = 2$					
0	-5	18	-24	14	-3			
1	-3	10	-12	6	-1			
2	-1	2	0	-2	1			
3	1	-6	12	-10	3			
4	3	-14	24	-18	5			
			$n = 5$ (6 Points) $D_n = 4$					
0	-17	71	-118	98	-41	7		
1	-7	25	-34	22	-7	1		
2	-1	-1	10	-14	7	-1		
3	1	-7	14	-10	1	1		
4	-1	7	-22	34	-25	7		
5	-7	41	-98	118	-71	17		
			$n = 6$ (7 Points) $D_n = 24$					
0	-147	696	-1383	1488	-921	312	-45	
1	-45	168	-249	192	-87	24	-3	
2	-3	-24	105	-144	87	-24	3	
3	3	-24	39	0	-39	24	-3	
4	-3	24	-87	144	-105	24	3	
5	3	-24	87	-192	249	-168	45	
6	45	-312	921	-1488	1383	-696	147	
			$n = 7$ (8 Points) $D_n = 120$					
0	-967	5104	-11787	15560	-12725	6432	-1849	232
1	-232	889	-1392	1205	-680	267	-64	7
2	-7	-176	693	-1000	715	-288	71	-8
3	8	-71	48	245	-440	267	-64	7
4	-7	64	-267	440	-245	-48	71	-8
5	8	-71	288	-715	1000	-693	176	7
6	-7	64	-267	680	-1205	1392	-889	232
7	-232	1849	-6432	12725	-15560	11787	-5104	967

TABLE XIII. INTEGRATION COEFFICIENTS (a_i)

$n = 2$ (3 Points)

a_i	0-1	0-2
a_0	.416666667	.333333333
a_1	.666666667	1.333333333
a_2	-.083333333	.333333333

$n = 3$ (4 Points)

a_i	0-1	0-2	0-3
a_0	.375000000	.333333333	.375000000
a_1	.791666667	1.333333333	1.125000000
a_2	-.208333333	.333333333	1.125000000
a_3	.041666667	0	.375000000

$n = 4$ (5 Points)

a_i	0-1	0-2	0-3	0-4
a_0	.348611111	.322222222	.337500000	.311111111
a_1	.897222222	1.377777778	1.275000000	1.422222222
a_2	-.366666667	.266666667	.900000000	.533333333
a_3	.147222222	.044444444	.525000000	1.422222222
a_4	-.026388889	-.011111111	-.037500000	.311111111

$n = 5$ (6 Points)

α_i	0-1	0-2	0-3	0-4	0-5
α_0	.329861111	.311111111	.318750000	.311111111	.329861111
α_1	.990972222	1.433333333	1.368750000	1.422222222	1.302083333
α_2	−.554166667	.155555556	.712500000	.533333333	.868055556
α_3	−.334722222	.155555556	.712500000	1.422222222	.868055556
α_4	−.120138889	−.066666667	−.131250000	.311111111	1.302083333
α_5	.018750000	.011111111	.018750000	0	.329861111

$n = 6$ (7 Points)

α_i	0-1	0-2	0-3	0-4	0-5	0-6
α_0	.315591931	.301322751	.305803571	.302645503	.307126323	.292857143
α_1	1.076587301	1.492063492	1.446428571	1.473015873	1.438492063	1.542857143
α_2	−.768204365	.008730159	.518303571	.406349206	.527033730	.192857143
α_3	.620105820	.351322751	.971428571	1.591534392	1.322751323	1.942857143
α_4	−.334176587	−.213492064	−.325446428	.184126984	.961061508	.192857143
α_5	.104365079	.069841270	.096428571	.050793651	.466269841	1.542857143
α_6	−.014269179	−.009788359	−.012946428	−.008465609	−.022734788	.292857143

TABLE XIII (continued).   INTEGRATION COEFFICIENTS (a_i)

$n = 7$ (8 Points)

a_i	0–1	0–2	0–3	0–4	0–5	0–6	0–7
a_0	.304224537	.292857143	.295558928	.294179894	.295758928	.292857143	.304224537
a_1	1.156159060	1.551322751	1.516741071	1.532275132	1.518063822	1.542857143	1.449016203
a_2	−1.006919642	−.169047619	.307366071	.228571428	.288318452	.192857143	.535937500
a_3	1.017964616	.647619047	1.322991071	1.887830687	1.720610119	1.942857143	1.210821759
a_4	−.732035383	−.509788359	−.677008928	−.112169312	.563202711	.192857143	1.210821759
a_5	−.343080357	−.247619048	.307366071	.228571428	.704985119	1.542857143	.535937500
a_6	−.093840939	−.069047619	−.083258928	−.067724867	−.102306547	.292857143	1.449016203
a_7	.011367394	.008465608	.010044643	.008465608	.011367394	0	.304224537

$n = 8$ (9 Points)

a_i	0–1	0–2	0–3	0–4	0–5	0–6	0–7	0–8
a_0	.294868000	.285511463	.287522321	.286631393	.287319499	.286428571	.288439428	.279082892
a_1	1.231011353	1.610088183	1.582633928	1.592663139	1.585579254	1.594285714	1.575297067	1.661516754
a_2	−1.268902667	−.374726631	.076741071	.017213404	.052201440	.012857143	.093954475	−.261869488
a_3	1.541930665	1.058977072	1.784241071	2.310546737	2.193218143	2.302857143	2.094787808	2.961834215
a_4	−1.386992945	−1.023985890	−1.253571428	−.640564373	−.027557319	−.257142857	.105864197	−1.281128747
a_5	.867046406	.658977072	.768616071	.651287477	1.177593143	1.902857143	1.419903549	2.961834215
a_6	−.355823964	−.274726631	−.313883928	−.279082892	−.338610560	.112857143	1.007033179	−.261869488
a_7	.086219687	.067231040	.075937500	.068853615	.078882826	.051428571	.430505401	1.661516754
a_8	−.009356536	−.007345679	−.008236607	−.007548501	−.008439429	−.006428571	−.015785108	.279082892

$n = 9$ (10 Points)

α_i	0–1	0–2	0–3	0–4	0–5
α_0	.28675446	.279082892	.280546875	.280000000	.280344053
α_1	1.302044339	1.667945326	1.645412946	1.652345679	1.648358272
α_2	−1.553034611	−.606155202	−.174375000	−.221516755	−.199101631
α_3	2.204905202	1.598977072	2.370178571	2.867583774	2.779155643
α_4	−2.381454750	−1.833985890	−2.132477678	−1.476119929	−.906463569
α_5	1.861508212	1.468977072	1.647522321	1.486843033	2.056499393
α_6	−1.018798500	−.814726631	−.899821428	−.836119929	−.924548059
α_7	.370351631	.298659612	.327053571	.307583774	.329998898
α_8	−.080389523	−.065202822	−.071015625	−.067231040	−.071218447
α_9	.007892554	.006428571	.006975446	.006631393	.006975446

α_i	0–6	0–7	0–8	0–9
α_0	.280000000	.280546875	.279082892	.28675446
α_1	1.652142857	1.646330054	1.661516754	1.581127232
α_2	−.218571429	−.190177469	−.261869488	.108482143
α_3	2.842857143	2.757762345	2.961834215	1.943035714
α_4	−1.067142857	−.888597608	−1.281128747	.580379464
α_5	2.712857143	2.414365354	2.961834215	.580379464
α_6	−.427142857	−.344058641	−.261869488	1.943035714
α_7	.282857143	.714637345	1.661516754	.108482143
α_8	−.064285714	−.086818094	.279082892	1.581127232
α_9	.006428571	.007892554	0	.28675446

TABLE XIII (continued).   INTEGRATION COEFFICIENTS (a_i)

$n = 10$ (11 Points)

α_i	0-1	0-2	0-3	0-4	0-5
a_0	.280189596	.273403746	.274510450	.274153172	.274342768
a_1	1.369902839	1.724736785	1.705777191	1.710813959	1.708371120
a_2	−1.858397861	−.861716770	−.446014103	−.484624017	−.469159445
a_3	3.019207201	2.280474587	3.094549512	3.569203142	3.499309814
a_4	−3.806483247	−3.026606541	−3.400126826	−2.703953823	−2.166733367
a_5	3.571542408	2.900121853	3.168701298	2.960243706	3.568823152
a_6	−2.443826997	−2.007347282	−2.167470576	−2.063953823	−2.184817858
a_7	1.184653629	.980157126	1.051424512	1.009203142	1.050153068
a_8	−.385752772	−.320764389	−.342654728	−.330338303	−.341276260
a_9	.075751054	.063220031	.067339691	.065099674	.066988295
a_{10}	−.006785850	−.005679146	−.006036424	−.0058468:8	−.006001285

	0-6	0-7	0-8	0-9	0-10
	.274188311	.274377908	.274020633	.275127333	.26841483
	1.710259740	1.708019723	1.712139383	1.699608360	1.775359414
	−.480097402	−.467780978	−.489671316	−.424682934	−.810435705
	3.540259740	3.498038370	3.569305755	3.364809253	4.549462882
	−2.287597402	−2.184080650	−2.344203944	−1.907724228	−4.351551226
	4.177402597	3.968945006	4.237524450	3.566103896	7.137646304
	−1.647597402	−.951424400	−1.324944684	−.545067978	−4.351551226
	.980259740	1.454913370	2.268988295	1.530255681	4.549462882
	−.325811688	−.364421603	.051281064	1.047962155	−.810435705
	.064545455	.069582222	.050622628	.405456574	1.775359414
	−.005811688	−.006168967	−.005062263	−.011848112	.26841483

SOME FORMULAS ON SUMS

The next two tables present powers and sums of powers of integers. On this page are listed some common formulas on sums dealing with integers.

1. $\displaystyle\sum_{i=1}^{n} i = \frac{1}{2}n(n+1).$

2. $\displaystyle\sum_{i=1}^{n} (2i-1) = n^2.$

3. $\displaystyle\sum_{i=1}^{n} 2i = n(n+1).$

4. $\displaystyle\sum_{i=1}^{n} i^2 = \frac{1}{6}n(n+1)(2n+1).$

5. $\displaystyle\sum_{i=1}^{n} (2i-1)^2 = \frac{1}{3}n(2n+1)(2n-1).$

6. $\displaystyle\sum_{i=1}^{n} (2i)^2 = \frac{2}{3}n(n+1)(2n+1).$

7. $\displaystyle\sum_{i=1}^{n} i^3 = \frac{1}{4}n^2(n+1)^2 = \left(\sum_{i=1}^{n} i\right)^2.$

8. $\displaystyle\sum_{i=1}^{n} i^4 = \frac{1}{5}\left(\sum_{i=1}^{n} i^2\right)\left(6\sum_{i=1}^{n} i - 1\right).$

9. $\displaystyle\sum_{i=1}^{n} i^k = \frac{1}{k+1}n^{k+1} + \frac{1}{2}n^k + \frac{1}{2}\binom{k}{1}B_1 n^{k-1} - \frac{1}{4}\binom{k}{3}B_2 n^{k-3} + \cdots,$

where B_i are the Bernoulli numbers (see Table XIX).

10. $\displaystyle\sum_{i=1}^{n} (2i-1)^k = \sum_{i=1}^{2n} i^k - 2^k \sum_{i=1}^{n} i^k.$

11. $\displaystyle\sum_{i=1}^{n} (2i)^k = 2^k \sum_{i=1}^{n} i^k.$

12. $\displaystyle\sum_{i=1}^{n} 2^{i-1} = 2^n - 1.$

13. $\displaystyle\sum_{i=1}^{n} (i+1)2^{i-1} = n2^n.$

14. $\displaystyle\sum_{i=1}^{n} \frac{1}{i(i+1)} = \frac{n}{n+1}.$

TABLE XIV. POWERS OF INTEGERS, N^i, $(i = 1, \ldots, 6)$

$(i = 1, \ldots, 6)$, $1 \leq N \leq 40$

N	N^2	N^3	N^4	N^5	N^6
1	1	1	1	1	1
2	4	8	16	32	64
3	9	27	81	243	729
4	16	64	256	1024	4096
5	25	125	625	3125	15625
6	36	216	1296	7776	46656
7	49	343	2401	16807	117649
8	64	512	4096	32768	262144
9	81	729	6561	59049	531441
10	100	1000	10000	100000	1000000
11	121	1331	14641	161051	1771561
12	144	1728	20736	248832	2985984
13	169	2197	28561	371293	4826809
14	196	2744	38416	537824	7529536
15	225	3375	50625	759375	11390625
16	256	4096	65536	1048576	16777216
17	289	4913	83521	1419857	24137569
18	324	5832	104976	1889568	34012224
19	361	6859	130321	2476099	47045881
20	400	8000	160000	3200000	64000000
21	441	9261	194481	4084101	85766121
22	484	10648	234256	5153632	113379904
23	529	12167	279841	6436343	148035889
24	576	13824	331776	7962624	191102976
25	625	15625	390625	9765625	244140625
26	676	17576	456976	11881376	308915776
27	729	19683	531441	14348907	387420489
28	784	21952	614656	17210368	481890304
29	841	24389	707281	20511149	594823321
30	900	27000	810000	24300000	729000000
31	961	29791	923521	28629151	887503681
32	1024	32768	1048576	33554432	1073741824
33	1089	35937	1185921	39135393	1291467969
34	1156	39304	1336336	45435424	1544804416
35	1225	42875	1500625	52521875	1838265625
36	1296	46656	1679616	60466176	2176782336
37	1369	50653	1874161	69343957	2565726409
38	1444	54872	2085136	79235168	3010936384
39	1521	59319	2313441	90224199	3518743761
40	1600	64000	2560000	102400000	4096000000

TABLE XV. SUM OF POWERS OF INTEGERS, $\sum\limits_{k=1}^{n} k^m$

$(m = 1, 2, 3, 4); \ 1 \le n \le 40$

n	Σk	Σk^2	Σk^3	Σk^4
1	1	1	1	1
2	3	5	9	17
3	6	14	36	98
4	10	30	100	354
5	15	55	225	979
6	21	91	441	2275
7	28	140	784	4676
8	36	204	1296	8772
9	45	285	2025	15333
10	55	385	3025	25333
11	66	506	4356	39974
12	78	650	6084	60710
13	91	819	8281	89271
14	105	1015	11025	127687
15	120	1240	14400	178312
16	136	1496	18496	243848
17	153	1785	23409	327369
18	171	2109	29241	432345
19	190	2470	36100	562666
20	210	2870	44100	722666
21	231	3311	53361	917147
22	253	3795	64009	1151403
23	276	4324	76176	1431244
24	300	4900	90000	1763020
25	325	5525	105625	2153645
26	351	6201	123201	2610621
27	378	6930	142884	3142062
28	406	7714	164836	3756718
29	435	8555	189225	4463999
30	465	9455	216225	5273999
31	496	10416	246016	6197520
32	528	11440	278784	7246096
33	561	12529	314721	8432017
34	595	13685	354025	9768353
35	630	14910	396900	11268978
36	666	16206	443556	12948594
37	703	17575	494209	14822755
38	741	19019	549081	16907891
39	780	20540	608400	19221332
40	820	22140	672400	21781332

TABLE XVI. N-G POLYNOMIAL FITTING CONSTANTS FOR $n = 1, 2, 3, 4$

m	S_2	A_{13}	A_{23}	A_{24}	A_{44}	A_{35}	A_{55}
5	5.00	2.000000	1.400000	3.40	1.440000	4.428571	.822857
6	8.75	2.916667	2.133333	5.05	3.702857	6.785714	4.702041
7	14.00	4.000000	3.000000	7.00	7.714286	9.571429	16.163265
8	21.00	5.250000	4.000000	9.25	14.142857	12.785714	43.102041
9	30.00	6.666667	5.133333	11.80	23.760000	16.428571	98.057143
10	41.25	8.250000	6.400000	14.65	37.440000	20.500000	199.680000
11	55.00	10.000000	7.800000	17.80	56.160000	25.000000	374.400000
12	71.50	11.916667	9.333333	21.25	81.000000	29.928571	658.285714
13	91.00	14.000000	11.000000	25.00	113.142857	35.285714	1099.102041
14	113.75	16.250000	12.800000	29.05	153.874286	41.071428	1758.563265
15	140.00	18.666667	14.733333	33.40	204.582857	47.285714	2714.782041
16	170.00	21.250000	16.800000	38.05	266.760000	53.928571	4064.914285
17	204.00	24.000000	19.000000	43.00	342.009000	61.000000	5928.000000
18	242.25	26.916667	21.333333	48.25	432.000000	68.500000	8448.000000
19	285.00	30.000000	23.800000	53.80	538.560000	76.428571	11797.028571
20	332.50	33.250000	26.400000	59.65	663.582857	84.785714	16178.782040
21	385.00	36.666667	29.133333	65.80	809.074286	93.571429	21832.163265
22	442.75	40.250000	32.000000	72.25	977.142857	102.785714	29035.102041
23	506.00	44.000000	35.000000	79.00	1170.000000	112.428571	38108.571429
24	575.00	47.916667	38.133333	86.05	1389.960000	122.500000	49420.800000
25	650.00	52.000000	41.400000	93.40	1639.440000	133.000000	63391.680000

26	731.25	56.250000	44.800000	101.05	1920.960000	143.928571	80497.371429
27	819.00	60.666667	48.333333	109.00	2237.142857	155.285714	101275.102041
28	913.50	65.250000	52.000000	117.25	2590.714286	167.071429	126328.163265
29	1015.00	70.000000	55.800000	125.80	2984.502857	179.285714	156331.102041
30	1123.75	74.916667	59.733333	134.65	3421.440000	191.928571	192035.108571
31	1240.00	80.000000	63.800000	143.80	3904.560000	205.000000	234273.600000
32	1364.00	85.250000	68.000000	153.25	4437.000000	218.500000	283968.000000
33	1496.00	90.666667	72.333333	163.00	5022.000000	232.428571	342133.714286
34	1636.25	96.250000	76.800000	173.05	5662.902857	246.785714	409886.302041
35	1785.00	102.000000	81.400000	183.40	6363.154286	261.571429	488447.843265
36	1942.50	107.916667	86.133333	194.05	7126.302857	276.785714	579153.502041
37	2109.00	114.000000	91.000000	205.00	7956.000000	292.428571	683458.285714
38	2284.75	120.250000	96.000000	216.25	8856.000000	308.500000	802944.000000
39	2470.00	126.666667	101.133333	227.80	9830.160000	325.000000	939326.400000
40	2665.00	133.250000	106.400000	239.65	10882.440000	341.928571	1094462.537143
41	2870.00	140.000000	111.800000	251.80	12016.902857	359.285714	1270358.302041
42	3085.25	146.916667	117.333333	264.25	13237.714286	377.071429	1469176.163265
43	3311.00	154.000000	123.000000	277.00	14549.142857	395.285714	1693243.102041
44	3547.50	161.250000	128.800000	290.05	15955.560000	413.928571	1945058.742857
45	3795.00	168.666667	134.733333	303.40	17461.440000	433.000000	2227303.680000
46	4053.75	176.250000	140.800000	317.05	19071.360000	452.500000	2542848.000000
47	4324.00	184.000000	147.000000	331.00	20790.000000	472.428571	2894760.000000
48	4606.00	191.916667	153.333333	345.25	22622.142857	492.785714	3286315.102041
49	4900.00	200.000000	159.800000	359.80	24572.674286	513.571429	3721004.963265
50	5206.25	208.250000	166.400000	374.65	26646.582857	534.785714	4202546.782041

TABLE XVI (continued). N-G POLYNOMIAL FITTING CONSTANTS FOR $n = 1, 2, 3, 4$

m	S_2	A_{13}	A_{33}	A_{24}	A_{44}	A_{35}	A_{55}
51	5525.00	216.666667	173.133333	389.80	28848.960000	556.428571	4734892.800000
52	5856.50	225.250000	180.000000	405.25	31185.000000	578.500000	5322240.000000
53	6201.00	234.000000	187.003000	421.00	33660.000000	601.000000	5969040.000000
54	6558.75	242.916667	194.133333	437.05	36279.360000	623.928571	6680009.142857
55	6930.00	252.000000	201.400000	453.40	39048.582857	647.285714	7460138.782041
56	7315.00	261.250000	208.800000	470.05	41973.274286	671.071429	8314705.763265
57	7714.00	270.666667	216.333333	487.00	45059.142857	695.285714	9249283.102041
58	8127.25	280.250000	224.000000	504.25	48312.000000	719.928571	10269750.857142
59	8555.00	290.000000	231.800000	521.80	51737.760000	745.000000	11382307.200000
60	8997.50	299.916667	239.733333	539.65	55342.440000	770.500000	12593479.680000
61	9455.00	310.000000	247.800000	557.80	59132.160000	796.428571	13910136.685714
62	9927.75	320.250000	256.000000	576.25	63113.142857	822.785714	15339499.102041
63	10416.00	330.666667	264.333333	595.00	67291.714286	849.571429	16889152.163265
64	10920.00	341.250000	272.800000	614.05	71674.302857	876.785714	18567057.502041
65	11440.00	352.000000	281.400000	633.40	76267.440000	904.428571	20381565.394286
66	11976.25	362.916667	290.133333	653.05	81077.760000	932.500000	22341427.200000
67	12529.00	374.000000	299.000000	673.00	86112.000000	961.000000	24455808.000000
68	13098.50	385.250000	308.000000	693.25	91377.000000	989.928571	26734299.428571
69	13685.00	396.666667	317.133333	713.80	96879.702857	1019.285714	29186932.702041
70	14288.75	408.250000	326.400000	734.65	102627.154286	1049.071429	31824191.843265
71	14910.00	420.000000	335.800000	755.80	108626.502857	1079.285714	34657027.102041
72	15549.00	431.916667	345.333333	777.25	114885.000000	1109.928571	37696868.571429
73	16206.00	444.000000	355.000000	799.00	121410.000000	1141.000000	40955640.000000
74	16881.25	456.250000	364.800000	821.05	128208.960000	1172.500000	44445772.800000
75	17575.00	468.666667	374.733333	843.40	135289.440000	1204.428571	48180220.251429

76	18287.50	481.250000	384.800000	866.05	142659.102857	1236.785714	52172471.902041
77	19019.00	494.000000	395.000000	889.00	150325.714286	1269.571429	56436568.163265
78	19769.75	506.916667	405.333333	912.25	158297.142857	1302.785714	60987115.102041
79	20540.00	520.000000	415.800000	935.80	166581.360000	1336.428571	65839299.428571
80	21330.00	533.250000	426.400000	959.65	175186.440000	1370.500000	71008903.680000
81	22140.00	546.666667	437.133333	983.80	184120.560000	1405.000000	76512321.600000
82	22970.25	560.250000	448.000000	1008.25	193392.000000	1439.928571	82366573.714286
83	23821.00	574.000000	459.000000	1033.00	203009.142857	1475.285714	88589323.102041
84	24692.50	587.916667	470.133333	1058.05	212980.474286	1511.071429	95198891.363265
85	25585.00	602.000000	481.400000	1083.40	223314.582857	1547.285714	102214274.782041
86	26498.75	616.250000	492.800000	1109.05	234020.160000	1583.928571	109655160.685714
87	27434.00	630.666667	504.333333	1135.00	245106.000000	1621.000000	117541944.000000
88	28391.00	645.250000	516.000000	1161.25	256581.000000	1658.500000	125895744.000000
89	29370.00	660.000000	527.800000	1187.80	268454.160000	1696.428571	134738421.257143
90	30371.25	674.916667	539.733333	1214.65	280734.582857	1734.785714	144092594.782041
91	31395.00	690.000000	551.800000	1241.80	293431.474286	1773.571429	153981659.363265
92	32441.50	705.250000	564.000000	1269.25	306554.142857	1812.785714	164429803.102041
93	33511.00	720.666667	576.333333	1297.00	320112.000000	1852.428571	175462025.142857
94	34603.75	736.250000	588.800000	1325.05	334114.560000	1892.500000	187104153.600000
95	35720.00	752.000000	601.400000	1353.40	348571.440000	1933.000000	199382863.680000
96	36860.00	767.916667	614.133333	1382.05	363492.360000	1973.928571	212325696.000000
97	38024.00	784.000000	627.000000	1411.00	378887.142857	2015.285714	225961075.102041
98	39212.25	800.250000	640.000000	1440.25	394765.714286	2057.071429	240318328.163265
99	40425.00	816.666667	653.133333	1469.80	411138.102857	2099.285714	255427703.902041
100	41662.50	833.250000	666.400000	1499.65	428014.440000	2141.928571	271320391.680000

TABLE XVI (continued).   N-G POLYNOMIAL FITTING CONSTANTS FOR $n = 5, 6$

m	A_{26}	A_{46}	A_{66}	A_{37}	A_{57}	A_{77}
6	29.20535711	8.05555556	3.26530625			
7	56.71428571	11.66666667	24.48979545	86.7142857	13.18181818	20.037105
8	99.70535714	15.83333333	106.12244898	155.6875000	18.29545455	187.012988
9	163.00000000	20.55555556	346.66666667	258.1428571	24.09090909	981.818182
10	252.06250000	25.83333333	945.45454545	403.1875000	30.56818182	3808.264462
11	373.000000	31.66666667	2269.090909	601.000000	37.72727273	12138.84297
12	532.562500	38.05555556	4945.454545	862.830357	45.56818182	33615.25746
13	738.142857	45.00000000	9991.836734	1201.000000	54.09090909	83637.96203
14	997.776786	52.50000000	18984.489795	1628.901784	63.29545455	191172.5642
15	1320.142857	60.55555556	34277.551020	2161.000000	73.18181818	407735.0649
16	1714.562500	69.16666667	59280.0000	2812.830354	83.75000000	820800.000
17	2191.000000	78.33333333	98800.0000	3601.000000	95.00000000	1573200.000
18	2760.062500	88.05555556	159466.0000	4543.187500	106.93181818	2890472.727
19	3433.000000	98.33333333	250240.0000	5658.142857	119.54545455	5118545.452
20	4221.705357	109.16666667	383020.4081	6965.687500	132.84090909	8774649.349
21	5138.714286	120.55555556	573369.9442	8486.71429	146.81818182	14614919.20
22	6197.205357	132.50000000	841358.0694	10243.18750	161.47727273	23722767.38
23	7411.000000	145.00000000	1212545.4545	12258.14236	176.81818182	37622826.44
24	8794.562500	158.05555556	1719120.0000	14555.68750	192.84090909	58426036.36
25	10363.000000	171.66666667	2401200.0000	17161.00000	209.54545455	89012316.08

	$\times 10^4$		$\times 10^6$	$\times 10^4$		$\times 10^8$
26	1.213206250	185.8333333	3.308320000	2.010033035	226.9318182	1.332582042
27	1.411814285	200.5555556	4.501115644	2.340100000	245.0000000	1.963178900
28	1.633827678	215.8333333	6.053224491	2.709140178	263.7500000	2.849671837
29	1.881014286	231.6666667	8.053420406	3.120100000	283.1818182	4.080211947
30	2.155206250	248.0555556	10.608000000	3.576033035	303.2954545	5.768378178
			$\times 10^7$			$\times 10^9$
31	2.458300000	265.0000000	1.384344000	4.081000000	324.0909091	0.805920545
32	2.792256250	282.5000000	1.790934545	4.635568750	345.5681818	1.113635662
33	3.159100000	300.5555556	2.298170909	5.245814286	367.7272727	1.523060538
34	3.560920535	319.1666667	2.926650300	5.914318750	390.5681818	2.062981469
35	3.999871429	338.3333333	3.700362448	6.644671429	414.0909091	2.769061437
				$\times 10^5$		
36	4.478170535	358.0555556	4.647121850	0.744056875	438.2954545	3.685200123
37	4.998100000	378.3333333	5.799040000	0.830581429	463.1818182	4.865110688
38	5.562006250	399.1666667	7.193040000	0.924431875	488.7500000	6.374140057
39	6.172300000	420.5555556	8.871416000	1.026010000	515.0000000	8.291361872
40	6.831456250	442.5000000	10.882440000	1.135728304	541.9318182	10.711973792
	$\times 10^5$		$\times 10^8$			$\times 10^{10}$
41	0.754201429	465.0000000	1.328101861	1.254010000	569.5454545	1.375003359
42	0.830657768	488.0555556	1.612940244	1.331275000	597.8409091	1.754157109
43	0.912781429	511.6666667	1.949795087	1.518010000	626.8181818	2.224811637
44	1.000845625	535.8333333	2.346595491	1.664628304	656.4772727	2.806068732
45	1.095130000	560.5555556	2.812252121	1.821610000	686.8181818	3.520428334
46	1.195920625	585.8333333	3.356752000	1.989431875	717.8409091	4.394293525
47	1.303510000	611.6666667	3.991260000	2.168581429	749.5454545	5.458536488
48	1.418197054	638.0555556	4.728227346	2.359556875	781.9318182	6.749131226
49	1.540287142	665.0000000	5.581507444	2.562867143	815.0000000	8.307859153
50	1.670092054	692.5000000	6.566479350	2.779031875	848.7500000	10.183094125

TABLE XVII.   MODIFIED ORTHOGONAL POLYNOMIALS*

m	4			5				6					7				
X	P'_1	P'_2	P'_3	P'_1	P'_2	P'_3	P'_4	P'_1	P'_2	P'_3	P'_4	P'_5	P'_1	P'_2	P'_3	P'_4	P'_5
1	1	−1	−3	0	−2	0	6	1	−4	−4	2	10	0	−4	0	6	0
2	3	1	1	1	−1	−2	−4	3	−1	−7	−3	−5	1	−3	−1	1	5
3				2	2	1	1	5	5	5	1	1	2	0	−1	−7	−4
4													3	5	1	3	1
$\Sigma P'^2$	20	4	20	10	14	10	70	70	84	180	28	252	28	84	6	154	84
λ	2	1	$\frac{10}{3}$	1	1	$\frac{5}{6}$	$\frac{35}{12}$	2	$\frac{3}{2}$	$\frac{5}{3}$	$\frac{7}{12}$	$\frac{21}{10}$	1	1	$\frac{1}{6}$	$\frac{7}{12}$	$\frac{7}{20}$

m	8					9					10				
X	P'_1	P'_2	P'_3	P'_4	P'_5	P'_1	P'_2	P'_3	P'_4	P'_5	P'_1	P'_2	P'_3	P'_4	P'_5
1	1	−5	−3	9	15	0	−20	0	18	0	1	−4	−12	18	6
2	3	−3	−7	−3	17	1	−17	−9	9	9	3	−3	−31	3	11
3	5	1	−5	−13	−23	2	−8	−13	−11	4	5	−1	−35	−17	1
4	7	7	7	7	7	3	7	−7	−21	−11	7	2	−14	−22	−14
5						4	28	14	14	4	9	6	42	18	6
$\Sigma P'^2$	168	168	264	616	2184	60	2,772	990	2,002	468	330	132	8,580	2,860	780
λ	2	1	$\frac{2}{3}$	$\frac{7}{12}$	$\frac{7}{10}$	1	3	$\frac{5}{6}$	$\frac{7}{12}$	$\frac{3}{20}$	2	$\frac{1}{2}$	$\frac{5}{3}$	$\frac{5}{12}$	$\frac{1}{10}$

m	11					12					13				
X	P'_1	P'_2	P'_3	P'_4	P'_5	P'_1	P'_2	P'_3	P'_4	P'_5	P'_1	P'_2	P'_3	P'_4	P'_5
1	0	−10	0	6	0	1	−35	−7	28	20	0	−14	0	84	0
2	1	−9	−14	4	4	3	−29	−19	12	44	1	−13	−4	64	20
3	2	−6	−23	−1	4	5	−17	−25	−13	29	2	−10	−7	11	26
4	3	−1	−22	−6	−1	7	1	−21	−33	−21	3	−5	−8	−54	11
5	4	6	−6	−6	−6	9	25	−3	−27	−57	4	2	−6	−96	−18
6	5	15	30	6	3	11	55	33	33	33	5	11	0	−66	−33
7											6	22	11	99	22
$\Sigma P'^2$	110	858	4,290	286	156	572	12,012	5,148	8,008	15,912	182	2,002	572	68,068	6,188
λ	1	1	$\frac{5}{6}$	$\frac{1}{12}$	$\frac{1}{40}$	2	3	$\frac{2}{3}$	$\frac{7}{24}$	$\frac{3}{20}$	1	1	$\frac{1}{6}$	$\frac{7}{12}$	$\frac{7}{120}$

* Table XVII is abridged from Table XXIII of Fisher and Yates: *Statistical Tables for Biological, Agricultural, and Medical Research*, published by Oliver and Boyd Limited, Edinburgh, by permission of the authors and publishers.

TABLE XVII (continued).   MODIFIED ORTHOGONAL POLYNOMIALS

m	14					15				
X	P'_1	P'_2	P'_3	P'_4	P'_5	P'_1	P'_2	P'_3	P'_4	P'_5
1	1	-8	-24	108	60	0	-56	0	756	0
2	3	-7	-67	63	145	1	-53	-27	621	675
3	5	-5	-95	-13	139	2	-44	-49	251	1000
4	7	-2	-98	-92	28	3	-29	-61	-249	751
5	9	2	-66	-132	-132	4	-8	-58	-704	-44
6	11	7	11	-77	-187	5	19	-35	-869	-979
7	13	13	143	143	143	6	52	13	-429	-1144
8						7	91	91	1001	1001
$\Sigma P'^2$	910	728	97,240	136,136	235,144	280	37,128	39,780	6,466,460	10,581,480
λ	2	$\dfrac{1}{2}$	$\dfrac{5}{3}$	$\dfrac{7}{12}$	$\dfrac{7}{30}$	1	3	$\dfrac{5}{6}$	$\dfrac{35}{12}$	$\dfrac{21}{20}$

m	16					17				
X	P'_1	P'_2	P'_3	P'_4	P'_5	P'_1	P'_2	P'_3	P'_4	P'_5
1	1	-21	-63	189	45	0	-24	0	36	0
2	3	-19	-179	129	115	1	-23	-7	31	55
3	5	-15	-265	23	131	2	-20	-13	17	88
4	7	-9	-301	-101	77	3	-15	-17	-3	83
5	9	-1	-267	-201	-33	4	-8	-18	-24	36
6	11	9	-143	-221	-143	5	1	-15	-39	-39
7	13	21	91	-91	-143	6	12	-7	-39	-104
8	15	35	455	273	143	7	25	7	-13	-91
9						8	40	28	52	104
$\Sigma P'^2$	1,360	5,712	1,007,760	470,288	201,552	408	7,752	3,876	16,796	100,776
λ	2	1	$\dfrac{10}{3}$	$\dfrac{7}{12}$	$\dfrac{1}{10}$	1	1	$\dfrac{1}{6}$	$\dfrac{1}{12}$	$\dfrac{1}{20}$

TABLE XVII (continued).   MODIFIED ORTHOGONAL POLYNOMIALS

m	18					19				
X	P'_1	P'_2	P'_3	P'_4	P'_5	P'_1	P'_2	P'_3	P'_4	P'_5
1	1	−40	−8	44	220	0	−30	0	396	0
2	3	−37	−23	33	583	1	−29	−44	352	44
3	5	−31	−35	13	733	2	−26	−83	227	74
4	7	−22	−42	−12	588	3	−21	−112	42	79
5	9	−10	−42	−36	156	4	−14	−126	−168	54
6	11	5	−33	−51	−429	5	−5	−120	−354	3
7	13	23	−13	−47	−871	6	6	−89	−453	−58
8	15	44	20	−12	−676	7	19	−28	−388	−98
9	17	68	68	68	884	8	34	68	−68	−68
10						9	51	204	612	102
$\Sigma P'^2$	1,938		23,256		6,953,544	570		213,180		89,148
		23,256		28,424			13,566		2,288,132	
λ	2	$\dfrac{3}{2}$	$\dfrac{1}{3}$	$\dfrac{1}{12}$	$\dfrac{3}{10}$	1	1	$\dfrac{5}{6}$	$\dfrac{7}{12}$	$\dfrac{1}{40}$

m	20					21				
X	P'_1	P'_2	P'_3	P'_4	P'_5	P'_1	P'_2	P'_3	P'_4	P'_5
1	1	−33	−99	1188	396	0	−110	0	594	0
2	3	−31	−287	948	1076	1	−107	−54	540	1404
3	5	−27	−445	503	1441	2	−98	−103	385	2444
4	7	−21	−553	−77	1351	3	−83	−142	150	2819
5	9	−13	−591	−687	771	4	−62	−166	−130	2354
6	11	−3	−539	−1187	−187	5	−35	−170	−406	1063
7	13	9	−377	−1402	−1222	6	−2	−149	−615	−788
8	15	23	−85	−1122	−1802	7	37	−98	−680	−2618
9	17	39	357	−102	−1122	8	82	−12	−510	−3468
10	19	57	969	1938	1938	9	133	114	0	−1938
11						10	190	285	969	3876
$\Sigma P'^2$	2,660		4,903,140		31,201,800	770		432,630		121,687,020
		17,556		22,881,320			201,894		5,720,330	
λ	2	1	$\dfrac{10}{3}$	$\dfrac{35}{24}$	$\dfrac{7}{20}$	1	3	$\dfrac{5}{6}$	$\dfrac{7}{12}$	$\dfrac{21}{40}$

TABLE XVII (continued).   MODIFIED ORTHOGONAL POLYNOMIALS

m	22					23				
X	P'_1	P'_2	P'_3	P'_4	P'_5	P'_1	P'_2	P'_3	P'_4	P'_5
1	1	−20	−12	702	390	0	−44	0	858	0
2	3	−19	−35	585	1079	1	−43	−13	793	65
3	5	−17	−55	365	1509	2	−40	−25	605	116
4	7	−14	−70	70	1554	3	−35	−35	315	141
5	9	−10	−78	−258	1158	4	−28	−42	−42	132
6	11	−5	−77	−563	363	5	−19	−45	−417	87
7	13	1	−65	−775	−663	6	−8	−43	−747	12
8	15	8	−40	−810	−1598	7	5	−35	−955	−77
9	17	16	0	−570	−1938	8	20	−20	−950	−152
10	19	25	57	57	−969	9	37	3	−627	−171
11	21	35	133	1197	2261	10	56	35	133	−76
12						11	77	77	1463	209
$\Sigma P'^2$	3,542		96,140		40,562,340	1,012		32,890		340,860
		7,084		8,748,740			35,420		13,123,110	
λ	2	$\dfrac{1}{2}$	$\dfrac{1}{3}$	$\dfrac{7}{12}$	$\dfrac{7}{30}$	1	1	$\dfrac{1}{6}$	$\dfrac{7}{12}$	$\dfrac{1}{60}$

m	24					25				
X	P'_1	P'_2	P'_3	P'_4	P'_5	P'_1	P'_2	P'_3	P'_4	P'_5
1	1	−143	−143	143	715	0	−52	0	858	0
2	3	−137	−419	123	2005	1	−51	−77	803	275
3	5	−125	−665	85	2893	2	−48	−149	643	500
4	7	−107	−861	33	3171	3	−43	−211	393	631
5	9	−83	−987	−27	2721	4	−36	−258	78	636
6	11	−53	−1023	−87	1551	5	−27	−285	−267	501
7	13	−17	−949	−137	−169	6	−16	−287	−597	236
8	15	25	−745	−165	−2071	7	−3	−259	−857	−119
9	17	73	−391	−157	−3553	8	12	−196	−982	−488
10	19	127	133	−97	−3743	9	29	−93	−897	−753
11	21	187	847	33	−1463	10	48	55	−517	−748
12	23	253	1771	253	4807	11	69	253	253	−253
13						12	92	506	1518	1012
$\Sigma P'^2$	4,600		17,760,600		177,928,920		53,820	14,307,150		
		394,680		394,680		1,300	1,480,050		7,803,900	
λ	2	3	$\dfrac{10}{3}$	$\dfrac{1}{12}$	$\dfrac{3}{10}$	1	1	$\dfrac{5}{6}$	$\dfrac{5}{12}$	$\dfrac{1}{20}$

TABLE XVII (continued).   MODIFIED ORTHOGONAL POLYNOMIALS

m	26					27				
X	P'_1	P'_2	P'_3	P'_4	P'_5	P'_1	P'_2	P'_3	P'_4	P'_5
1	1	−28	−84	1386	330	0	−182	0	1638	0
2	3	−27	−247	1221	935	1	−179	−18	1548	3960
3	5	−25	−395	905	1381	2	−170	−35	1285	7304
4	7	−22	−518	466	1582	3	−155	−50	870	9479
5	9	−18	−606	−54	1482	4	−134	−62	338	10058
6	11	−13	−649	−599	1067	5	−107	−70	−262	8803
7	13	−7	−637	−1099	377	6	−74	−73	−867	5728
8	15	0	−560	−1470	−482	7	−35	−70	−1400	1162
9	17	8	−408	−1614	−1326	8	10	−60	−1770	−4188
10	19	17	−171	−1419	−1881	9	61	−42	−1872	−9174
11	21	27	161	−759	−1771	10	118	−15	−1587	−12144
12	23	38	598	506	−506	11	181	22	−782	−10879
13	25	50	1150	2530	2530	12	250	70	690	−2530
14						13	325	130	2990	16445
$\Sigma P'^2$	5,850	7,803,900		48,384,180		1,638	101,790		2,032,135,560	
		16,380	40,060,020				712,530	56,448,210		
λ	2	$\frac{1}{2}$	$\frac{5}{3}$	$\frac{7}{12}$	$\frac{1}{10}$	1	3	$\frac{1}{6}$	$\frac{7}{12}$	$\frac{21}{40}$

m	28					29				
X	P'_1	P'_2	P'_3	P'_4	P'_5	P'_1	P'_2	P'_3	P'_4	P'_5
1	1	−65	−39	936	1560	0	−70	0	2184	0
2	3	−63	−115	840	4456	1	−69	−104	2080	1768
3	5	−59	−185	655	6701	2	−66	−203	1775	3298
4	7	−53	−245	395	7931	3	−61	−292	1290	4373
5	9	−45	−291	81	7887	4	−54	−366	660	4818
6	11	−35	−319	−259	6457	5	−45	−420	−66	4521
7	13	−23	−325	−590	3718	6	−34	−449	−825	3454
8	15	−9	−305	−870	−22	7	−21	−448	−1540	1694
9	17	7	−255	−1050	−4182	8	−6	−412	−2120	−556
10	19	25	−171	−1074	−7866	9	11	−336	−2460	−2946
11	21	45	−49	−879	−9821	10	30	−215	−2441	−4958
12	23	67	115	−395	−8395	11	51	−44	−1930	−5885
13	25	91	325	455	−1495	12	74	182	−780	−4810
14	27	117	585	1755	13455	13	99	468	1170	−585
15						14	126	819	4095	8190
$\Sigma P'^2$	7,308	2,103,660		1,354,757,040		2,030	4,207,320		500,671,080	
		95,004	19,634,160				113,274	107,987,880		
λ	2	1	$\frac{2}{3}$	$\frac{7}{24}$	$\frac{7}{20}$	1	1	$\frac{5}{6}$	$\frac{7}{12}$	$\frac{7}{40}$

TABLE XVII (continued). MODIFIED ORTHOGONAL POLYNOMIALS

m			30					31		
X	P'_1	P'_2	P'_3	P'_4	P'_5	P'_1	P'_2	P'_3	P'_4	P'_5
1	1	−112	−112	12376	1768	0	−80	0	408	0
2	3	−109	−331	11271	5083	1	−79	−119	391	221
3	5	−103	−535	9131	7753	2	−76	−233	341	416
4	7	−94	−714	6096	9408	3	−71	−337	261	561
5	9	−82	−858	2376	9768	4	−64	−426	156	636
6	11	−67	−957	−1749	8679	5	−55	−495	33	627
7	13	−49	−1001	−5929	6149	6	−44	−539	−99	528
8	15	−28	−980	−9744	2384	7	−31	−553	−229	343
9	17	−4	−884	−12704	−2176	8	−16	−532	−344	88
10	19	23	−703	−14249	−6821	9	1	−471	−429	−207
11	21	53	−427	−13749	−10535	10	20	−365	−467	−496
12	23	86	−46	−10504	−11960	11	41	−209	−439	−715
13	25	122	450	−3744	−9360	12	64	2	−324	−780
14	27	161	1071	7371	−585	13	89	273	−99	−585
15	29	203	1827	23751	16965	14	116	609	261	0
16						15	145	1015	783	1131
$\Sigma P'^2$	8,990	21,360,240		2,145,733,200		2,480	6,724,520		9,536,592	
		302,064		3,671,537,920			158,224		4,034,712	
λ	2	$\dfrac{3}{2}$	$\dfrac{5}{3}$	$\dfrac{35}{12}$	$\dfrac{3}{10}$	1	1	$\dfrac{5}{6}$	$\dfrac{1}{12}$	$\dfrac{1}{60}$

SOME PHYSICAL CONSTANTS

STP = standard temperature and pressure = 0°C and 760 mm Hg

C = velocity of light = 2.99793×10^{10} cm/sec = 186,284 mi/sec

Velocity of sound in air (STP) = 331.7 m/sec = 1088 ft/sec

g = acceleration due to gravity (SL) = 32.174 ft/sec^2

m_E = mass of earth = 5.975×10^{27} g

International nautical mile = 1852 meters = 6076.10333 ft

U. S. nautical mile = 1853.248 meters = 6080.20 ft

TABLE XVII (continued). MODIFIED ORTHOGONAL POLYNOMIALS

m	32					33				
X	P_1'	P_2'	P_3'	P_4'	P_5'	P_1'	P_2'	P_3'	P_4'	P_5'
1	1	−85	−51	459	255	0	−272	0	3672	0
2	3	−83	−151	423	737	1	−269	−27	3537	2565
3	5	−79	−245	353	1137	2	−260	−53	3139	4864
4	7	−73	−329	253	1407	3	−245	−77	2499	6649
5	9	−65	−399	129	1509	4	−224	−98	1652	7708
6	11	−55	−451	−11	1419	5	−197	−115	647	7883
7	13	−43	−481	−157	1131	6	−164	−127	−453	7088
8	15	−29	−485	−297	661	7	−125	−133	−1571	5327
9	17	−13	−459	−417	51	8	−80	−132	−2616	2712
10	19	5	−399	−501	−627	9	−29	−123	−3483	−519
11	21	25	−301	−531	−1267	10	28	−105	−4053	−3984
12	23	47	−161	−487	−1725	11	91	−77	−4193	−7139
13	25	71	25	−347	−1815	12	160	−38	−3756	−9260
14	27	97	261	−87	−1305	13	235	13	−2581	−9425
15	29	125	551	319	87	14	316	77	−493	−6496
16	31	155	899	899	2697	15	403	155	2697	899
17						16	496	248	7192	14384
$\Sigma P'^2$	10,912	5,379,616		54,285,216		2,992		417,384		1,547,128,656
		185,504	5,379,616				1,947,792		348,330,136	
λ	2	1	$\frac{2}{3}$	$\frac{1}{12}$	$\frac{1}{30}$	1	3	$\frac{1}{6}$	$\frac{7}{12}$	$\frac{3}{20}$

VALUE OF PREFIXES

PREFIX	VALUE	PREFIX	VALUE
Tera	10^{12}	Deci (d)	10^{-1}
Giga	10^9	Centi (c)	10^{-2}
Mega (M)	10^6	Milli (m)	10^{-3}
Kilo (k)	10^3	Micro (μ)	10^{-6}
Hecto (h)	10^2	Nano	10^{-9}
Deka (dk)	10^1	Pico	10^{-12}

Sponsored by the International Union of Physics and International Electrotechnical Commission.

TABLE XVIII. ANGLES, $\frac{n}{12}\pi$

n	RADIAN	DEGREES	SIN	COS	TAN	COT
0	0	0	0	1	0	∞
1	.261799	15	.2588190	.9659258	.2679492	3.7320508
2	.523599	30	.5000000	.8660254	.5773503	1.7320508
3	.785398	45	.7071068	.7071068	1	1
4	1.047198	60	.8660254	.5000000	1.7320508	.5773503
5	1.308997	75	.9659258	.2588190	3.7320508	.2679492
6	1.570796	90	1	0	∞	0
7	1.832596	105	.9659258	−.2588190	−3.7320508	−.2679492
8	2.094395	120	.8660254	−.5000000	−1.7320508	−.5773503
9	2.356194	135	.7071068	−.7071068	−1	−1
10	2.617994	150	.5000000	−.8660254	−.5773503	−1.7320508
11	2.879793	165	.2588190	−.9659258	−.2679492	−3.7320508
12	3.141593	180	0	−1	0	∞
13	3.403392	195	−.2588190	−.9659258	.2679492	3.7320508
14	3.665191	210	−.5000000	−.8660254	.5773503	1.7320508
15	3.926991	225	−.7071068	−.7071068	1	1
16	4.188790	240	−.8660254	−.5000000	1.7320508	.5773503
17	4.450590	255	−.9659258	−.2588190	3.7320508	.2679492
18	4.712389	270	−1	0	∞	0
19	4.974188	285	−.9659258	.2588190	−3.7320508	−.2679492
20	5.235988	300	−.8660254	.5000000	−1.7320508	−.5773503
21	5.497787	315	−.7071068	.7071068	−1	−1
22	5.759587	330	−.5000000	.8660254	−.5773503	−1.7320508
23	6.021386	345	−.2588190	.9659258	−.2679492	−3.7320508
24	6.283185	360	0	1	0	∞

n	$n!$	n	$n!$
1	1	11	399 16800
2	2	12	4790 01600
3	6	13	62270 20800
4	24	14	8 71782 91200
5	120	15	130 76743 68000
6	720	16	2092 27898 88000
7	5040	17	35568 74280 96000
8	40320	18	6 40237 37057 28000
9	3 62880	19	121 64510 04088 32000
10	36 28800	20	2432 90200 81766 40000

TABLE XIX. CONSTANTS

TERM	VALUE	RECIPROCAL
$\dfrac{\pi}{2}$	1.57079 63268	.63661 97724
π	3.14159 26536	.31830 98862
2π	6.28318 53072	.15915 49431
$(\pi/2)^2$	2.46740 11003	.40528 47346
π^2	9.86960 44011	.10132 11836
$(2\pi)^2$	39.47841 76044	.02533 02959
$\sqrt{\pi/2}$	1.25331 41373	.79788 45608
$\sqrt{\pi}$	1.77245 38509	.56418 95835
$\sqrt{2\pi}$	2.50662 82746	.39894 22804
e	2.71828 18285	.36787 94412
e^2	7.38905 60989	.13533 52832
$\sqrt{e}$	1.64872 12707	.60653 06597
$\log_{10} e$	.43429 44819	2.30258 50930

1 radian = 57.29577 95131 degrees
1 degree = .01745 32925 radians

Bernoulli Numbers

$B_1 = \dfrac{1}{6}$	$B_6 = \dfrac{691}{2730}$
$B_2 = \dfrac{1}{30}$	$B_7 = \dfrac{7}{6}$
$B_3 = \dfrac{1}{42}$	$B_8 = \dfrac{3617}{510}$
$B_4 = \dfrac{1}{30}$	$B_9 = \dfrac{43867}{798}$
$B_5 = \dfrac{5}{66}$	$B_{10} = \dfrac{174611}{330}$

Euler Numbers

$E_1 = 1$	$E_4 = 1385$
$E_2 = 5$	$E_5 = 50521$
$E_3 = 61$	$E_6 = 2702765$

TABLE XX. CONVERSION FACTORS

Fundamental Units

QUANTITY	METRIC (absolute)		ENGLISH	
	cgs	mks	POUND FORCE (gravitational)	POUND MASS (absolute)
Mass	gram (g)	kilogram (kg)	slug	pound (lb)
Length	centimeter (cm)	meter (m)	foot (ft)	foot (ft)
Time	second (sec)	second (sec)	second (sec)	second (sec)
Area	cm^2	m^2	ft^2	ft^2
Volume	cm^3	m^3	ft^3	ft^3
Density	$g\ cm^{-3}$	$kg\ m^{-3}$	$slug\ ft^{-3}$	$lb\ ft^{-3}$
Speed	cm/sec	m/sec	ft/sec	ft/sec
Acceleration	cm/sec^2	m/sec^2	ft/sec^2	ft/sec^2
Force	dyne	newton	pound (lb)	poundal
Pressure	barge	$newton/m^2$	lb/ft^2	$poundal/ft^2$
Work	erg	joule	ft lb	ft poundal
Power	erg/sec	watt	horsepower (hp) 550 ft lb/sec	ft poundal/sec
Torque	dyne cm	newton m	lb ft	poundal ft
Moment of inertia	$g\ cm^2$	$kg\ m^2$	$slug\ ft^2$	$lb\ ft^2$
Momentum	g cm/sec	kg m/sec	slug ft/sec	lb ft/sec
Angular mom.	$g\ cm^2/sec$	$kg\ m^2/sec$	$slug\ ft^2/sec$	$lb\ ft^2/sec$
Heat (energy)	calorie	calorie	. . .	BTU
Temperature	°Centigrade	°Kelvin	°Fahrenheit	°Rankine

Atmosphere: Pressure exerted by air at sea level under standard conditions.

British thermal unit (BTU): Energy required to raise temperature of 1 lb mass of water 1°F (averaged from 32 to 212°F).

Calorie: Energy required to raise 1 g mass of water 1°C (averaged from 0 to 100°C).

Dyne: Force necessary to give 1 g mass acceleration of $1\ cm/sec^2$.

Erg: Work done by force of 1 dyne applied over distance of 1 cm.

Joule: Unit of energy or work equal to 10^7 ergs.

Kilowatthour: Work done in 1 hr at power level of 10^3 watts.

Newton: Force necessary to give 1 kg mass acceleration of $1\ m/sec^2$.

Watt: Rate of doing work, or power expended, in amount of 10^7 ergs/sec.

CONVERSION FACTORS

MULTIPLY	BY	TO OBTAIN	MULTIPLY	BY	TO OBTAIN

LENGTH (L)

MULTIPLY	BY	TO OBTAIN
Angstroms	10^{-8}	centimeters
Centimeters	.3937	inches
Feet	30.48006	centimeters
Inches	2.540005	centimeters
Kilometers	3280.833	feet
	.621372	miles
Meters	3.280833	feet
	39.37	inches
Miles	5280	feet
	1.60935	kilometers
Millimeters	.03937	inches
Rods	16.5	feet
Yards	.914402	meters

AREA (L^2)

MULTIPLY	BY	TO OBTAIN
Acres	43560	sq ft
Sq cm	.155000	sq in.
Sq ft	929.034	sq cm
Sq in.	6.451626	sq cm
Sq km	247.1044	acres
Sq m	10.76387	sq ft
Sq mi	640	acres
Sq mm	0.001550	sq in.
Sq rods	272.25	sq ft
Sq yd	.8361307	sq m

VOLUME (L^3)

MULTIPLY	BY	TO OBTAIN
cc	.06102	cu in.
	.033815	ounces
Cu ft	.028317	cu m
	28.317	liters
Cu in.	16.387	cc
	.016387	liters
Cu m	35.314	cu ft
	264.2	gallons
Cu yd	.76456	cu m
Liters	61.0234	cu in.
	1.05671	quarts
Gallons	3.78543	liters

MASS (M)

MULTIPLY	BY	TO OBTAIN
Grams	15.43236	grains
	0.035274	ounces
Pounds	453.5924	grams
Ounces	28.34953	grams
Tons	1016.047	kg

DENSITY (ML^{-3})

MULTIPLY	BY	TO OBTAIN
G/cm^3	.03613	lb/in^3
	62.43	lb/ft^3
lb/ft^3	16.018	kg/m^3

VELOCITY (LT^{-1})

MULTIPLY	BY	TO OBTAIN
m/sec	2.2369	mi/hr
mi/hr	1.46667	ft/sec
Knots	1.1508	mi/hr
RPM	.10472	rad/sec

WORK (ML^2T^{-2})

MULTIPLY	BY	TO OBTAIN
(Abs) joules	.73756	ft lb
G calories	.003968	BTU
Kwhr	3413.0	BTU

FORCE (MLT^{-2})

MULTIPLY	BY	TO OBTAIN
Newtons	.22481	lb wt
g wt	.07932	poundals
lb wt	32.174	poundals
Poundals	.031081	lb wt

PRESSURE ($ML^{-1}T^{-2}$)

MULTIPLY	BY	TO OBTAIN
Atmosphere	29.921	in Hg
	14.696	lb/in^2
	760	mm Hg
lb wt/in^2	70.307	g/cm^2

CAPACITY—DRY

MULTIPLY	BY	TO OBTAIN
Bushels	35.2383	liters
Dekaliters	1.13513	pecks
Liters	.908102	quarts

Answers to the Exercises

In some cases the answers are given to more decimal values than is warranted by statement of the problem; this is done so that the student can check his round-off errors.

EXERCISE I

1. 38.462, 2.3742, .0023714, .70003.

2. 30.437.

3. $8\sqrt{1.1109}$, 8.4.

4. 62, 419, 183.5625, 3.2620.

5. $P^{(5)}(x) + 12P^{(4)}(x) + 30P^{(3)}(x) + 16P^{(2)}(x) + 3P^{(1)}(x) + 4P^{(0)}(x)$.

9. .8432.

10. $R_{10}(.5) < 1.29 \times 10^{-10}$.

13. 12950.

14. 25%.

15. $P_4(x) = \frac{1}{8}(35x^4 - 30x^2 + 3)$.

17. $D_4(x) = \frac{1}{6}x^3 - \frac{3}{4}x^2 + \frac{11}{12}x - \frac{1}{4}$.

20. $i(.01) = -7.9438$, $i(5) = 4.3$.

22. 1 and -124.44.

23. $3x^3 - 14x^2 + 11x$.

EXERCISE II

1.

x	y	Δy	$\Delta^2 y$	$\Delta^3 y$	$\Delta^4 y$
1.0	1.0000				
		5191			
1.1	1.5191		354		
		5545		-24	
1.2	2.0736		330		24
		5875		0	
1.3	2.6611		330		24
		6205		24	
1.4	3.2816		354		24
		6559		48	
1.5	3.9375		402		24
		6961		72	
1.6	4.6336		474		24
		7435		96	
1.7	5.3771		570		
		8005			
1.8	6.1776				

2. (a) $y(1.7) = -1.06743$; (b) $y(5) = 77$.

3. (a)

x	0	.1	.2	.3	.4	.5
y	-5.000	-4.928	-4.904	-4.916	-4.952	-5.000

x	.6	.7	.8	.9	1.0
y	-5.048	-5.084	-5.096	-5.072	-5.000

(b)

x	0	.01	.02	.03	.04	.05
y	−.3000	−.2998	−.2991	−.2980	−.2964	−.2942

x	.06	.07	.08	.09	.10
y	−.2915	−.2881	−.2842	−.2796	−.2743

4.

x \ y	0	1	2	3			
0	0	−3	−3	−9	−12	−15	−27
	2		3		4		5
1	2	−2	0	−8	−8	−14	−22
	6		7		8		9
2	8	−1	7	−7	0	−13	−13
	10		11		12		13
3	18	0	18	−6	12	−12	0
	14		15		16		17
4	32	1	33	−5	28	−11	17

5.

x	y	$\Delta[x_i x_i]$	$\Delta^2[x_i x_k]$	$\Delta^3[x_i x_k]$	$\Delta^4[x_i x_k]$	$\Delta^5[x_i x_k]$
−4	−4320					
		2040				
−2	−240		−480			
		120		64		
0	0		−32		−8	
		−40		−8		1
−3	−120		−88		4	
		−480		32		
5	−1080		168			
		360				
8	0					

9.

x	y	$\Delta[x_ix_j]$	$\Delta^2[x_ix_j]$	$\Delta^3[x_ix_j]$
0	1.00000			
		−.000762		
5	.99619		−.0001514	
		−.002276		.0000001
10	.98481		−.0001500	
		−.003776		.0000002
15	.96593		−.0001472	
		−.005248		.0000003
20	.93969		−.0001428	
		−.006676		.0000003
25	.90631		−.0001380	
		−.008056		
30	.86603			

10.

p	A_0	ΔA_0	$\Delta^2 A_0$	$\Delta^3 A_0$
0	1.0000000			
		−.0001250		
.01	.9998750		−.0002500	
		−.0003750		.0000002
.02	.9995000		−.0002498	
		−.0006248		0
.03	.9988752		−.0002498	
		−.0008746		.0000004
.04	.9980006		−.0002494	
		−.0011240		0
.05	.9968766		−.0002494	
		−.0013734		.0000006
.06	.9955032		−.0002488	
		−.0016222		.0000002
.07	.9938810		−.0002486	
		−.0018708		.0000006
.08	.9920102		−.0002480	
		−.0021188		.0000004
.09	.9898914		−.0002476	
		−.0023664		
.10	.9875250			

13. With $u_0 = \frac{1}{9}$, $\ln 2 = 0.693147169$.

EXERCISE III

1. 18449.9, 24782.4, 25761.8, 27640.2.

2. 18469.0, 27645.8.

3. (a) .988845, .972405, .888873, .912580, .939931.
   (b) 1.509643, 50.784809, -2.420785, -5.203276, -5.407975.

5. .91725.

EXERCISE IV

1. (a) -4.6449, -2.8969, -1.3831.
   (b) 71.65006, 153.714717.

2. 1.747022.

3. 1.2068 (true value); calculated value is 1.1919.

4. .167, .235.

EXERCISE V

1. $-.5771$, $-.3306$, .0324, .04885, .0731.

2. -12.373, 143.53.

10. $\sum_{i=0}^{4} y_i H_i M_i$ where $M_i = \sum_{k=0}^{4} \cot(x - x_k]_{k \neq i}$.

11. For $x = x_1 : H_i M_i = d_i^{-1} \prod_{k=0}^{4} \sin(x_1 - x_k)_{k \neq i,1}$, $(i = 0, 2, 3, 4)$ and

$H_1 M_1 = M_1(x_1)$ where $d = \Pi \sin(x_i - x_k)_{k \neq i}$.

EXERCISE VI

1. (a) 8.638566; (b) 530.220748; (c) 609.788585;
   (d) 298.900693; (e) 8.637235; (f) 530.247168.

2. 242.7165.

3. 0.5.

4. 0.54938 7278.

EXERCISE VII

1. .888874, .912581.

2. -2.422880, -5.212814, -5.424428.

3. -3.8125.

4. 1.231 (with $p = -.62$); 1.225 (with $p = -.63$).

5. -2.9212 (omit value at $x = 2.0$); 153.71470.
6. $y'(0) = -.57711, y'(.5) = .0324$.
7. -12.373.
8. (a) 8.637301.
12. $r = \sqrt{30}/3, h = 2\sqrt{30}/3$.

EXERCISE VIII

1. 1.380278.
2. $.142857$ (double root).
3. 1.5236.
4. 1.873097.
5. 2.219106.
7. $.50382; .24698$.
8. 1.177115.
9. No real positive root.
10. $.212139; .256861$.
16. $(1.444, .155)$.
18. $(-.46558, 1.04132, 2.18812, -1.03563)$.
20. (b) $(1, -3, 0, 2, -1)$.

EXERCISE IX

1. (a) $1.914751, .001817$; are there more solutions?
(c) $1.285714286, 1.571428571$.
(d) $\left(\dfrac{22}{7}, -\dfrac{45}{7}\right)$

2. (a) $.62348902 \pm .781831487\, i,\ -.222423440 \pm .974950160\, i,$
$-.900968868 \pm .433883739\, i$.
(b) $1, 1.414214, -1.414214, .5 \pm .8660254\, i$.
(d) $\frac{1}{7}(3 \pm 4\, i), \frac{1}{2}(-1 \pm \sqrt{3}\, i)$

EXERCISE X

1. (a) True solution.

x	1.0	1.1	1.2	1.3	1.4	1.5
y	-3.0	-2.47934	-2.08333	-1.77515	-1.53061	-1.33333

(b) Runge-Kutta Method.

x	.1	.2	.3	.4	.5
y	.99534	.98279	.96445	.94224	.91796

x	.6	.7	.8	.9	1.0
y	.89301	.86858	.84565	.82508	.80769

2. True value at $t = 1.0$ is $x = 20.22087$.
3. True value at $t = 0.8$ is $x = 11.22507$.

EXERCISE XI

1. (a) $y = 2.3335 + 1.6713x$.
2. $y = 3.9429 - 3.0422x + 2.0180x^2$.
3. By the Nielsen-Goldstein method

$y = -.003788x^4 + .034383x^3 - 9.731655x^2 - 97.659134x + 2.580355$.
$y = -.041375x^3 - 9.258163x^2 + 96.712139x + 2.853135$.
$y = -9.878788x^2 + 99.078789x + 1.363636$.

4. The Nielsen-Goldstein method yields

$$y = -.003041x^3 + .019176x^2 + .008818x + .132066.$$

EXERCISE XII

1. (a) $y = 1.6691(1.2733)^x$.
2. $y = 3.2x + 1.5\ln 2x$.
4.

i	0	1	2	3	4	5	6
a_i	96.17	173.01	24.17	32.5	-16.67	10.49	-7.67
b_i		-139.63	19.63	-32.5	-6.06	-8.87	

7. $y = 1.02636x + .34212$.
8. $y = 1.75x^2 - .37x + .62$.

EXERCISE XIII

1. (a) Triangle, $(-2, 3), (2, -3), (6, 2)$.
2. (a) $f_{max} = 95.35$.   (b) $f_{max} = 130.4$.
3. $f_{max} = 112.83$.
4. $f_{max} = 127.27$.
5. $f_{max} = 149.35$.

Index